W9-AFV-236

Books by Alex Karmel

Mary Ann

Last Words

My Revolution

MY REVOLUTION

Restif de la Bretonne, by Binet.

Alex Karmel

MY REVOLUTION

PROMENADES IN PARIS 1789–1794

BEING THE DIARY OF

RESTIF DE LA BRETONNE

Author of THE PORNOGRAPHER, THE PERVERTED PEASANT, PARIS NIGHTS, FANCHETTE'S SLIPPER...

McGRAW-HILL BOOK COMPANY
New York St. Louis San Francisco
Toronto Mexico Panama Düsseldorf

to Richard de Combray

MY REVOLUTION

Copyright © 1970 by Alex Karmel.
All rights reserved.
Printed in the United States of America.
No part of this publication may be reproduced, stored
in a retrieval system, or transmitted, in any form or
by any means, electronic, mechanical, photocopying,
recording, or otherwise, without the prior
written permission of the publisher.

Library of Congress Catalog Card Number: 71-127971

FIRST EDITION

33336

CONTENTS

A HARD WINTER:
January–March 1789 1

A HOPEFUL SPRING:
April–June 1789 17

THE FALL OF THE BASTILLE:
July 1789 43

"CONSUMMATUM EST . . .":
August–December 1789 63

MON CALENDRIER:
1790 93

DECEPTIONS AND SHAMS:
1791 133

BONNETS AND PIKES:
January–July 1792 175

AUGUST AND SEPTEMBER:
August–September 1792 207

TO KILL A KING:
October 1792–January 1793 241

SETBACKS:
February–August 1793 271

DIARY OF THE TERROR:
September 1793–March 1794 311

BAL A LA VICTIME:
April–December 1794 351

A FEW DATES

1789

May 4	The Estates General assemble at Versailles
June 20	"Tennis Court Oath" proclaiming the National Assembly
July 12	Necker dismissed; Paris revolts
July 14	The Bastille falls
August 4	The nobility renounces many of its privileges
October 3–5	The women of Paris march on Versailles; the king and the Assembly move to Paris

1790

February 4	The king swears allegiance to the unfinished constitution
July 14	"Fête de la Fédération"

1791

April 2	Death of Mirabeau
June 20–25	The king flees, is arrested at Varennes, brought back to Paris
July 17	Massacre of the Champ de Mars
September 14	The Constitution proclaimed, accepted by the king
October 1	The Legislative Assembly meets

A FEW DATES

1792

April 20	France declares war on Austria
June 20	The people invade the Tuileries Palace
July 24	Prussia enters the war
August 10	The king deposed by an insurrection
September 2	Verdun falls to the Prussians
September 3–6	September massacres
September 20	Battle of Valmy; the Prussians retreat
September 22	The Convention meets, proclaims France a republic
December 11–16	Trial of the king

1793

January 21	The king executed
February 1	France declares war on England and Holland
April 3	Treason of Dumouriez
May 31–June 2	The Girondins expelled from the Convention
July 13	Assassination of Marat
September 5	Proclamation of the Terror
October 16	Marie-Antoinette executed
October 31	Girondin deputies executed

1794

March 24	Hébert executed
April 3	Danton and Desmoulins executed
June 8	Fête de l'Etre Suprême
July 28	Robespierre executed (Tenth of Thermidor)
November 12	Jacobin Club closed

Parlerai-je ici de la RÉVOLUTION, *de cet événement étrange, dont le bruit grondera longtemps encore dans la suite des siècles? . . . Non: je l'ai décrite dans les deux derniers volumes des* Nuits, *dans* un Ouvrage manuscrit achevé en 96 . . .

—MONSIEUR NICOLAS, Ninth Epoch

A HARD WINTER

JANUARY–MARCH 1789

WAS there ever before a city like Paris, capital of an immense country, center of civilization, site of dozens of monuments (each of which would make the fame of a provincial town), but at the same time so sordid, ill-organized, filthy, unhealthy and unsafe that one wonders why its population doesn't diminish instead of growing all the time? The food supply is so badly managed that famine has been a real threat for the past three years; the police so incompetent that it is unwise to carry any money in one's purse, even in broad daylight; the streets are a dump for garbage of all kinds; the Seine, so lovely to the eye, receives the raw wastes of 800,000 human bodies and is little better than an open sewer; vice is so prevalent and profitable that thousands of young girls prefer selling their bodies to working or marrying: reckless cabriolets driven by haughty young gentlemen take their toll of killed and maimed every day; and even when one is indoors the din of passing carriages and street vendors hawking their wares makes all repose impossible except in the dead of night. Profligacy and waste abound. The rich load their tables with more delicacies than they can consume; they nourish useless pets with scraps that would be a feast on the tables of the poor, then let these animals roam free, adding to the filth of the streets; warehouses are stuffed with slowly rotting grain while speculators wait for the price to rise; and a thousand sacks of flour are used each day to powder wigs.

In January we had a minor reform in the right direction. The municipality ordered that all horses be fitted out with sleigh bells so pedestrians will have some warning that they are about to be trampled down. But it is not enough simply to give the man on foot a sporting chance so that he can leap to the side of the road to be covered with dust on fine days or spattered with mud when it rains. There should be a strict limitation on the pace of all vehicles and also single horsemen within the city, with fines high enough to discourage even the rich, who are the worst offenders. Then the most populous quarters, such as that around the Palais-Royal, should be closed to carriages and horsemen altogether. Not only would this make those districts more pleasant for everyone, but it would also abate the current mania for private coaches. (The streets of Paris today are more congested than they were thirty years ago when I first came from Auxerre and each year it takes longer to get from one place to another.) If Monsieur and Madame knew that they could promenade, shop and pay visits without fear of returning home covered with filth they would put their money into fine clothes instead of a bright new carriage and an insolent coachman. The tailors and seamstresses would benefit and so would everyone else.

This has been the worst winter in the memory of any living man. There was snow on November 26th, exceptionally early; then chunks of ice appeared in the Seine, which was unusually shallow because of last summer's drought. The merchants immediately raised their prices on all goods that arrive by water—flour, wine, firewood, coal—all the necessities of life. The cold grew more intense each day after that. On December 12th a man on horseback trying to cross from the Quai des Quatre Nations to the Quai du Louvre broke through the ice and was drowned. Just a few days later he would have crossed safely. The Seine became a Dutch landscape: children on skates, a path across the ice from the Ile de la Cité to the Ile St.-Louis to avoid the scandalous toll on the Pont-Rouge. At the Pont-Marie the sailors of vessels trapped by the ice kept a huge bonfire going night and day. The cries of peddlers sounded more piercing than ever in the cold air. All streets were solid ice from house to house, lined with piles of frozen garbage and filth that grew each day with the accretions of all the chamber-pots of Paris. A terrible time for beggars; the police gathered a score of frozen bodies each morning. A bad time for streetwalkers.

The thaw began January 13th, was complete the 16th. The accumulated sewage in the streets dissolved in the flood of melting ice and snow. Even the rue St.-Jacques became nothing more than an icy cesspool. The carriages of the rich tossed up great waves of slush that spattered the clothes of everyone they passed. The stench was sickening. As usual the Auvergnats set out planks to make toll bridges at street crossings that were impassable. To make this service indispensable these scoundrels blocked the natural drains, creating icy swamps even where there would have been a solid footing. Along the rue St.-Honoré at the rue des Poulies I saw a pretty young girl tripping across one of these improvised bridges. The Auvergnat demanded his fee; the girl had left her purse at home. With that the brute shoved her into the slush. The girl's feet slipped out of her shoes; the hem of her skirt was drenched; she walked away with icy water dripping on her exposed legs.

On January 20th I went to the Ile St.-Louis for the first time in more than a month. The ice on the Seine had broken up, but huge chunks were caught at all the bridges, blocking the stream. These white floes, many over a foot thick, piled up on top of one another reaching the level of the quais, so that it seemed that the houses there and on the bridges were suspended in a quarry of ice. Five large boats were trapped in this white flood beside the Pont-Marie, and another, filled with lime, had been carried downstream to the Pont-Nôtre-Dame where it was stranded across one of the arches of the bridge. Later it broke apart from the pressure of the ice.

Even after the thaw the price of everything stayed high.

On November 9th I had finished printing Part XIV of *Les Nuits de Paris,* a monumental work in eight volumes, the fruit of thirty years of observing what takes place in Paris when most honest citizens are in bed. Without boasting I can say that my observations are valuable, because I am not your typical Parisian man of letters, son of a judge or a merchant, eager to gain entrée into the salons of the Faubourg St.-Germain by means of his talent. I was born a peasant, I spent fifteen years as a workingman before I began to write, I have always been a man of the people and I am proud of it. (For the same reason I do not have that sentimental notion of the *goodness* of the people so fashionable today among our salon philosophers.)

I always work on several projects at the same time. One that occupies me at present is *Le Thesmographe*—a complement to *L'Andrographe,* published in 1781. In that work I described the ideal society where property is abolished and men live in communities, sharing all goods. But those ideas were too visionary. Ignored by the critics, rejected by the booksellers, I had to be content with the thanks of Mr. Benjamin Franklin, to whom I sent a copy. The present work is addressed to the Estates General and does not aim so high; I outline only reforms. And yet I fear that it will suffer the same fate, even before writing it. What is needed today is reform, but what reform! Above all a more equitable distribution of property, as prescribed by the Christian religion in its maxim: "Do unto others as you would have others do unto you!" And this especially as regards land. But what a demand to make in this eighteenth century, where inequality is carried to the very edge of slavery! Nonetheless *that* is the revolution that sooner or later must be accomplished.

There has been much talk of the Estates, called for next April to devise some way to avoid a governmental bankruptcy. This medieval body has been moribund for a century and a half; the lawyers have been busy digging out old parchments to try to find out just what it is. The great question is the relation of the three Orders: the Clergy, the Nobility, and the Third Estate—everyone else! The debate concerns the number of delegates of each Order and how they shall vote. In September the Parlement of Paris declared that the *Tiers* should have no more deputies than either of the others. In December they changed their minds, and decided that the Third Estate should have double the number of delegates of either of the first two. Thus that collection of bewigged and berobed judges again became the heroes of the crowd of clerks, young lawyers, apprentice goldsmiths and watchmakers that infests the Place Dauphine behind the Palais de Justice and considers itself the *people.*

They are a strange generation, these young men of today's Paris; a spoiled, stubborn, insolent, closed-minded generation that refuses to listen to those who are older; a self-confident generation that displays either an innocent folly, masked by the education they have received, or else an immature wisdom, acrid and green, like grape juice in mid-August. I call them "the children of Jean-Jacques Rousseau" because they are the spawn of *Emile* and the theories of education without any discipline first stated in that work. I will admit that I too was enchanted by the book when it appeared, by the idea of bringing children up according to the dictates of Nature. But that was thirty years ago; at that time infants were still wrapped in swaddling clothes that impeded their growth, children still compelled to act like little adults, to remain inactive and silent for most of the day. Jean-Jacques put his case strongly, as is necessary if one wants to be heard, but since then his principles have been much abused. What is the result? In fashionable Parisian households children are allowed to run naked with their hair floating loose in a manner that is both hideous and repulsive. You are invited as a guest and you find that the brats have the run of the house, making deafening noises and climbing all over you with their dirty bare feet. If you try to talk to the mother or father about some important matter you find that the parents prefer to answer some absurd question posed by their adored son, their adored daughter. . . . We now begin to see the results of that education.

The Princes of the Royal Family opposed the doubling of the representation of the Third Estate, but Necker, our Swiss financial wizard of a minister, prevailed upon the king to accept the ruling of the judges of Paris. The whole issue was altered with the appearance of the pamphlet by the Abbé de Sieyès, *Qu'est-ce que le Tiers-Etat?* His catechism was immediately known by everyone: "What is the Third Estate? Everything. What has it been until now? Nothing. What does it want? To become *something.*" The whole question ceased to be a legal matter; what Sieyès asked was, "Who should govern France?"

I have my own ideas on the matter, which will be found in the *Thesmographe*. I propose a Fourth Estate, to represent the peasantry, nine out of ten of the productive workers of the nation, and a Fifth Estate, to represent the feminine sex, half the nation and not to be ignored. But perhaps my proposals will come too late.

Carnival fell on February 23rd. Despite the cold, the scarcity of bread, all the disasters of the past year, the merry-makers were as numerous as ever. There were maskers all along the rue St.-Honoré and rue de la Savonnerie as far as the rue St.-Martin, on foot, horse, donkeys, even in carriages—grotesque costumes, some of gauzy cloth that revealed too much. The next day, Mardi Gras, none of my employees showed up for work. One of the great faults of the Catholic religion is that half the year is spent in festivals. At about six in the evening a masker fell from a carriage in the rue St.-Honoré and was crushed to death by the coach that followed.

One afternoon in March, returning from the Ile St.-Louis by the Port-au-Bled, I see a crowd on the Grève. They are awaiting the execution of a thief, a spectacle that I detest. While I examined the crowd, the poor creature was led down the steps of the Hôtel de Ville. No doubt he had been tortured; he looked half dead and walked only because he was held up by the priest and the executioner. At the foot of the steps the priest embraced him, a truly Christian gesture: the poor soul seemed devoured by a fever and was as filthy as the cell from which he had been released. I tried to leave, but the crowd was too thick. The punishment was mitigated; as an act of mercy the victim was strangled with a tourniquet before his body was delivered to the lash and the rack. A pretty young girl and her lover joked and giggled even as the whip flailed the half-naked corpse. Outraged by the barbarous display, I vented my spleen on the girl.

"You must have the heart of a monster, Mademoiselle! If I were your lover I would leave you forever!"

The two of them were so startled by my remarks that they said nothing. I slipped away. . . .

I must tell you about the Ile St.-Louis, "my isle" as I call it, site of my sentimental promenades. It was in 1779, November 5th, at the onset of my chest illness, that I inscribed my first *date* on the parapet of the quai d'Orléans. That first *inscription* was on the tenth stone to the left of the Pont-Rouge, looking toward the Ile de la Cité. I traced the letters with the thought, "Will I live to see this mark next year?" It seemed to me that if I did live that long the experience would be pleasurable, and pleasure is so rare in the autumn of life that there is no harm in creating occasions to feel it. This *date* was only these words: *"5a 9bris malum"* (5 November, sick).

During the following year, 1780, the inscriptions on the isle are few. But after January 1781 they become more frequent, often succeeding each other daily. This was because of my liaison with the young Sara Debée and the passion she aroused in my breast, an affair that brought me two months of joy in return for two years of misery. (And yet I still can't write her name without trembling.) I learned that she had seduced me on the orders of her mother who thought that I was rich; I learned that she was unfaithful; I learned that she was a whore—with each new painful revelation my attachment only grew stronger! What began as a lighthearted affair with a pretty child of nineteen who flattered me by reading my books ended as a daily torment from which I couldn't escape. The story is recounted in *The Last Adventure of a Man of Forty-five.*

All the events of this past decade are recorded on the stones of my isle: the marriage of my daughter Agnès without my permission, my reconciliation with her, her taking refuge with me after the torture of her marriage became too much for her to bear, the desertion of my wife, who left me with a pile of unpaid bills, my affair with Félicette . . . and also anniversaries of earlier events . . . all noted in abbreviations of Latin legible only to myself, scratched on the parapets of the quais with an iron hook that I had fashioned for the purpose when I found my house key insufficient. So that when I make a complete tour of my lovely isle, observing all the while the changing light and currents of the Seine, it recalls my entire life.

I've always had a passion for anniversaries. I find the

future a deep and terrifying emptiness that I hardly dare contemplate. But just as a man who fears water can stand on the shore and skip pebbles with a certain pleasure, so I cast stones into the abyss of the future in the form of my dates. I inscribe them; then I return a year later on the same day. I savor the present; I turn toward the past; I experience simultaneously what is and what exists no more . . . and then, if I am in a proper frame of mind, I throw a new *date* into the future, a new pebble that the river of Time, flowing onward, will wash up on the shore in its turn.

Alas! even this modest pleasure could not long remain unpolluted. Who would believe that in a supposedly civilized city like Paris the police are so lax that an honest citizen can be hounded by bands of children? And yet that has happened to me, and not only once. I have been followed, hooted at, called "Griffon!" and other names, and worst of all found my *dates* maliciously effaced. Nor, as I first believed, is this persecution just an accident, mischief of the idle scamps who laze on the quais or the scullery maids forever gossiping at kitchen windows. No, these attacks have all been instigated by the MONSTER Augé, tormenter of my daughter's existence and of my own!

Nonetheless I continue my promenades.

I turned fifty-four on November 22nd. My daughters made a truffled turkey for dinner; we were five at table: Agnès and Marion, my nephew Edmond, my friend Mercier and myself. Yes, I do mean Louis-Sébastien Mercier, celebrated author of *Le Tableau de Paris*. I am proud to say that he was one of the first men of letters to praise my works, writing me a letter that extolled *Le Paysan Perverti* at a time when I was completely unknown. It must be admitted that very few of that tribe have followed his example. In Germany and Switzerland I am renowned as a genius, but here in Paris I am considered a cheap scribbler; "*le Rousseau du ruisseau*" as one wit put it ("the Rousseau of the gutter"); it was meant as an insult but I take it as a compliment. I have this reputation because I write about shopgirls and apprentices instead of marquises and counts, because I

PLATE 2: Restif on the Ile St. Louis, at the Hotel Lambert, somewhat distracted from his *dates*. The firewood stacked up in the background is on the Ile Louviers, then a depot for merchandise, now attached to the Right Bank. The Owl is the symbol of the "Nocturnal Spectator," the name Restif awarded himself in *Les Nuits de Paris*. From Volume II of *Les Nuits de Paris,* 1788.

live on the rue de la Bûcherie instead of the Chaussée d'Antin, because I run my own press and continue to work with my own hands, because I wear old clothes, and because *Le Paysan* and *Les Contemporaines* were so popular, not only with the literati but among ordinary folk.

After dinner Mercier joined me for a tour of my isle. Only he and my exiled friend Grimod de la Reynière have ever shared that pleasure with me. We agreed that getting older was unpleasant. I suffer from hemorrhoids, a weak chest and occasional pains in the testicles which I fear are the aftereffects of a shameful malady given me by that other MONSTER, *my wife,* twenty years ago.

Shameful woman! parasite! hussy!

On January 1st I resolved that beginning with the new year I myself should be a new man and fill my days with other cares than the ridiculous pursuit of sexual satisfaction. It is not that I despise *love,* which would be a blasphemy. The first law that governs mankind is that of survival; the second, reproduction. But there arrives an age when love becomes ridiculous, when it becomes, in fact, a vice—that is to say my age, with its limitations and infirmities. What makes sticking to this resolution difficult is the constant presence of my daughters, who provoke feelings that should only be reminiscences. I awaken in the morning in an aroused state; Marion brings my breakfast; as she leans forward the sight of a peach-shaped breast slipping out of her nightgown makes me breathe deeply to restrain myself. I promise myself that in the evening I shall try, on my promenade . . . and it is all right. But sometimes there are accidents under the bedclothes. . . .

Reader! do not be shocked at my frankness! do not be ashamed, either for myself or for you! I describe human nature as it is, not as it is supposed to be by puritans. I describe what I see in the streets of Paris and I describe myself, because those are the two subjects I know best. "Nothing human is foreign to me," as the poet says.

There are no impulses I find unnatural, even if to act on

them would be that. And sometimes a false virtue that keeps us from action is the most unnatural of all!

Only those two MONSTERS, my wife and son-in-law, accuse me of having committed incest. Agnès Lebègue, before we separated, actually tried to provoke me into this crime, so she could hold it against me afterward. For anything to have occurred, my daughters would have to have desired it also. Far from that; they have always been modesty itself. But monsters cannot conceive that the whole world is not as vicious as they.

Until a few years ago I was always in love, and even while consumed with passion I could not be indifferent to any woman tastefully turned out, especially if she had a pretty foot. Because of this I could not imagine that anyone could go to bed at nine without having seen the streets of Paris, mixed in the crowds, visited several cafés, and then wandered through certain districts to see what might be taking place. Now all that is past. There are several young girls with whom I like to pass a pleasant hour, but my tenderness is purely paternal; since the episode of Sara I have not tried to combine that sentiment with physical pleasure.

I am still capable of an occasional rakery when the impulse strikes me. And then there are my three *amuseuses* who know me well: Mme. Dumoulin, an ash-blonde with a well-preserved figure; Mme. Dupont-Lambert, a brunette, pretty breasts, a fancy laundress whose white body always smells of soap; and Mme. Damourette, who sells paintings, prints and miniatures. Good luck brought me these three acquaintances at the music halls of Audinot and Nicolet, on the balcony, which I prefer to the orchestra, because of the *grisettes* at the bar who want you to buy them drinks.

Mme. Dumoulin is from Liège, wife of a printer from whom she is separated. She makes watch hands and wears high button shoes that reveal an exquisite taste. The evening that we met she tripped while taking her seat. I caught her in my arms. During the *entr'actes* we chatted; she put her hand in mine. I didn't think her a *fille* (in Paris *les filles* are not given to caresses) but a young widow looking for someone to live with. I took her home after the show. She lives on rue Mazarine. She noticed that I was looking at her shoes; she asked me if I liked them. I answered that I was crazy about them.

"In that case, you must desire me, because those who like my shoes are not disappointed in the rest of me."

I answered that I found everything about her appetizing. She took me in her arms; we went to bed.

During the act she said, "Well, well, dear author of *Le Pied de Fanchette,* you really aren't bad!"

I asked her how she had recognized me. She said a watchmaker had pointed me out to her one afternoon when I walked across the Place Dauphine. As I said good-bye she made me a little speech.

"You are beyond the age when women are your chief concern and I don't want to be tied to anyone. Come see me from time to time; I'll remind you that you are still a man."

I met Mme. Dupont-Lambert in a similar fashion. She was buying her ticket; I noticed that she was alone and asked for a seat in the same part of the theater. Later she asked me to live with her, but I knew that would interfere with my work. . . . The story was not very different with Mme. Damourette. . . . Later I discovered that these three were acquaintances. . . . The world is small. . . .

There is also a *lupanar,* rue de la Parcheminerie, where the madame is an old friend. She knows my tastes. . . . So I am well protected from the temptations of living alone with my daughters. . . .

This February Damourette introduced me to a young girl, tall but superb, who wanted to meet me because she had read my books. We met, we talked, I took her home; what follows followed. . . . Afterwards Damourette told me I was the girl's first lover. I was surprised; Damourette said that knowing I might have scruples the girl had applied a pommade to the "bottleneck." . . . I didn't see her again. If the story is true it is repulsive; if not, the pretense disgusts me. I am natural and frank; I am a man and not a saint; but subterfuge makes me cold.

On February 19th, as I made my tour of my isle, a souvenir, alive this time: Sara! How many tears have I wept since July

23, 1782, when I resolved never to see her again, a *date* still visible and marked by the words *Sara laissée*. It was like seeing a ghost. In these six years she has changed, aged—she must now be twenty-six or -seven—she has lost all that remains of childhood, that bloom of adolescence, all that made the moments of torment worth it for those few times when she was tender and called me her "dear papa." We walked toward each other; I waited for her to say something; our eyes met, then turned away; we passed in silence like the strangers we have become. Under the former *inscription* I wrote: *"19 f. Sara videns."* . . .

March 29th was the tenth anniversary of the death of Mairobert. I weep for him still. He was a loyal friend and of help to me on many occasions. Secretary to the duc de Chartres, Royal Censor, he put his signature to my productions whatever they contained. On March 27, 1779, I paid him a visit; I was sick and unhappy; I told him my misfortunes. He wept with me; offered me money; then added, "How many men who seem happy are really desperate!" Two days later he slit his veins in the baths at Poitevin, then put a pistol in his mouth and pulled the trigger. . . .

A HOPEFUL SPRING

APRIL–JUNE 1789

ON Holy Thursday, April 9th, the Countess de Beauharnais had the kindness to take my two daughters and myself to the annual promenade of fine carriages in the *allées* of the Bois de Boulogne. It was cloudy that morning, but the sky cleared by noon and the temperature rose, so that the excursion was altogether agreeable. The favor was more for Agnès and Marion than for me; Mme. de Beauharnais is fond of both of them and aware of the misfortunes they have suffered. The parade of coaches was even more crowded than usual; we moved at a snail's pace. But then the idea was to see and be seen, not to get anywhere. There were fewer of those fast cabriolets called *shishkis* so popular last year, but then there were many brilliant sedan chairs of a new style that is considered very elegant. How absurd that there should be *styles* of vehicles that change every year, so that people of fashion must keep buying new coaches in order to be up to date! There was also a great number of ordinary city hacks, dubbed "representatives of the Third Estate" in reference to the quarrels over the elections. These were forced to take the back road to the Bois through the Faubourg St.-Honoré instead of ascending the Champs-Elysées, reserved for private coaches.

It was Mercier who introduced me to Fanny de Beauharnais in the summer of 1787. Since my friend Grimod was exiled by a *lettre de cachet,* hers is the only elegant house in Paris where I am received. I go there on Fridays, the evening when she offers supper to her friends. Her mansion on the rue de Tournon, two steps from the Luxembourg Palace, is not impressive from the street, but her salon and dining room, all blue and silver, are exquisite. I enjoy the company for the same reasons that I myself am admitted: one's credentials are not birth or wealth but rather wit, learning and talent.

You arrive at about ten, chat with whoever is there. At eleven-thirty supper is served, a light and delicious repast. At twelve-fifteen you return to the salon. If the conversation is interesting you're welcome to stay all night. The hostess will not desert you; I've often left at five in the morning. This time is often occupied by writers reading from their manuscripts. It is true that hour is not conducive to perceptive criticism. Everyone always admires everything and there are occasions, I must admit, when they admire while snoring. But when you read from a manuscript at three in the morning, you don't really want criticism, only praise and then more praise.

That salon has been a whole education for me. One evening I heard the old marquis de la Grange spin anecdotes of the court of the old king, Louis XV, called the "*Bien-Aimé*" during the first years of his reign, detested afterwards. He told us that when the king took Du Barry for his mistress, his greatest pleasure was to see the ladies of the court kneeling at the feet of a woman of easy virtue. "If I made a cow my mistress," he said, "they'd find that she was graceful. I take a whore instead and they find her a model of virtue."

There I met old Cazotte, who has become my dear friend. The man is an *illuminé*. One evening he told me of his theories, that all substances, be they mineral, animal or vegetable, form part of a living Whole, an electric fluid pervading the entire universe, with Man the ultimate product of billions of years of change of that single substance. He said there must be other planets out in the vastness of interstellar space and that he believed that after death we could communicate with the inhabitants of those other worlds, we would become decrystallized souls who would speak to one another across those vast distances as he and I were speaking across a table. He gave me a fascinating idea for a book that I may write some day: A man who knows he is going to die tells his wife that he must take a long voyage to a faraway land; he writes a series of letters that are to be posted to her over a period of two years, teaching her the philosophy that will reconcile her to the fact that he no longer exists in his corporal form. In the last letter, and only then, she learns the truth. The Countess and I both found the idea genial.

On Easter Sunday, as I have every year since 1776, I went to the church of the Carmelite friars to hear the hymn, "*O filii!*" As a boy I tended my father's goats and pigs and found a hidden valley that I decided belonged to me; there I erected an altar of stones and prayed, with full sincerity, to the Divinity of the Place (who is the Divinity of all places); there I saw, one magic afternoon, two wild pigs coupling with the full innocence of the garden of Eden while my little herd grazed in peace and the little field rabbits hopped about, nibbling the tender spring grass. . . . When will I see my natal village again, the long line of fieldstone houses on the flank of the hill? when will I see la Bretonne, the farmhouse where I was born, the muddy court between it and the hayloft, the gnarled pear tree beside the well? After thirty years in Paris I remain a peasant in my bones and would be ready to return to the sweet, if often indecent, games of my childhood. . . . That Easter hymn, sung by those hidden voices, could convert the most determined atheist if he did not know that there is a religion more catholic than that of the Church of Rome, the religion of the Gospels and of Nature itself. . . . Memories of the divine JEANETTE ROUSSEAU whom I have loved all my life, although I never exchanged more than two words with her, and those the most banal.

I saw her for the first time on Easter Sunday, 1748. I was fourteen, an advanced and passionate lad of fourteen, inebriated by the solemnity of the Mass, the incense, the choir. The host was offered to the flock; the men advanced first, then the women, then the young girls. Among them was one whom I had never seen before and who effaced all the others—her virginal face, her pale complexion, the simplicity of her dress—all that crystallized into the image already formed in my imagination out of the yearning of my young heart and the new impulses of my body. That moment decided my fate, but who will ever understand this except myself?

Whenever I have loved a woman, and there have been many, it was always *Jeanette* whom I loved. I dreamt one night that Agnès Lebègue had died and that I had married my childhood sweetheart. And that is possible! I learned last year that she has returned to my native region after twenty years in Clermont-en-Auvergne working as governess for a rich family. She has never married. The idea enchants me. I have run from adventure to adventure, affair to affair, debauchery to debauchery; all the while Jeanette has lived an innocent, quiet life. I have tried to acquire fame while she has practiced the virtues of obscurity. . . . Some day she will read what I have written about her and she will cry, "He loves me still! He has always loved me!"

The events of April 27–29 were a surprise to everyone but myself.

For years I have written that the growing insolence of the rich and insubordination of the poor must lead to a great clash. The workingmen of this city have become intractable because they have read, in well-meaning books, a truth that is too strong for them; that the worker is an indispensable man. And since they've read that they seem determined to prove that it's a lie, neglecting their labor and reducing its value by half. Our salon philosophers do not know the people as I know them; they do not realize the effect of their words on untrained minds because their love of humanity leads them astray. And now we see the consequences of this error.

The manufacturer Réveillon speaks out in the electoral meeting of his district; what he has to say is reasonable to anyone who is educated but misunderstood by the Faubourg St.-Antoine. The result: his house and factory are pillaged, he is fortunate to escape with his life, and hundreds are dead.

There is much talk of a conspiracy behind these events. It is said that they were sparked by the Court to postpone the Estates, or by the aristocrats to discredit the *Tiers,* or by the duc d'Orléans to turn the people against the king. But even if one of these theories is true, the spark could do nothing unless the tinder were there.

The meetings of the electors of the sixty districts set off a strong emotion even among the great mass that could not vote.

PLATE 3: A family dinner at La Bretonne in Sacy—Restif's father and mother, a few servants, the children of his father's first and second marriages. From *Le Paysan Perverti,* 1784.

It made me uneasy to see it, uneasy because I know the hatred of the people for all who are well-off, an eternal and violent hatred that awaits only the occasion to make itself felt. Not that I rejoice at having been proved right; no, the event is much too grave for that.

One of my workers is called Daniol le Manceau, a bright boy but with a temper as fiery as his red hair; on occasion we have come to blows when he refused to obey an order. On the 24th he arrived at work enraged at a report that Réveillon had proposed that wages be reduced to ten sous a day; people had been up all night talking about it in the *faubourg*. "How can a man live on ten sous when a loaf of bread costs fifteen?" I was sure his story must be wrong but did not contradict him.

(What I suspected then was true. Réveillon had proposed that *both* wages and prices be reduced, to encourage commerce. But that was too complicated for the crowd to understand.)

I went to my isle but all was quiet. At Mme. de Beauharnais's that night the talk was all of the elections. I was called a shirker when I said I hadn't bothered to register and an aristocrat when I mentioned my fears about the *faubourg*. No one there knew anything of what was happening.

Saturday Daniol reported that St.-Marceau and the Gobelins had been aroused. But Sunday all was calm. Representatives from all sixty districts met at the Archevêché, beside Notre-Dame. It seemed that the danger had passed.

Monday morning I worked at home. When I went out, at three, many shops were closed. I heard the sound of a drum from the Place Maubert. A motley parade passed by, several hundred workers descending the rue de la Montagne-Ste.-Geneviève, armed with homemade clubs. One carried a gibbet with a crude effigy stuffed with cotton hanging by its neck; alongside, a placard that read: DECREE OF THE THIRD ESTATE CONDEMNING RÉVEILLON TO BE HANGED AND BURNED! The roughest group imaginable, tanners and cobblers, ragged Auvergnats and soot-blackened Savoyards. They shout as they march, slogans like "Kill the rich! Bread for two sous! Drown the priests!"

A group of Electors from the Archevêché arrived; they talked with some of the marchers. Some dispersed but others continued by the rue de Bièvre. One of the marchers addressed the spectators.

"We don't want to hurt anyone except Réveillon, because he wants us to starve!"

Reassured by this moderation, I followed the parade—at a certain distance. They went to the Hôtel de Ville, where they planted their gibbet on the usual site of executions, then set the effigy on fire. That was all. Returning home I saw that the Gardes Françaises had been called out; their battalions clattered down the rue St.-Jacques. With their appearance many shops reopened their doors.

Tuesday none of my workers showed up. I went to my isle and made a tour. No work being done on the docks. Crossed the Pont-Marie to the Marais, went out the rue St.-Antoine. The police everywhere, also detachments of the Gardes. The news of the disturbances had not reached the fashionable neighborhoods; a long file of elegant carriages trooped down the street, going to the races at Vincennes. Despite the presence of the Gardes, the carriages were often forced to stop, engulfed by hostile crowds, the horses made skittish by the press of bodies, the coachmen trying to control them while pretending nothing was happening. Shouts of "Cheap bread!" A group of men in shirt sleeves grabs the reins of an elegant coach, holds them until its mistress leans out the window and shouts, "Long live the Third Estate!"

(One sees in this the irrationality of the whole event. It was at an assembly of the voters of the Third Estate that poor Réveillon made his unfortunate remarks. I've learned since that he paid his workers more than the going wage and took care of them during the slow season when there was no work. But the emotions of the people know no logic.)

Who should come along but the duc d'Orléans, also off to the races. The king's brother and the richest man in France after the monarch. Cheers. The duke urges the crowd to be calm while his servants distribute coins left and right. Everyone says that he would like to see his brother deposed and take his place. But can he really believe that the road to Versailles passes through the Faubourg St.-Antoine?

That is all I saw. . . . In the evening we heard the sound of rifles coming from the east.

The next day we learned what had happened. Réveillon's house and factory completely devastated by the rioters. Hundreds killed by the troops before the disorders ceased. Many picked up in the cellars, dead or dead-drunk on Réveillon's wine. Nothing remained but the four walls.

The meeting of the Estates was postponed to May 4.

But Paris went back to work; the shops reopened, the markets were busy. On May 1st there was a crush of carriages in the Faubourg St.-Antoine as crowds trooped from all over Paris to see the ruins of Réveillon's house. Friends greeted each other as if at the theater, vendors sold refreshments. In Paris anything at all becomes an *entertainment,* even the aftereffects of a riot.

All was quiet but there were police everywhere. Two of the rioters were hung in the heart of the Faubourg St.-Antoine instead of the usual spot on the Grève, their bodies left exposed and rotting as a warning to the district. In my neighborhood the rue des Prêtres St.-Séverin was closed off for a house-to-house search for rioters. They arrested two workers and one woman. I heard that the curé of St.-Séverin was questioned about several suspects, notwithstanding the secret of the confessional. But where were the police before the disturbances, where have they been all those times I was attacked on my isle?

The sixty districts were still meeting to draw up their *Cahiers,* also their representatives at the Archevêché. The delegates from Paris for the Third Estate had not yet been chosen. Nonetheless the Estates opened on May 4th. The police patrols were doubled and redoubled, joined by cavalry of the Gardes riding three or five abreast. These precautions proved unnecessary; the only manifestation that day was a parade of carriages going to Versailles as everyone who could get away went to observe the procession of the delegates. That afternoon the streets here in Paris were unusually quiet.

For nine months the opening of the Estates had been hailed as the birth of a new era, but the first weeks of the babe's existence proved disappointing. For a few days there was a new journal hawked by streetboys everywhere, *Les Etats-Généraux;*

its author, the Comte de Mirabeau of Provence, an immediate leader of the Third Estate despite his title. Mirabeau dared attack the antique forms designed to humiliate the *Tiers* and to criticize the inaugural speech by Necker, which was so long and dull that several delegates were put to sleep. The journal was suppressed; the suppression protested; in the end the censorship was relaxed, but only to the extent of permitting excerpts from the minutes of the Estates, without commentary. Limited liberty that, and poor reading—a month passed in disputes on procedure, voting by head or order, etc.

Most people lost interest and returned to their daily cares. The price of bread continued to rise.

May 16: Surprising letter from Eberts in Neuwied. He wants to republish a selection of the costume engravings of Moreau, the ones for which I wrote *Tableaux de la bonne compagnie* two years ago. Reduced format this time, so the price can be lower. All he asks is twenty-six vignettes, this version to be called *Tableaux de la vie*. In the typical fashion of publishers he flatters me by speaking of the great success of my *Contemporaines* across the Rhine—a success from which I derived small profit; half the edition was pirated—his compatriots consider me a genius. Good for them! After that bouquet, that costs him nothing, he offers 150 livres for the new work, on condition that I get it to him by the middle of July. He could have written a bit sooner! At least he offers to pay in advance. I decide I must do it; I need the money. Small recompense for a *genius*. . . .

My answer: I shall do it, but will write nothing until his draft arrives. A piece of hackwork but difficult since I must affect that elegant style so beloved by the Germans, who think that the latest fashion from France is the epitome of civilization. When I write from the heart, as my nature dictates, I can cover pages and pages in a morning. But elegance does not come easy.

The *Thesmographe* was taking longer than I'd planned. I decided that if my notion of a Fourth Order of peasants were to be considered by the Estates, it must appear immediately, as a pamphlet. The writing took two days, printing it two more.

PLATE 4: "Les Adieux" by Moreau le Jeune, one of the plates from *Les Tableaux de la Vie*. The quality of the engravings made the collection a success throughout Europe. This was Restif's only work to appear in English until the twentieth century.

The title: *The Strongest of All Pamphlets*, because I believe it is that. Took the copies around myself, to Duchesne, Mérigot, Guillot, Madaran and the booksellers of the Palais-Royal. A labor of love, or rather duty, but I'm afraid the work got lost in the crush; the bookstalls of Paris groan under the weight of pamphlets of all sorts, no one seems to read anything else. A bad time for literature.

What can I say about the booksellers of Paris? A strange tribe, they live off writers but despise them, have no loyalty. Consider the widow Duchesne: she made a fortune on *Les Contemporaines* but refused to handle *Les Nuits de Paris,* even though much of that work was written in a room I rented above her shop. Guillot is a schemer, Madaran a cheat. And yet a writer who works for a living is bound hand and foot to these parasites.

The Electors of Paris voted unanimously in favor of full liberty of the press, declaring it indispensable to the action of the Estates. Indeed it is, and to literature also! What misery the censors have caused me for twenty-five years! I envy the fate of ordinary men whose profession does not subject them to the whim of arbitrary officials who can deprive them of liberty at any time. There are times when I rejoice in my maladies, because I imagine they will keep me out of prison; to tell the truth I fear death less than the Bastille. What I write here I keep in a secret place and would never dare publish. But I have been courageous at times; when the censors demanded cuts in *L'Ecole des Pères* that I found unacceptable, I printed up fifty or so copies with the offending paragraphs omitted, distributed them to the police, then sold the rest of the edition in its original state. But I trembled for months, afraid my ruse would be discovered.

I consider myself as much a printer as a writer, even if the former has less glory to it. My first novel was not written until I was thirty, but I had been working at the press since the age of seventeen, first an apprentice in Auxerre, then a journeyman, then foreman; now I have my own shop, which is small and a disaster.

At the time when I decided to write I was working for F. A.

Quillau, rue du Fouarre, a young man who left absolutely everything up to me. My job, as foreman, involved: (1) reading the first proofs; (2) supervising sixty-six workers; (3) distributing the type and keeping it in good condition; (4) choosing type faces and sizes for titles, chapter heads, etc.; (5) doing the payroll on Saturdays; (6) seeing that the workers did not sleep on the job; (7) correcting the *tierces* or final proofs; (8) talking to suppliers and customers, which should have been the job of the boss but which he neglected; (9) setting any citations in Greek. In addition I chose the paper, fixed the margins, and supervised the apprentices when they cleaned up, usually on Sundays. When I was done with all that I was too tired to have any fun. Sometimes I stayed at the press and wrote letters to pretty girls before going home to Agnès Lebègue, who was already unfaithful; that was my only amusement.

It was those letters that led to my second career. I had seen Rose Bourgeois out walking with her mother and sister one Sunday afternoon in the rue Contrescarpe. I trembled with desire at the first sight of her, followed the three women until they returned home to the rue de la Traversière, some rooms behind a silk shop. I began to write love letters, unsigned, leaving them in the shop or sometimes the kitchen, which I entered by the back door when no one was watching. I began to be noticed but could not keep away. I wrote that I was invisible, a spirit of the air, but passionately in love. Once I saw Rose reading one of my epistles; her cheeks were flushed; when her sister came into the room Rose hid the note. I grew bolder and finally was caught as I deposited letter number twelve.

It was in October at about five, the hour when the lamps are lit. I was seized by the collar, found myself held by two shopboys who shouted, "Be quiet or we'll call the police!"

I let myself be led inside without protesting; Rose looked down at the floor as I went past her. They took me to the dining room in back and stood guard until M. Bourgeois arrived.

"Here he is!" With a wave of his arm M. Bourgeois sent everyone out of the room. He presented my letters to me and asked if I was the "spirit of the air," their author. I acknowledged that he had the right man.

"By what right do you take it upon yourself to arouse in the heart of my daughter a feeling as dangerous as love?"——"By no right, sir, but that of the imperious sentiment of my own heart!"——"Young man, you speak vehemently!"——"I speak from my heart, sir!"——"Your conduct would be inexcusable, if I were less indulgent . . ."

And then, to my astonishment, the good man advised me that my letters displayed a great *talent* as a writer; they had enchanted his daughter, nay, his daughters (Rose had confided in her sister). He advised me to put my gifts to better use than writing *billets-doux* and to return when I had made something of myself. In the meanwhile I was not to see his daughter or communicate with her in any way.

With that he let me go. I was glad that I hadn't been forced to tell him that I was thirty and married; it would have spoiled everything.

How many times since have I passed that building, now occupied by others, and exclaimed: *"Salve, o domus, quae me fecisti scriptorum!*—Hail, O house, where I became a writer!"

Thus finished the shameful epoch of my life, years of nothingness, misery, abasement, years without pride that had led to a dreadful marriage. I began to feel that it was not too late to amount to something.

One evening, walking along the quai de Gèvres, I saw a pretty young woman inside a shop buying herself a hat. She reminded me of Rose, just as Rose had called forth the image of Jeanette Rousseau. This time, instead of writing letters, I began a novel.

As soon as I had that idea the quai was no longer a simple row of shops, it seemed an enchanted palace. The shopgirls, the other customers, even the crowd in the street—everyone was beautiful. The light of the lamps transformed them; I felt that I was at a fête given by the emperor of China. Thus the first person to enjoy my book was myself, and I had not yet written a word.

I began in a state of inconceivable exaltation, that state of effervescence necessary to writers and poets, but it did not last long. Nonetheless I persisted. The result was *La Famille ver-*

tueuse, published by Duchesne, 1755, two thousand copies. It was not very good; I had not yet found my own style but imitated all the books I had read.

All of my works have been inspired by women and by the streets of Paris. . . .

The draft from Eberts did not arrive until the middle of June. At the same time Mérigot agreed to take the *Nuits de Paris*. I was happy about that for a day, until I realized that what with the cost of printing the eight volumes and what I paid for the engravings, I was losing money . . .

June 13th: An astonishing letter from my wife, Agnès Lebègue, informing me that two days before, the 11th, she was attacked in broad daylight by the despicable Augé, only two steps from here, rue St.-Victor near the Place Maubert. I must admit I regret that I was not a witness to the scene; it would have brought me a delicious satisfaction. The two MONSTERS battling it out in the mud!

Augé "collared her violently, heaped abuse on her, and demanded his wife back!" The frightened old woman took refuge in a pastry shop and sent for the police. Enraged and persistent, Augé waited outside. When the gendarme arrived, Augé got to him before his victim, filed a complaint that she was keeping her daughter, his wife, in her house. (It would be to the credit of A. Lebègue if this were so, but it is I who am responsible for saving our daughter's life.) She was dragged from precinct to precinct, first to the station house at the Place Maubert, which was closed (oh! the Paris police!), then to rue de la Vieille Bûcherie, also closed, then to rue St.-André-des-Arts.

En route, "among other insults," the madman accused her of pimping for *me*. She complained that she felt weak and he shouted, "Hold on to the officer! you're used to giving yourself to everyone!"

At the station she was treated like a whore and could hardly manage to obtain a glass of water. Augé made out a formal complaint against her on the subject of Agnès and she one against him for his abuse and blows; the captain must have been bewildered by this lovely family scene.

So now it is all on record that they are both crazy and no one can say that my griefs are all my own invention. A. Lebègue deserved all she got but it came too late to do any good—the damage has been done and Agnès and I are the ones who must suffer. And yet my wife is only malicious, scheming, stubborn, headstrong, while Augé is a wild beast. . . .

Twice this spring, April 14 and June 6, I have been attacked on the Ile St.-Louis while making my sentimental promenades among my *dates*. On the latter occasion it was at the rue de Bretonvilliers that a horde of vicious children swarmed about me, like a swarm of angry bees, hooting and shouting insults. I stood where I was and turned my eyes to heaven, the only witness of the infamy I am forced to suffer, fearing that at any moment I might suffer bodily harm. In the midst of the shouts from the crowd of nasty little savages, smelling of sweat and urine, I heard one call to another, "Is this the one the dark man told us about?" So my suspicions were confirmed; it is Augé who is the instigator of these assaults! Fortunately a washerwoman came by and ordered the little devils to leave me alone. Her language was crude but effective. Thank heaven for that good woman who has a heart beneath her ugly exterior! I escaped by the Pont de la Tournelle.

Thus the MONSTER continues to persecute me, and all because I have saved my daughter Agnès from his perverse and violent treatment, because I wish to protect my own flesh and blood from being degraded like the most abject and depraved whore, and by a man who has no fortune and cannot hold a job! And there is nothing I can do to prevent this scene from occurring again.

There is a district in the center of Paris that has always been the quintessence of French civilization. It is not the Court but something better; often in advance on matters of fashion and intellect, it corrects Versailles and leads it, drawing its authority from the customs of the nation. This neighborhood, the brain of Paris, is that of the rue St.-Honoré and the Palais-Royal. The rue St.-Honoré, at first sight, appears only the province of fashionable shops, but there are an infinity of men of good taste who live above these shops, and especially in the adjoining streets. Added to them are others, who spend all day in the district, eating in the restaurants, gambling in private clubs, chatting in the cafés, promenading in the narrow streets. They go home late at night and know nothing more of the Marais, the Faubourg St.-Germaine, or Montmartre than their own apartment.

At the beginning of this decade, the duc d'Orléans added the new galleries to the Palais-Royal, three massive blocks of buildings in the latest style around the edge of the garden, with a continuous wide arcade that reaches up to the top of the *entresol* forming an all-weather promenade. When the Opéra burned down in 1786 a theater was added. The duke did everything with great style; the new palace was quickly filled with the most elegant shops and became the most frequented rendezvous in Paris, above all for foreigners, libertines, courtesans, gamblers, in short all that floating society that sets the fad and fashion and never seems to be short of ready money, however large its debts. Every apartment, shop, room and attic was let for the highest rents and the duke found himself even more wealthy than before.

This neighborhood and the Palais-Royal have long been the object of my promenades. Of late it underwent yet another transformation. The duke fancies himself a great liberal and does all he can to make himself popular among the leaders of the Third Estate; many suspect that he would like to see his brother deposed and himself on the throne at the demand of the people.

The Palais-Royal is private property; order is kept by guards in the employ of the duke; the police must remain in the streets outside the gates. The result: a plethora of bookstalls where all sorts of pamphlets and books are sold without approval of the censors. Also a number of cafés that have become veritable debating societies, above all le Caveau and the Café de Foy. Thus the Palais-Royal has become the political center of Paris, rivaled only by the Hôtel de Ville. But it has not, by any means, been deserted by its former habitués; the libertines and street-walkers are as numerous as ever. A strange combination, perhaps, but do not all visitors always marvel at *la légèreté française?*

All I know about politics is what I read in the journals at the Café Manoury, Place des Ecoles, where I say hello to a few acquaintances, glance at the games of chess and checkers, then retire to my favorite seat in a corner. The debates of the Estates in Versailles are already history; they are not my concern. But I observe the capital of this great kingdom, and this spring I have noted two thermometers of political fever, the cafés of the Palais-Royal and the market at the Place Maubert.

Bread is scarce and dear. If bread were not scarce and dear nine out of ten Parisians would care nothing for what takes place in Versailles.

May 13: Two hundred troops stationed at the Place Maubert, especially at the doors of the bakeries. The price of bread up.

June 6: Troops again, Place Maubert, market day.

June 10: Bread in short supply and dear. The loaves Marion brought home taste sour; rotten flour mixed in the dough. People talk of a plot to starve Paris, the Prévôt Flesnelles and the Intendant Berthier making millions by speculating in grain while the people go hungry.

The women waiting in line say there would be plenty for everyone if not for the regulations that stop grain at the customs barriers about the city. The harvest is still two months off; last year's harvest was a disaster. Never before have I heard women talk about the problem of supplying the capital, but then bread has never been so scarce. We live by bread; everything else is only a sauce.

June 13: Patrols at the markets, the price of bread up again.

June 19: At my shop my workmen talk about nothing but the price of bread. Daniol le Manceau wants to hang all the bakers and the speculators.

June 25: A housewife says that now that the Third Estate

has become the National Assembly perhaps there will be bread.

June 28: Many people sick because of the flour from rotten grain mixed into the dough. The loaves Marion brought home are dark, crumbly and sour. Assembly or no, everyone is unhappy and angry.

June 29: I pass a horrible night; dysentery—diarrhea, cramps, flatulence. My daughters are angels but I am ashamed to ask them for the services I need. Felt very old.

June 30: Patrols of six of the Gardes Françaises stationed at all bakeries to keep order. Rumors that the Court itself is speculating in grain to pay its debts.

Thus the Place Maubert. At the Palais-Royal other scenes, other concerns:

June 10: Tried to check on the sale of my pamphlet, but could not even find it among the great chaos of tracts of all kinds. According to one bookseller thirteen came out yesterday, sixteen the day before, ninety-two last week. At Desennes' I could hardly squeeze from the door to the bureau, so crowded were the aisles with purchasers and those who stand at the counters, reading. Almost all of these tracts violent against the clergy and the nobility; I see that I have been much too timid so far in the *Thesmographe*.

In the arcades and the garden at least twice the usual crowd. Not only are the cafés completely filled, but a press of spectators crowds the doors and windows listening to the orators, who stand on tables and chairs. These are mostly young men, their clothes in a calculated disarray, their unkempt hair floating wildly about their heads. They express the boldest ideas, denounce the Estates as a trick on the people, ridicule the queen and the clergy, call for an English-style government or a Swedish-style government or no government at all, insist that there is a plot to starve Paris, a *Pacte de la Famine* (which is where they and the housewives of the Place Maubert agree); and the more outrageous their sentiments the louder the applause from the crowds.

Meanwhile the peripatetics and nymphs continue to ply their trade to assuage the passions of those exhausted by political discussions. . . .

June 20: The crowds as dense as ever but in a fevered state, alarm and apprehension on every face. News from Versailles that the king has decided to be done with the Estates, has locked the delegates out of the Palace and posted troops with bayonets to make certain that none should enter. Rumors that the delegates of the *Tiers* have all been arrested, that they are fleeing to Nantes, that the Bastille is being readied for mass arrests, that German mercenaries are marching on Paris, that no flour has been permitted to enter the city, that the queen has sent to Vienna for help, etc.—each fresh report shouted by some hysterical messenger, all believed at once by the crowd and the orators.

Later it was learned that the delegates of the Third Estate had found an unused building near the Palace, an indoor tennis court as it happened, crowded inside and there declared themselves to be a National Assembly, swearing that they would never be dissolved except by their own consent, whatever the king might order. With that news the spirits of the crowd picked up a bit, although the alarms about the king's intentions continued. I returned home half expecting to find the streets patrolled by German troops, but all was quiet.

June 24: At least ten thousand people in the district waiting for news; the agitated crowd spilling out of the Palais-Royal to the surrounding streets. Word in the morning that the king had sent the Marquis de Brézé to order the Assembly to disperse, Mirabeau had declared they would leave only by the force of bayonets, the delegates had voted themselves immune to arrest.

A number of the Gardes Françaises desert their barracks and come to the garden of liberty to show their sympathy for the popular cause—they are received with open arms. Astonishing to see those soldiers in their blue uniforms applauding orators whose sentiments border on treason, plied with wine by the men and embraced by all the women, respectable bourgeoises as well as the usual flotilla of whores. Late in the afternoon I saw one of these troops, half-drunk, a stout matron on one arm and the sleaziest of *filles* on the other, reeling along the arcade, shouting *"Vive le peuple!"* and *"Vive l'Assemblé!"* between hiccups.

June 26: It's all over, the Court has given in, the king has ordered the nobility and clergy to join the delegates of the Third Estate, has recognized the Assembly. . . . The news spread through Paris like wildfire.

In the evening the Palais-Royal presents a fantastic spectacle, every window illuminated and the most brilliant display of fireworks I've ever seen; the expense must be enormous, but that will hardly bother the duc d'Orléans.

June 27: Yet another fête, courtesy of the duke. As usual on such occasions, the pickpockets are out in force, slipping like eels through the close-packed throng. Each time a rocket went off ten thousand voices sighed "Ah! Ah!" while clever hands slipped into gussets and pockets; by the light of the next flare the careless discovered that purses, watches, shoe buckles and even garters had disappeared.

Others took advantage of the press of the crowd for different amusements. I saw several girls surrounded by circles of young rogues who could not have cared less about politics. As the rockets burst these nymphs were levitated several feet above the ground; one seemed to float almost horizontally, like a goddess on a ceiling of painted clouds. What they were subject to out of sight in the moments of darkness can only be imagined; their cries were lost in the roar of the crowd. It is true that I couldn't tell if they were cries of indignation or delight.

June 28: Sunday promenade with Agnès, who wanted to see the famous place. Unfortunately we found the gates shut; the guards said there were already too many people inside for safety.

June 30: Recovering from my illness but tempted by the fine weather I go to the Café Manoury to read the papers, then to the Palais-Royal. By some miracle I found a seat at the Café de Foy, not without some questioning glances directed at my old clothes. There were the usual orators, to whom I no longer listened.

But at about seven a distraught young man climbs up on a table, breathless and unkempt, demands the attention of the crowd. Just a week ago, he declaims, we were honored by the visit of the Gardes Françaises! (Cheers for the Gardes.)

Since then eleven of these patriots have been imprisoned in

the Abbaye for swearing allegiance to the Assembly! (Groans and shouts of *"Vive l'Assemblé!"*)

This afternoon the order has been given to transfer these men to Bicêtre, to be mixed with the thieves, pimps and scum imprisoned there. (Shouts of "No! No!")

"They ask for your help!"

At this a whole battalion of young men leaps to its feet.

"To the Abbaye!" they shout, like the chorus at the Opéra. And off they go.

To my astonishment they are back in half an hour, with the eleven Gardes, plus another old soldier who had been imprisoned for so long that he could hardly walk. I have no idea how they managed it.

The released prisoners were of course cheered as so many heros of antiquity, offered food and wine, surrounded by the prettiest girls. As I left I heard some young men making arrangements for the Gardes to spend the night in the Palais, considered safe territory. No doubt they will be passed from one call girl to another, hidden from the police for as long as necessary. And given the location, it will take years for them to run out of companions, even if they stay with each only one night. What a life!

Mercier informs me that we have had a Revolution, one of the most notable in history, all the more remarkable because no blood was spilled.

THE FALL OF THE BASTILLE

JULY 1789

I missed it. Working to finish the *Tableaux de la Vie*—Eberts kept sending frantic letters from Neuwied—I stayed at home writing until three in the afternoon.

Mercier had been a bit hasty in concluding that the Revolution was over, but then Mercier is marvelously good-natured, and therefore an optimist. For all the fireworks at the Palais-Royal, bread remained scarce, dear and bad at the Place Maubert. The papers I read at the Café Manoury were full of the speeches of Mirabeau, Sieyès, Bailly, but the Assembly was ten miles away in Versailles. The Gardes Françaises might support the people, but there were other troops loyal to the Court all around the capital. After the few days of euphoria at the end of June the Palais-Royal became suspicious again; on July 5 I heard an orator denounce the *plot* of the "Queen's Party," a plan to dismiss Necker and the Assembly, besiege Paris and starve it into submission. On July 10 there was a huge crowd before the Hôtel de Ville, completely filling the Place de Grève and spreading out on the adjoining quais; the Electors were protesting the presence of mercenary troops on the approaches to Paris. At the Place Maubert there were now twelve men with bayonets in front of every bakery. The housewives shouted they had never seen anything like it and blamed it all on the queen.

Thus a cloud of misfortunes gathered over this unfortunate capital, the most free, the most agreeable, the most voluptuous of cities. On the tenth the agitation was a murmur; the next day it became louder. At ten in the evening a young aristocrat, freshly arrived from Versailles, tried to calm the crowd at the

Palais-Royal. "All is well!" he shouted. I admired his courage, considering the place, but doubted that he knew anything. The next day the storm broke.

I report only what I've seen:

July 12: Worked on the *Tableaux* all day, taking advantage of the Sunday quiet. Out at six; crossed the Pont Neuf, going to the Café M. On the quai du Louvre I am caught in a crowd fleeing toward the east, whole families dressed for their Sunday promenade, children crying, women pale, men carrying babies on their shoulders, all looking as if the earth were about to swallow them up. I stop a young father to ask what has happened, hear only: "Tuileries! . . . cavalry . . . Lambesc! . . . Germans!" Then he races onward. At the corner of the rue de l'Arbre-Sec a young girl in a flowing white dress climbs up on a balustrade, begins to shout, "Cowards! Cowards!"—A young man calls to her, blows her a kiss. "We'll be back with guns, my angel!" This calms her, but she remains where she is, tapping her foot impatiently. . . .

What caused this Sunday crowd to flee?

Enticed by a blue sky, the city-dweller takes his wife and children to breathe the pure air in the gardens designed by Le Nôtre. Children sail their boats, fountains shimmer in the shade of the ancient trees. But on the terrace that overlooks the Seine some hotheads provoke the troops that are stationed about the park by an unwise commander. They are mercenaries, the Royal Allemands. A stone hits the helmet of Lambesc, the officer in charge. Indignant, he trembles. His temper overcomes his reason; he leads his troops into the Garden of Kings . . . sacred shelter, made for games, laughter and love where Mars should be found only as a statue . . . he advances, saber in hand . . . young mothers cry out in terror, snatch up their children, who cry at having to forgo their innocent games. Lambesc orders his troops to halt. But it is too late, an old man has already been trampled under the horses' hooves.

I went on the Palais-Royal to catch up on the news. In the morning word had come that Necker was dismissed and already on the road back to Switzerland. All the rumors of the "Court plot" were confirmed. In the afternoon there had been an impromptu parade through the streets of the district and along

PLATE 5: Lambesc's *Royal Allemands* charging into the Tuileries Gardens, July 12, 1789. Drawn by Moreau le Jeune, who had done the engravings of *Les Tableaux de la Vie*. Eyewitness accounts contradict Restif's version of this incident.

the boulevards; the young men of the Palais-Royal had taken the busts of Necker and d'Orléans from the wax museum of Curtius and held them aloft, calling on the people to arm themselves. The Palais-Royal was transformed. Instead of a debating club and pleasure palace it had become a military GHQ. The wild-haired young men who for weeks had been making motions and proposals as if the spot were a second Assembly now played at being generals and aides-de-camp. Everyone had a bit of a leaf in his hat or hair; this, I learned, had been designated the symbol of hope and patriotism by one of the orators calling the people to arms. I hastened to procure one for myself, but with some difficulty; the lower branches of the trees were all bare.

Messengers arrive, orders are given, emissaries sent out. The sound of gunfire. A courier runs up with the report that the Gardes Françaises have chased Lambesc's Royal Allemands from the Tuileries and the Champs-Elysées; they have retreated to the other side of the river. Much shouting of battles to be fought, heads to fall, Liberty, the Nation, etc. Despite their fiery words, sloppy dress, disheveled hair, I am reassured that these are young men of good family and education, not the bandits of the *faubourgs* . . .

At eleven I decide I must get home. The city has become an armed camp. An improvised troop waits for God knows what, rue des Petits-Champs, armed with sticks and swords. Rue des Vieux Augustins I am almost killed by a stray pistol shot. In the Halles the meat packers and greengrocers have organized a militia. Fortunately my clothes are old and worn—they let me pass.

By midnight I have gone no further than the rue des Prouvaires. A young tough seizes me by the collar. "An abbé!" he shouts. "He's too old!" a voice replies in the darkness, "Let him go!"

I fall in the mud, get up, brush myself off. The air is acrid with the smoke of torches. The blacksmiths are all at work, their forges casting an orange glow into the dark streets, but they are hammering pikes, not horseshoes. At the Pont-Notre-Dame another improvised troop. The green leaf in my hat and some well-chosen words persuade them that I am a good fellow. On the Cité I see a group of men breaking into a gunsmith's. Are they thieves or patriots? By half past twelve I am home; Agnès and Marion are up, trembling for my safety. I tell them I tremble more for Paris than for myself. . . .

July 13: After a fitful sleep, I am awakened by the alarm cannon fired at the Hôtel de Ville. Soon after, the tocsin punctuates the dawn, the deep bourdon of Notre-Dame leading the solemn chorus of bells. My chest was bothering me after so little sleep, but I could not stay in bed, nor did I think of working. The damp wind carried the odor of smoke; I learned later that the customs barriers had all been burned that night. It grew light but the sky remained overcast.

At eight a troop of beggars, tramps and bandits from the Faubourg St.-Marcel passed by on the rue des Rats; among them I recognized some of the burly savages who gather the wood floated to the Ile Louvois. They shouted, "Cheap bread! Arm the people! Open the prisons!" To me they seemed to announce the day of judgment for the rich and the privileged, all who sleep under feather quilts; I saw the city I love caught between the armies of the king and the threat of anarchy.

But others had seen the danger. At ten a drummer went by, calling on all Electors to report to their district. This time I regretted not having registered; it was no longer a matter of selecting a delegate but of saving Paris from famine, pillage and rape.

I went off anyway, to the Mathurin church; the confusion was such that I managed to get inside; so did many others without cards. The nave resembled the Café de Foy with its orators standing on chairs; the coming and going in the aisles was like the arcades of the Palais-Royal. Motions, proposals, reports—the barriers burned, some prisons emptied, convents invaded by brigands in search of hoarded grain, crowds at the Invalides and the Arsenal demanding arms. No sure reports on the royal troops; for the moment they seem to remain in their encampments.

A delegate from the Electors at the Hôtel de Ville arrives, manages to obtain attention. The municipal government has assumed responsibility for law and order as well as defense; the Gardes Françaises have offered their support, some of the Swiss troops may come over also; most important, a Milice Bourgeois is being formed, made up of responsible citizens.

Reassured by this news, I return home. There are bands of men with pikes who cry *"Vive le Tiers Etat!"* . . . The sky remains heavy, reminiscent of the hailstorm a year ago this day that destroyed crops all around Paris, the commencement of our present troubles. . . . Late in the afternoon I see the first formation of the new militia on the rue St.-Jacques; in their hats a cockade of red and blue, colors of the city of Paris.

As the sun sets, at least three hundred of the Gardes march to the Hôtel de Ville, drums beating, cheered by the people in the rue St.-Jacques; they also wear the red and blue cockade. . . . In the evening all windows are lit by order of the Hôtel de Ville; the purpose: to aid the new militia in its rounds. At the corner of the rue Galande an improvised forge; ruddy-faced men work through the night, fabricating pikes. No one seems to sleep—a sinister carnival.

Thus the first two days of the crisis; the next would be more terrible yet. To be honest, I must admit I thought instead that everything would calm down. With every hour that passed an attack on Paris grew less likely; now that the citizens were armed there would be a bloody defense, and how could Louis gain from that? The new militia, whose patrols passed all night, seemed ready to stop a popular insurrection like that of April. I went to sleep exhausted but reassured.

Here is a tale of that night, as told by the Owl of the *Nuits de Paris,* the Nocturnal Spectator. Did it happen or not? I deny nothing:

"Reassured by the creation of the *milice,* I dared wander through the streets of the capital. But alas! every law can be abused, every drug contains a poison. In a quiet street of the Marais I hear shouts. Six men are chasing a young girl who looks like a chambermaid. Just as the hunted hare seeks any refuge, so the girl throws herself into my arms. I had no weapons and was helpless to defend her. The pursuers wear the blue and red cockade; they carry pikes. 'We wish her no harm,' their leader explains, 'but we must search this house; there may be arms inside.'—'Alas, messieurs! I am alone. All the other servants left this morning with the master and mistress. I'm afraid to be alone in the house and was going to my friend's house when you saw me leave.'—'All the same we must search!' The girl was forced to open the door of the house and go in with the six men. I remained in the shadows outside and listened. I hear the girl's voice shout for help from within. Just then another patrol goes by. I stop them. 'Messieurs, a patrol has just entered this house but I think they are thieves in disguise; the chambermaid who opened for them has shouted for help.' They force the door. There is a shot—the thieves had posted a sentinel who fired in the air as a signal—then loud footsteps as the others run out to the garden, dropping their loot as they escape. The girl had recognized them, all servants from houses in the neighborhood who knew her masters were away. Not content to steal, they wanted to rape her; that was when she had shouted, despite their threats. The true patrol put all in order, locked the doors, escorted the girl to her friend's house. The ordinary police would not have done as well."

July 14: I must admit that on this great day I slept late, then stayed in bed working on the *Tableaux*. It was three-thirty when I went out, my head still heavy, stumbling along as if drunk. A leaden day, gray sky threatening rain, no breeze. Crossed the Cité, then the Pont-Notre-Dame; the bright light by the river wakes me up a bit.

I'm about to go to my isle when I notice a noisy crowd on the Grève. Mostly laborers, some women, a few children darting in and out like swallows; muskets, pikes, shouting. I draw closer and suddenly notice—bobbing up and down like Punch and Judy puppets but dripping blood—two heads stuck onto pikes. . . .

There are triumphant shouts, "The Bastille has fallen!" I don't believe it. The crowd passes on, with their horrible trophies.

CAFE
DE FOY

PLATE 6: July 12, 1789, at the Palais-Royal. Standing on a table, Camille Desmoulins calls the people to arms. From *Tableaux Historiques de la Révolution Francaise,* Paris, 1801.

By the Hôtel de Ville, lying in a stream of muddy water, a uniformed corpse. It has no head. Five or six men stand about, as if it were a dead pig. One pokes at the boots with a stick.

I ask who it is. "The commander of the Bastille."

Another noisy ragtail cluster crosses the place, emerging from the rue des Martyrs. A pirate of a man with a long black mustache waves a sword about; at its tip, a bouquet of dripping viscera. No one but me trembles at this barbaric sight.

The gray sky is like a curtain of steel. I go up the rue St.-Antoine. Every window in every dingy house is open and crowded with spectators. I pass stretchers bearing some of the casualties of the siege. Behind them, some of the Swiss troops, defenders of the fortress, now prisoners. Shouts of "Hang them! Hang them!" Young and pretty girls at the windows join in the cry.

A giant of a Swiss soldier, his head covered by a butcher's apron, is led along by a young rascal who can't be older than thirteen. This little tiger shouts obscenities while beating his captive's shins with a stick.

I arrive, finally, at the Bastille. There it is, that prison I so feared three years ago that I hardly dared glance at it when I passed by every evening, rue Neuve-St.-Gilles. The siege, indeed, is over; the fortress is being looted. From the high towers precious documents float down into the moats. I find it difficult to believe what my eyes see.

After this day an attack by the royal troops no longer seems unlikely. Paving stones are pried up to form barricades, chairs taken from churches piled on top of them; every street is patrolled, every man is armed. Paris has taken its prize; now it waits. . . .

Shall I speak of what took place that evening on my isle? No, this is not a time for personal affairs. . . .

The night of the 14th was all alarms and patrols. The next day the shops remained closed, the sky gray. No traffic, because of the barricades. But in the afternoon the delegates of Paris brought the word that the king had promised to withdraw his troops. The bells of Notre-Dame tolled while a *Te Deum* celebrated the deliverance of the capital.

On the 16th life began again; the shops opened, mail was delivered, there were long lines at the bakeries but no disturbances, the barricades were dismantled. It was announced that Lafayette the general and Bailly the astronomer had been chosen to hold the reins of the municipality, Lafayette as commander of the *milice,* Bailly as mayor. Necker was recalled; Polignac and d'Artois, leaders of the queen's party, fled abroad. Louis promised to come to Paris; the victory of the city appeared complete.

I went to the Palais-Royal. In the cafés a great dispute. "The king is coming to Paris. He wants to show us he bears no grudge for the capture of the Bastille!"—"Let him come," the skeptics cried. "But he won't come!"—"We know the goodness of his heart," answered those who had faith.

For once the skeptics are proven wrong. The 17th, under a serene sky that promises the end of all our troubles, Louis comes to visit the people of Paris. Without troops, without any guards other than an escort of one hundred deputies of the Assembly, the king arrives at the capital.

On this day the *white* of the standard of the monarchy is added to the *red* and *blue* of Paris to create the TRICOLOR, new symbol of the Nation.

I was there when the cortège arrived at the Hôtel de Ville, just one of the immense crowd that overflowed the Grève, hung from every lamppost and window, had been waiting since noon. First Lafayette, Liberator of America and now of Paris, noble and handsome, mounted on a white horse. Then Bailly, the new mayor, preceding the royal carriage on foot. Along the route of the procession, a double line of the Gardes, their rifles held upside-down as a sign of peace. Among the huge crush of spectators, a sprinkling of monks and nuns, the tricolor cockade pinned to their habits—a strange sight, but then the churches also were decorated with the national colors. Shouts from the crowd: *"VIVE LA NATION! VIVE LA LIBERTE!"*

On the steps of the Hôtel de Ville, Bailly gives Louis the bright ribbon worn by everyone else, and with a show of cheerful good will the monarch pins it to his hat. He enters the Hôtel de Ville under an arch of crossed swords. A few minutes later he appears at a balcony and waves to the crowd.

This time they shout, *"VIVE LE ROI!"*

When Louis descends to regain his carriage, the crowd breaks through the line of Gardes. A young woman in rags who looks as if she sells turnips in some market throws her arms around the king's neck. Youngsters pour wine for the coachmen. For fifteen minutes no one can move. Forgotten are all the fears of famine, of the troops around Paris, of the Austrian queen, of her courtiers, of the many millions wasted on jewels.

The next morning, a normal market, Place Maubert, only a small patrol of the *milice* to keep order and that unnecessary. Bread suddenly cheaper and plentiful. The cause, no doubt, the destruction of the customs barriers, but many housewives attributed it to the king's visit. . . . A great crowd at the church of St.-Séverin for the funeral of an apprentice tailor of the rue de la Huchette killed at the Bastille. The procession passed under my windows on the rue de la Bûcherie and included a detachment of the *milice* led by muffled drums; the district paid for the ceremony. This young man had planned to be married on Tuesday; had it not been for the present events he would have worked as a tailor, fathered a brood of children and died unnoticed by anyone. Today he is a hero. If things had gone otherwise on the 14th he would have been tossed into an unmarked grave as a rebel. . . .

Sunday to the Tuileries with Marion; it is only a week since the attack of Lambesc's cavalry but it seems as if a century had passed. The only troops in evidence today the *milice,* plus a few of the Gardes strolling with pretty girls. Every man wearing a tricolor cockade; the women all ribbons of the same colors. One girl, a pretty blonde, had a tricolor *dress*—left arm and side red, right arm and side blue, center white. Perhaps a seamstress who ran it up in a hurry. She was applauded wherever she went and seemed to enjoy the attention. . . .

There remains to be recounted a day that soiled the glory of this month; two hideous murders like two spots of blood on a banner. I was witness to one; I wish that neither had occurred,

I wish that I had witnessed nothing, I wish that I did not have to write about it.

I admit to being weak in these matters; I have never been able to stand the sight of blood, mine or another's; I've never been a soldier, never killed a human being or even an animal—and all that is daily fare for others. There is a frivolity and ferocity in the people, in certain of the people—I would not wish to accuse all of them, far from it—a savage exaltation at the taste of blood that makes me tremble, makes me tremble more than the blood itself. I can understand the desire to take justice into one's own hands when it has so long been denied, but the cruelty of the spectacle is insupportable. . . .

We have all been so badly trained: public torture of all kinds, dismemberment, the rack, gibbets on the public square, men burned at the stake—all of this a show for the entire populace, women and children included, a veritable school of barbarism. Instead of civilizing us our masters have trained us to become cruel, because they are cruel themselves. . . . I remember the Tartar Tourangeot in the days of my apprenticeship at Auxerre, not a bad sort as workmen go, a great drinker and skirt-chaser, I remember him recounting his exploits in Flanders as an infantryman, the houses he had burned, the peasants he had killed, the women he had raped, the villages looted and deserted after the army had passed, all these crimes so many heroic exploits because he had worn the uniform of the king. And those nights in the dormitory under the eaves the other apprentices hung on his every word, envying his *good fortune* to have enjoyed such great adventures in his youth. . . . The powerful of the earth reap what they have sown and I fear that this may only be the beginning. But it makes me sick to see it. . . .

The Intendant Berthier had long been blamed for the shortage of bread, accused of trying to starve the capital instead of assuring its provisions. His father-in-law, Foulon, was hated as a financier, suspected of speculating in grain; he was reported to have said that if the people of Paris were hungry they had only to eat hay. He had the misfortune to be appointed minister after the dismissal of Necker, a post that he held for three days without doing anything.

After the fall of the Bastille, Foulon retired to his estate at Viry. Fearing an attempt on his life he took the extreme precaution of announcing that he was dead. The story was not improbable; the man was seventy-four and in bad health. His servants put on black; there was a burial; meanwhile he tried to flee to Belgium. But he was betrayed by one of the men he had trusted, seized by a band of peasants who sent him back to Paris to be judged. Because of his celebrated *mot,* he was transported in a hay wain, his shirt stuffed with dry grass, hooted and ridiculed all along the road.

He arrives, is taken to the Hôtel de Ville. The Electors are embarrassed by the presence of this unwanted prisoner, as is Bailly, the mayor of a week, as is Lafayette, general of the Militia but still unsure of his authority. They don't want to hand him over to the judgment of the mob; they don't want to lose the precarious confidence of the people. The workers remain armed and the orators of the Palais-Royal shout that heads must roll for justice to be done.

For six hours they debate. The crowd outside grows ever larger. They begin to shout that they are betrayed, the prisoner has been permitted to escape. (Here I recount what I learned from Daniol, who is proud to have been part of the mob.) Lafayette himself goes out on the stairs with the prisoner to show the crowd that Foulon is still there; he pleads for patience, talks of respect for the judgment of the law. Someone shouts, "This man was judged when he said we should eat hay!" A tough little man darts out of the crowd, races up the stairs, grabs the prisoner. Others follow; Foulon is dragged down the steps, across the square, strung up on the lamppost at the corner of the rue de la Vannerie. Lafayette stood where he was and watched.

(I wonder what passed through the mind of the friend of Washington and Franklin at that moment. Could such a scene ever occur in the American Republic?)

As is the bloody custom these days, the head was severed and paraded through the streets. It was lost somewhere in the Palais-Royal, after amusing the strollers of the arcades. The trunk was left in the mud. . . .

Meanwhile Berthier, intendant of Paris, son-in-law of Foulon, is arrested at Compiègne; he also was fleeing abroad; he also is returned to Paris to be judged. The whores who populate the rue St.-Martin, a variety much more crude than those of the Palais-Royal, hang out their windows as the carriage passes. "Kill him!" they shout, "Kill him!" If the story is to be believed, a beggar in rags shows him the severed head of his wife's father, the mouth stuffed with hay. The sides of the coach have been knocked out so the people can have a good look at their prey; there are placards reading: "He betrayed his country!—He devoured the food of the people! He stole from everyone!"

The carriage arrives at the Hôtel de Ville. From here on I am an ocular witness. I went out at six, to read the papers at the Café Manoury. But I saw the crowd on the Grève, joined it to find out what was going on. There are times when I regret that curiosity that leads me to gawk at everything like all Parisians. I notice that the windows of the Hôtel de Ville are all open because of the heat; the Electors are meeting inside; a detachment of the Gardes tries to maintain order. The crowd is mixed, some beggars, many workmen, but also some well-dressed youths whom I should rather expect to encounter in the neighborhood of the Bourse.

Berthier arrives in his singular conveyance; an immense cry of scorn and hatred rises from the crowd. It is difficult to see anything but I manage to catch a glimpse. Berthier seems half-dead already, his head bent forward and his eyes closed. Someone throws a crust of black bread at the coach. "Monster! Here is the bread you made us eat!"

Somehow the Gardes get the prisoner up the steps. The crowd becomes turbulent. Ten minutes later the unfortunate man is led out again. The Gardes seem more to hold him erect than to escort him. An officer shouts that the criminal is to be taken to the Abbaye jail, demands that the crowd let him pass. Shouts of rage. The Gardes and their charge begin to descend the steps as the jeers grow louder. Berthier shakes himself out of his daze like someone trying to wake up.

"These people are strange, with their cries!"

Like a frightened child, he seizes the hand of one of the grenadiers.

"I'm scared, my friend; take care of me!"

The grenadier nods his consent, perhaps ironically. They reach the foot of the steps. A group of about thirty men, who seem to have planned their actions, push through the front of the crowd, shove the guards aside, grab the prisoner. Like a dead branch caught in the swift current of a rain-choked stream he is carried across the square, bobbing up and down, to the fatal lamppost.

A lad of fifteen whom no one has noticed until now is perched on the cross-bar, a rope in his hand. The crowd falls silent, an expectant silence with only a few shouts from those who have planned the action.

When he sees death before him, Berthier come alive. He seizes a musket from one of his assailants, flails about. They slip the noose over his head, tug on the dangling rope. The victim reaches up, tries to support his weight with a clenched fist. A bayonet slashes at his arm and cuts the rope. The victim falls, claws at the men who grab him; he is overcome, hoisted up a second time but the rope again breaks. He is slaughtered at the foot of the gibbet. . . .

All I can see is a furious scuffle; then someone holds the bloody head aloft. The crowd screams with joy at the immolation of its victim.

I skip the details I did not witness. I ran from the Grève to the Palais-Royal. The news has somehow preceded me; all is joy in that fiery garden. A few minutes later the head of Berthier is announced. The *filles* pause to applaud with their white hands so expert at stimulating desire. I leave immediately, not wishing to see the horrible trophy again. Avoiding the quais, I return by the rue Dauphine, then the rue St.-André. But at the rue de l'Eperon I encounter a score of the thugs that I had seen at the Grève. They march in a V formation and drag something after them. "Come see the intendant of Paris!" they shout.

The rope is tied to the feet of a headless corpse. I jump back, trembling, to avoid stepping on the sordid debris; I see only the back but the band cries that the chest has been opened and the heart ripped out. Despite myself I cannot take my eyes from the bloody cadaver, the livid skin, the hands that flop along after it. . . .

All my self-command had vanished by the time I got back to the rue de la Bûcherie; I was trembling and sick. My daughters were there to take care of me. . . .

Do not imagine that I side with the tyrants, oppressors of the people! Far from that! I believe I was one of the first to denounce their crimes before it became fashionable. But I have pity for the man whom I see slaughtered before my eyes. I have pity for the man—there is no human being whose agony I cannot pity. My fellow citizens, let us remain men; if we do that we can accomplish whatever we wish. . . .

Saturday the 25th, bread cheaper again by a half-sou; the housewives attribute it to the lynching of the intendant. How are the people to be taught respect for the law, when things change only after violence? . . . A solemn service at the Mathurins for all who died in the attack on the Bastille. If one were to believe every butcher's boy who claims he was there that afternoon, the fortress would have been reduced by sheer weight of numbers. . . .

On the 30th I went to the Bastille, now open to sightseers every evening from seven to nine. I puffed up to the top of those towers I had so often observed from afar, then went down to the dungeons, black and fetid, where my back itched with the expectation of rats and vermin. A steady stream of visitors completed the same circuit, whole families looking for the heaps of skeletons, secret tunnels, iron masks, of legend. In fact, there were only seven prisoners liberated on the 14th, five common criminals and two men who had gone mad. The governor's apartments are completely looted. It has been decided that the symbol of tyranny is to be razed; the demolition has already begun. . . .

"CONSUMMATUM EST..."

AUGUST–DECEMBER 1789

AUGE the *monster:* it is not lightly that I give him this title—he has been guilty of acts of such unnatural cruelty that "monstrous" is the only way to describe them. Agnès finally left him in '84 after receiving a blow so violent that her face remained swollen and bruised for two months. But what hadn't she suffered before that, keeping it hidden from the world and even from myself out of a sense of duty to her execrable husband? It was more a martyrdom than a marriage and the girl was a saint to have borne it as long as she did.

For example, bits of bread thrown at her face during meals, kicks in the belly during her pregnancy, pinches with a pair of pliers to make her quiver during the performance of her marital duties.

Also, drunken dinners with Augé's libertine friends at which he would describe the most secret parts of her body in intimate and obscene detail; invitations to those same friends to sample her charms, followed by insane scenes of jealousy. One evening Augé drags her from the table into the next room, leaving the door open, and virtually rapes her in the sight of all.

Also his abusing her body to satisfy his unnatural tastes, initiating her into the practices of the lowest of whores, proclaiming that he will use her in this way so as to have proof that she is unfaithful if she becomes pregnant.

Also, a chamberpot and its contents thrown at her shins with such force that it cracks, knocking her down covered with filth, her legs bleeding—at which sight the MONSTER becomes sexually aroused and throws himself on top of her.

Infamies worthy of Commodius, Nero, Heliogabalus! I, who

pride myself on my knowledge of the workings of the human heart, unafraid to face whatever facts are necessary—I must confess that I can understand nothing about such a man!

In 1786 I wrote a novel about this horrible marriage, *L'Ingénue Saxancour.* I printed a small edition myself. It was approved without cuts by the censor, which shows how delicately it was written. I've been asked why I must deal with such a repulsive subject, but for me writing has always been the ultimate consummation of all experience, be it happy or not. Even before I became a novelist I kept detailed notebooks recording everything of importance in my life. All of my books are, so to speak, one long autobiography. *Monsieur Nicolas, or The Human Heart Unveiled* (begun in 1783) will be my masterpiece, recounting the truth behind all those fictions.

Mercier advised me not to distribute *L'Ingénue Saxancour.* "If Augé were to die," he said, "Agnès would have difficulty finding another husband after what you've written." I hadn't thought of that because it never occurred to me that Augé might die. I think of him as an indestructible demon. But I accepted Mercier's advice as that of a man of good sense—especially as no bookseller would handle the book, for fear of a scandal—until a singular event forced me to change my mind.

It was the evening of the fall of the Bastille. I went out for a second promenade at about nine, this time to my isle by the Pont-Rouge. As I descend the rue St.-Louis I am interrogated by a patrol. To my surprise Augé is one of them. He smiles maliciously but says nothing. A horseman gallops up with some new rumor; the patrol runs off. I continue my tour of my *dates* as far as the Hôtel Lambert, then decide to return home.

On the island side of the Pont de la Tournelle an evil-looking sentry bars my path, orders me into a guardhouse at the edge of the quai. He has been told to stop anyone in a red suit. Inside I find a stranger also wearing red and as bewildered as I at being detained. The sentry brings in the sergeant. I ask why I am there. The sergeant pays me no attention but dismisses the other man. One of the young rascals who has hounded me for years comes to the door, calls for the sergeant. He goes out,

PLATE 7: The Owl of Paris—Restif in his role as the Nocturnal Spectator of *Les Nuits de Paris*. Frontispiece of *Les Nuits de Paris,* 1788.

then returns a changed man. "I'm letting this one go too," he announces.

The sentry grabs me by the collar. "This man is a spy for the king!" he shouts. "I've been informed by the patrol!"

I tell the sergeant that I am the Owl of the streets of Paris, the Nocturnal Spectator who spies on vice but has never meddled in politics. "Obey your superior!" I order and manage to escape from the sentry's grip.

Outside I encounter the beautiful Froment, daughter of one of the residents of the isle, a young girl whom I have often observed during my promenades.

"Let me accompany you home," she says. "An evil man has denounced you!"

She explains that from her window, across from the guard-house, she overheard a twisted, swarthy man describe me to the sentry, the same man whom she had seen at other times inciting the scamps of the isle to attack me during my promenades. When she saw me arrested she went out and sent the streetboy to call the sergeant. It was she who procured my release, explaining that I was only the *dateur* whom the children of the isle called "Griffon" and certainly innocent.

So my earlier suspicions of Augé were confirmed. Now he was trying to take advantage of the troubled state of the city to have me sent to jail! But my isle had protected me in the person of the beautiful Suzanne Froment.

"Do you remember who I am?" I asked. We had met once, five years before.

"The author of *Le Paysan perverti*. My father is one of your admirers. You must call when you return for your *dates*."

"I never shall!" I answered, tears streaming down my face. "My isle has been profaned forever!" And I knelt and kissed the last stone of the bridge.

After that I decided to distribute *L'Ingénue Saxancour,* come what might.

Madaran, 33 rue des Noyers, finally agreed to accept it, but only on condition that it be sold under the counter, with neither his name nor mine on the title page. Also I had to agree to give him *Les Provinciales,* a work I had completed on July

7th—six hundred ten short stories, each named for a city or town in France. This is the sort of work that has always sold very well, but the advance was minimal.

I had the copies of *Sax.* bound at my own expense before delivering the volumes. When they were ready I sent one to my wife, so that she could learn the horrible details of the marriage she arranged against my will. (But she is less a *monster* than Augé.)

Perhaps that was a mistake. It was not long before l'Echiné showed his hand again. (*L'Echiné*—the spiny one—another name for my son-in-law.)

The night of July 31st I was troubled by erotic dreams. In the morning the sight of Marion in her nightgown was almost more than I could bear. Twenty years ago I would have forgotten my work and rushed out, nostrils quivering for the scent of a woman, until I found some scullery maid or shopgirl pleased to be led to an alcove and pumped on the spot. Those days have passed. That evening I called on Mme. Dumoulin, who was out, then Mme. Dupont-Lambert, my pretty laundress always smelling of soap, who was indisposed. My third *amuseuse* had left Paris. Returning from Mme. Dupont's, rue Mazarine, I made a detour to the *lupanar,* rue de la Parcheminerie.

Unfortunately the place was already occupied by a detachment of the Gardes who had chosen to conduct their patrol in the brothel instead of in the streets. The girls were too busy with these patriots to have any time for me. I left, humiliated, vowing never to return. (Like my vow never to return to the Ile St.-Louis this was soon broken.)

All that day, wherever I went, I had the feeling that I was observed. This warning of the sixth sense alerted me again when I was out in the street. I hesitated, then started home.

In the shadow of an abutment, midway between two flickering lanterns, I was beset by five or six assassins.

At first I took them for common thieves, offered the little money I had. But they paid no attention, throwing me to the ground and flogging me without mercy. I heard one whisper, "You're sure this is the man who wrote that book?"

I survive to tell the tale only because a patrol arrived and my assailants fled. I dragged myself home, spent two days in bed. Fortunately I have always had a strong constitution. I told Agnès only that I had been attacked by thieves. The poor girl has suffered enough as it is. But I knew that it was the work of the MONSTER.

This was confirmed when I saw Madaran. He said that Augé had been to see him twice, demanded that the entire edition of *L'Ingénue Saxancour* be turned over to him, threatened to call the police if Madaran continued to sell the book. Madaran told me that he was suspending all sales, which means nothing since there haven't been any.

How did Augé learn the novel was on sale? (No one else knew about it.) If the MONSTER were a rational person he would realize that he was admitting to having committed the most abominable turpitudes by identifying himself with the Moresquin of the book. But he insists on slandering himself. Miserable fool!

After attacking my wife (June 11th), accusing me to the Gardes (July 14th), sending cutthroats to assassinate me (August 1st) the MONSTER now tried to silence my pen! Why must my miserable existence be poisoned by this vile creature year after year?

Ten days later Madaran tells me that l'Echiné has been back, again demanding that all copies of the book be turned over to him. I have the feeling that Madaran might just agree to this. I asked him to return all the copies to me, where at least they will be safe. But that isn't all. Madaran says he can't find a printer in Paris to take on the *Provinciales*. They are all busy with political tracts, pamphlets, newspapers. He suggests that I print the work myself, claiming that I will stand to profit both as author and printer. But that means that I must put up the money for paper, ink and labor. And he refuses to share these expenses. In effect he has broken our contract. After twenty-five years as a writer, and a successful writer, I find myself always beginning again. . . .

As is my custom, I go to the Café Manoury two or three times a week to read the papers. This summer there seemed to be a new one every week, most of them really pamphlets of one tendency or another. Censorship hasn't been abolished but quite simply forgotten. The most interesting among the newcomers: Mirabeau's *Courier de Provence* and Prudhomme's *Révolutions de Paris*. In the latter many of the documents discovered in the Bastille, those not destroyed by the besiegers. Meanwhile the staid *Journal de Paris* continues day after day, as if nothing had changed, with its obituaries, stock quotations, reports of the meetings of the Academies, appreciation of a tenor singing the *Barber of Seville* at the Opéra or Duscis playing *Hamlet* at the Théâtre Français, lists of the winning numbers in the National Lottery, etc. A bit livelier nonetheless; at the beginning of August they reported that after the murder of Berthier some of his assassins were seen in a café of the rue St.-Honoré flavoring their drinks with pieces of his heart. Improbable but not impossible for those CANNIBALS I saw the day he was lynched.

The Assembly was at work on a Constitution. I confess that I did not read all their debates; for example, I learned of the famous night of August 4th only from the recitation by Mercier at Mme. de Beauharnais's supper the following Friday.

Mercier had gone to Versailles with his friend Carra, one of the Electors of the Hôtel de Ville. There had been reports from all over France of peasants burning châteaux, manors, monasteries, seeking above all the documents that prescribed their feudal duties. The day before, the Assembly had voted to apply the full force of the law against these outbreaks—what else would one expect from a legislature where half the members are either Nobility or Clergy and those who till the soil are totally excluded? (My PAMPHLET was justified, for the moment at least.) Everyone expected the worst, a program of repression that would put the whole Revolution in the balance.

But at eight in the evening—Mercier is a grand storyteller, above all in company—at eight in the evening the duc d'Aiguillon took the floor (after the king and the duc d'Orléans, d'Aiguillon is the greatest landowner in France). He asked if the humble men who had done this violence were truly guilty of a crime. And he continued with an attack on the whole structure of feudalism, which is to say against himself.

The duke was followed by an obscure nobleman from Brittany, dressed in the costume of his province, one of those *hoberaux* who maintain their dignity by ragged cloaks and are as poor as the peasants who work their lands. He proposed that the Nobility make a sacrificial bonfire of all those hated parchments, offer them as a gift instead of watching them be destroyed by force. There was a moment of hesitation; then the deluge.

The enthusiasm of sacrifice spread from bench to bench. The Vicomte de Beauharnais proposed that the law be the same for noblemen and commoners and that all grades in the army be open to everyone. (He is the nephew of the countess; the divine Fanny had tears in her eyes at this moment as Mercier spoke.) There was a queue at the tribune, a crush of all those delegates of the Nobility who had been so adamant in opposing the union of the three orders in May and June, one proposing that gentlemen no longer be exempt from taxes, the next that hunting rights be given up, the next offering his dovecote, all agreeing to the abolition of those ancient feudal duties that are a chief source of their wealth.

The delegates of the provinces renounced their special privileges, all wanting only to be equal to the rest of France. It has been said since that these gifts only confirmed what was already accomplished in July, and to be sure I thought of the recklessness of young gamblers, who stake their whole fortune on a turn of the wheel. Nonetheless the narration of this generosity made me proud to be a Frenchman. In one night the immense oak of feudalism was cut down, that evil tree whose branches covered the sky with its cold shadow, whose roots penetrated the depths of the earth. And by whom?—by those few who enjoyed its fruits!

Only the Clergy was reticent, claiming that their property was but a trust. But that must follow before long. . . .

A strange-looking man presented himself to me in the middle of August, thin gray hair, a perfectly yellow complexion, cadaverous eyes staring out of a skull that his skin seemed hard-put to cover, clothes as ragged and old-fashioned as my own. His name: Dr. Jean Paul Marat, a physician. He had no idea who I was, but I remembered having met him at one of Fanny's suppers some years before. At that time he was writing about medicine—theories of physiology and psychology, all tainted with spiritualism. Now, like everyone else, he wants to put out a newspaper and is looking for someone to print it. The man is not shy, even if he looks as if he might expire at any moment; he told me that he alone understood the Revolution and that his sheet would guide its future. I scanned what he had written about the session of August 4th—he denounces everyone and everything, calls the Constitution a fraud, the Assembly a pack of aristocrats, demands radical action to relieve the misery of the people instead of theoretical debates about the Rights of Man. His eyes devoured me as I read; the man can write but he seems a bit mad. Whatever they say about the freedom of the press I would fear prison every day if I printed things like that. I told him that I had too much work, unfortunately a lie unless I count my own productions. . . .

The *milice bourgeois* has been fused with the Gardes Françaises, all of it under the command of Lafayette, given uniforms and rifles as well as the responsibility of maintaining order in the capital. The effect of this has not always been desirable. Give a shopkeeper or a foreman a rifle, a sash, a jacket with epaulettes, and suddenly he is no longer your brother but a superior, intent on using his new power. My walk home from the Palais-Royal was a succession of shouts, "Who goes there! Keep to the left! Keep to the right!" as if my passage threatened the public peace. On the rue Ste.-Marguerite two sentinels shout from either end of the street, "To the left!—To the right!" so that I am obliged, as a compromise, to walk in the mud.

All the same the uniforms are necessary, the regular police have almost ceased to function, the Garde Nationale, as it is now called, is the only protection we have. The papers report disorders of one kind or another from all over France; royal prisons and arsenals stormed by mobs, sometimes delivered to them, châteaux set afire, riots, lynchings. A letter from the mayor of Senlis in the *Journal de Paris* denies stories that the city is infested with bandits, surrounded by troops. In Versailles a curious incident: A man attacks his mistress with a kitchen knife in the heat of a quarrel. His father tries to parry the blow and is killed by error. The murderer is condemned as a parricide, sentenced to be turned on the rack until dead. The crowd that gathers to witness the execution decides that the punishment is more barbarous than the crime, mobs the executioner, destroys the instrument of torture as a relic of the past.

On Assumption Day the usual procession set out from Notre-Dame. There are still old women to kneel in the street as the choirboys and the chalice go by but there are also shouts of "Down with the priests!" and "String them up on the lamppost!" The Assembly was discussing the privileges of the Clergy and the people seemed to have wind of the determination of the Church to hold on to all it has. For once I was delighted by the popular fury; since my two years as a student in an Augustinian seminary I've detested those hypocrites clad in black.

The Palais-Royal continues to be the impromptu third legislature of France, after the Assembly and the Hôtel de Ville; sometimes it seems the first. All these fine August evenings the place has been as busy as it was in June. In the arcades you hear all the tongues of Europe, are invited to try in a score of casinos, have your choice of a swarm of delicious girls dressed in the latest fashions. In the cafés the debate continues as if the Constitution were being written there; you hear the word LIBERTY over and over and there is a kind of intoxication in this *liberty,* a belief that the world is beginning anew, that anything can be done if only it is proposed. It is impossible to resist this spirit when you are there; the Palais-Royal is a Garden of Eden before the serpent where the humanity of centuries to come will find its form.

One evening it was the scene of the most curious demonstration of all; a troop of several hundred valets, footmen, coachmen, many wearing the livery of their masters, asking for the support of the patriots of the cafés. They demand to be admitted to the Gardes, want all Savoyards sent back to Savoy as unfair competition, are trying to organize a guild to regulate their so-called profession. They had been first to the Hôtel de Ville to present their demands to Bailly, but he had turned them down. Strange revolutionaries, that horde of lackeys; they could not quite manage the style. But their grievances are real; many have no work. The rich have been moving out of Paris for fear of more troubles; everywhere you see great houses that are shuttered.

The world may have been created in six days but one would think a month was a short time to write a Constitution for a kingdom that had got on a thousand years without one. Yet by the end of August people grew impatient with the Assembly because it was still debating the Rights of Man. The Palais-Royal talked of this and that, but the real issue was bread. The price remained at twelve sous the four-pound loaf by order of the Hôtel de Ville, but there was not enough to go around. Several times Marion came home empty-handed from the bakery at the rue Galande because other women had stood in line since four in the morning. The Gardes were out in force every market day at the Place Maubert; it began to look like June all over again. They say that this year's harvest has been good, but the new flour has not yet arrived in Paris.

On September 4th Marion and Agnès both got up before dawn to join the queue at the bakery. All was orderly at first, the Gardes on patrol. At seven, the usual hour for the bakery to open, the doors remained shut. The crowd became restless; there was squabbling among the women, then a fight when a strong-armed market woman demanded a place near the head of the line, claiming she had been there earlier and had left for a call of nature. The patrol intervened; the vegetable seller was hauled off screaming, "Tomorrow I'll piss on your shoes and shit in the street!" At seven-thirty a baker's boy shouted out that the flour had been delivered late and the bread was still in the oven. At eight one of the women screamed that someone was sneaking loaves out the back door of the shop. With that the queue dissolved, an Amazon mêlée began, the women in front trying to kick the door in, those behind trying to climb over the others. The Gardes attacked, using their musket butts as clubs. One wouldn't think that they would injure their mothers and sisters —the men are recruited in the district—but Agnès says they were brutal; something strange happens to a man when he is armed. Agnès was knocked down and trampled, but escaped with nothing more than bruises; Marion got a shaft in her belly and had to spend the day in bed.

On August 31st the streets around the Palais-Royal were shut off by the Gardes. There had been a petition at the Café de Foy to elect a new set of delegates for Paris who would veto all discussion of the *Veto*. Lafayette ordered all political assemblies banned, sent in his troops. What a change from the bright days of June and July, when the Gardes were the darlings of the crowds under the arcades!

(This question of the *Veto* has become the focus of everything. Mirabeau is in favor of it, saying that if the king has no power there will be no reason to have a monarchy. There are rumors that he has received money from the Court for taking his position. One hears it discussed everywhere, even by shopgirls and the women who sell fish at the Place Maubert. At times you might think the *Veto* was a man, or goddess, or a mythological animal. Whatever it is, man, woman or beast, the people are against it.)

At my shop, Daniol reported that a woman of the Halles had been beaten because she shouted insults at a patrol of the Gardes. He said that Lafayette should be strung up on the lamppost at the Grève just like Berthier and Foulon. That was too much for the others; they told him to be quiet. . . . There is a curious cartoon displayed in the window of the shop on the rue St.-Jacques that sells engravings. Its title: PATROLISM DRIVING PATRIOTISM OUT OF THE PALAIS-ROYAL. The Gardes Nationales in their blue uniforms are depicted wearing blindfolds and miters instead of caps. The leader of the patrol, obviously Lafayette, holds the point of his sword at the breast of a defenseless citizen who clutches a book entitled, *The Rights of*

Man, the Constitution, Liberty. (The Café de Foy was raided several times in September.)

During August I completely revised the second half of the *Thesmographe,* proposing much bolder reforms than I would have dared mention when the work was begun. Among them, a total revision of the status of the clergy, including the *marriage* of priests, monks, abbés, etc., who must cease being parasites feeding on the productive sectors of society. Also the legalization of divorce, permitting the dissolution of unhappy households, a subject with which I have only too much experience, both in my own marriage and the disastrous experience of my daughter; the grounds: (1) sterility, (2) madness, bad temper, an insupportable character, (3) adultery. The rights of minors must be protected, but I believe that divorce is better for children than a forced union where the parents have come to detest each other. It will take some time for these ideas to be accepted, but their day must come.

Another proposal dear to my heart is the establishment of a worker's printing plant, owned cooperatively, with apprentices, workmen, foremen and the chief of the enterprise all sharing in the profits of their labor, the capital to be created by subscription or loans to be paid off over the years. I include a provision for pensions for all those who can no longer work because of age or sickness. This is no doubt the most practical of all my projected reforms, since I have a thorough knowledge of the printing industry, having worked my way up from the very bottom. Once in operation it can serve as a model for similar enterprises in other industries.

But I wonder if the times are right for these ideas. In the past my proposals were always labeled "too advanced." Now, suddenly, I find myself at the tail end of the parade because I offer reforms instead of a total upheaval. What is surprising is that those in the avant garde are not only eccentrics (like Dr. Jean Paul Marat), but the offspring of quite respectable families.

Everyone has read the *Discours de la lanterne aux Parisiens,* a violent defense of popular justice in the style of the orators of the Palais-Royal. The anonymous author claims the atrocious title of "district attorney of the lamppost"; he boasts that it was the severed heads of Flesselles and De Launey, Foulon and Berthier that rid France of the Polignacs, Condés, d'Artois, etc.—a benefit that one would have thought would cost several battles. He pictures foreigners coming to Paris to gaze in ecstasy at that lantern on the Grève, "that beacon that did more in two days than all their heroes in a century."

From the style of this notorious work it was easy to guess that its author was Camille Desmoulins, who had earlier published *La France Libre,* another daring pamphlet that relates the crimes, errors and vices of the kings of France from Henri III and his *mignons* to Louis XV and his private brothel, the *"parc aux cerfs."* This Desmoulins claims to be the man who stood on a table at the Palais-Royal on July 12, plucked a leaf from a tree to make the first green cockade, and shouted "To arms!" I pictured him as one of the wild young men of the Café de Foy, distinguished only by his talent for sensational journalism.

In September the countess gave a farewell supper, rue de Tournon; she is leaving for Italy. The silver-and-blue salon was as resplendent as ever, the supper delicious and abundant, the wines exquisite, the service discreet and Fanny the Divine loveliness itself. Imagine my surprise when Mercier arrives—Mercier the wise, the elegant, the witty, the knowing, the perfect Parisian man of letters—when Mercier introduces a well-dressed young man and who is he? Camille Desmoulins.

To tell the truth I was the only one who appeared surprised; perhaps Mme. de Beauharnais did not know she was entertaining the district attorney of the lamppost. He was not all that young, almost thirty; well-educated, a graduate of Louis le Grand; well-mannered, the son of a Picard magistrate. Most surprising, from the man who claims to have instigated the attack on the Bastille—he stutters. But it is a charming stutter, disarming and friendly; indeed everything about him was charming. "Camille"—everyone called him that almost at once—soon had a circle of women about him. Half-boasting, half-mocking, he talked of his friendship with Mirabeau, whose choice wines, at the dinners he gave in Versailles, "had tempted him to stray from the path of Revolutionary virtue." As he spoke he had a glass of the countess's excellent claret in his hand.

I took Mercier aside to tell him of my astonishment. He said I was out of touch, claimed that his young friend has immense talent and a great future, predicted that in twenty years he will be one of the great men of letters of France. It is true that I have never known much about *men of letters*. . . .

My own troubles were far from over. On September 10th Marion went to the Marais to see her dressmaker about a new coat. Going down the rue du Roi de Sicile, always crowded in the afternoon, she was seized by a short, ugly, twisted man who shouted at her, "Aha! little tart! you dare come to my district! I'll have you locked up!"

It was the MONSTER, half-drunk as usual. Too stunned to reply, she listened as he called her a whore, a procuress, an incestuous bitch. When she recovered her wits and shouted for help, the son of a shopkeeper of the rue St.-Antoine came to her aid, knocked the vile Augé to the ground and brought her home. I am eternally grateful to that lad, who reassures me as to the goodness of human nature.

On September 19th I received a note from the Vicomte de Toustain-Richbourg, asking me to call. It was Toustain who finally obtained approval for *Le Paysan* in 1786. Leaving my work, I departed immediately. I enter the noble house, am offered a cup of chocolate, then shown a missive from Augé that had arrived two days before.

In the letter the twisted pervert accuses me of slander, kidnaping and ignoring a magistrate's order to return Agnès to him. (What order? the man is mad!) To top it all he declares himself a friend of Necker, Bailly and Lafayette (and who else?), threatens to appeal to others if Toustain will not help him. All in good time!

The Vicomte was very kind, assuring me of his sympathy. We spoke briefly of public affairs and I saw that Toustain, recently so powerful, was now a lost man who didn't know which way to turn.

I answered the letter myself, that same day:

"To l'Echiné, rue des Singes No. 23" (well-named, he is indeed an ape) : "I have in my possession your letter of 16 Sept. to M. le V-C de T.R. and I notice that you agree to *forgive* your wife if she returns to you. You say you love her and yet it was you who made her pass a night on the stairs outside your apartment in her nightgown—and in the month of February—while she was recovering from the birth of your son! There are witnesses. You mistreated her so that her milk turned sour. Villain! coward! liar! You mention *my* wife—how dare you after your conduct on June 11th? I am keeping your letter as evidence in the hope that before long our august Assembly will arrive at the chapter of Divorce and permit the dissolution of the evil bond between you and my dear child.

"In the meantime, Monsieur, leave me alone! I provide for my wife and I provide for *yours*. I provide for my younger daughter whom you insulted, I nourish my nephew, I give work to honest men by my own labors. What do you do? evil and nothing more!"

I have put it all in the *Thesmographe!* This will be another book that he can run from bookstore to bookstore trying to suppress. Monster, *monster,* MONSTER! If there were any justice he would be exposed in a cage on the Grève.

September 28th, a M. Rollin, officer of the Gardes, informs me that Augé has denounced me to his district. But the Gardes have no jurisdiction in private affairs. I note that if I had been suspected of some political crime one would have seen Augé renew the ancient horrors of Marius and Sulla, bringing an accusation against the father of his wife.

But worse was to follow. On October 1st the weather turned cold and damp so that the old pain in my shoulders came back. Instead of making my usual promenade I was in bed by nine. At eleven-thirty there is a knock at the door. It is Desmarquets, the lawyer who lives downstairs, quite upset. As he came home an evil-looking man had tried to question him. Desmarquets managed to slip inside and throw the bolt. Once in his own rooms he looked out. The stranger was talking with four toughs at the corner of the rue des Grands-Degrés. Noticing Desmarquets at his window he returned to question him again.

"Is Restif de la Bretonne at home?"

"I don't know, sir. If you have something to tell him come back in the morning."

"One talks to scoundrels only at night!"

I looked out. In the street below I saw Augé with four accomplices, perhaps the same thugs who had attacked me in the rue de la Parcheminerie. He caught sight of me and began shouting insults. Desmarquets offered to hide my girls in his apartment, then went down with my nephew Edmond to tell Augé that they will alert the patrol when they pass. Augé shouts that he has come to blow my brains out.

The next day everyone in the neighborhood knows what has happened. I learn that Augé has been around on other occasions. My landlord, Frazé, chased him away just two days before after an exchange in which Augé said I had abducted Agnès so that I could sleep with her. His words: "Let him screw his other daughter but not my wife!"

The old-clothes man at the rue des Rats was questioned about my habits. He heard Augé mutter that he would do me in. . . .

Page, the tailor, heard Augé say that Marion was a whore. . . .

They all advise me to file a complaint, promise to testify. But my wife filed a complaint against the MONSTER on June 11th after he had attacked her on the street in broad daylight and nothing ever came of it! I've been assaulted six times this year on the Ile St.-Louis, once on the rue de la Parcheminerie, and never a policeman in sight. We might as well be living in a jungle!

By the end of September we were back at the end of June. There were again patrols at the Place Maubert every market day, fights at the bakeries where there never seemed to be enough bread, huge crowds at the Hôtel de Ville protesting the shortage, demanding that the king come to Paris. And again talk of a Court plot to undo the Revolution, a plan to spirit the king off to Metz where he can call on the Austrians for help, send the Assembly packing, surround Paris with regiments of musketeers staffed by noblemen, starve it into submission. What was different was the ubiquitous newspapers, hawked on every streetcorner, available in every café, speaking to an audience far larger than the habitués of the Café de Foy.

Les Révolutions de Paris: "We need a second revolutionary spasm, and everything is ready for it."

The *Chronique de Paris,* more moderate, "invited" the king and queen to spend the winter in Paris, to reassure the people.

Marat, that mad physician, had found a printer less circumspect than I; his journal, *L'Ami du Peuple,* was the most violent of all and immediately popular in the Faubourg St.-Antoine (Daniol began to quote him with the very first number). He accused Lafayette, Bailly and half the Assembly of treachery, called on the people to act before winter made everything worse. And there was no question what he meant by "act." . . .

The "second revolutionary spasm" was not long in coming.

On October 4th, a gray Sunday afternoon, I took Agnès to the Tuileries and the Champs-Elysées. Among the rather thin crowd a number of men with *black* cockades pinned to their hats—the mournful livery of the Habsburgs and Marie Antoinette. I examined the faces beneath the brims of those hats, the dry, white, twisted faces that had been in hiding all summer; their reappearance on this gloomy day seemed a bad omen.

Afterwards to the Palais-Royal. Even *there,* in the arcades not two steps from the Café du Foy, black cockades on the *chapeaux* of elegant young men who bantered with the whores as they went up to try their luck at the gaming tables. . . . An orator thundered against a dinner held the night before in Versailles, the regiment of Flanders banqueting in the palace, all wearing the white cockade of the Bourbons and the black of the Habsburgs, Marie Antoinette and the young prince cheered when they came into the hall, oaths of fidelity to the king, to the queen, the Gardes Nationales chased out of the palace by these drunken royalist troops, the whole event a scandal. . . .

The next morning at about ten I hear the *générale* in the street below, a drummer of the Gardes calling on the men of the district to assemble. I go out; there is a huge crowd around the Hôtel de Ville, covering the Grève and the bridges—or rather two crowds, on either side of the square, one mostly like market women, the other workers of the Faubourg St.-Antoine. There are troops all about, cavalry of the Gardes before the Hôtel de Ville, a grim scene under a menacing sky but apparently peaceful.

I circulate. Two demonstrations are going on at the same time. The workers speak of a dispute at the demolition of the Bastille, a mason arrested on some charge or other; they want him freed. The woman are more violent. They shout for bread, for arms, for Lafayette, for Bailly; one proposes burning the Hôtel de Ville, another marching to Versailles to bring back the king. In the crowd I notice a sprinkling of whores, still powdered from the labors of the night, also some men in women's clothes, not the pederasts who hold court in a certain corner of the Tuileries but toughs who might be either pimps or agitators.

The place is tense; I go home. The shops that usually open on Mondays are closed. On the Place Maubert, another gathering of women. Some I recognize; they tend the stalls on market day. They are shouting about bread, but they seem quite cheerful, pleased that they can show the men that women also can make a riot. Three red-cheeked emissaries come puffing up the rue Galande, skirts fluttering; they declare they come from the Hôtel de Ville. "Join us!" they shout, "We're going to Versailles to fetch the baker and the baker's wife!" (*i.e.,* the king and queen).

Of course every window was open. "Come with us, women of Paris!" a voice shouted, in the same tones that usually cry, "Onions! Fresh and strong! Onions!"

Not content merely to give the call, the Amazons swarm up the stairs of the buildings about the square, dragging out every chambermaid, scullery maid, seamstress and laundress, sometimes even the mistress of the household.

I run home, tell Marion and Agnès to hide under the beds, bolt the door. We escaped from the furies, but from the window I saw the daughter of Guillaume-Page, the tailor across the street, dragged out of his shop by three hussies who shouted they would cut off her hair if she wouldn't go with them.

We waited. . . . We heard a battalion of the Gardes pass by. . . . Curiosity overcoming prudence I went out again, ordering Agnès and Marion to remain indoors.

The crowd had left the Hôtel de Ville; one of the Gardes at the staircase said the men had dispersed quietly but the women had broken in, stolen some guns.

I ran to the Palais-Royal. On the rue St.-Honoré I encountered some of the market women, mixed now with workers armed with pikes, hammers, axes, etc. There was a small field cannon, at least a century old, drawn by two horses. A pretty girl was perched on the shaft, shouting, "To Versailles!"

A battalion of the Gardes were stationed at the rue des Petits-Champs; they whistled at the girl as she went by. Not the least embarrassed, she pointed at that secret treasure most women pretend does not exist and cried, "For the Grenadier who does his duty!" The windows rattled with the Gardes's cheering.

It had begun to drizzle, but no one paid attention. I followed the artillery nymph a while further. The crowds grew thicker at the approaches to the Champs-Elysées. I heard gunfire; decided to return. By then I had to make a long detour around the Halles; the streets were all choked with crowds going the other way.

By the time I descended the rue St.-Martin and reached the Hôtel de Ville the rain was heavy. A battalion of the Gardes marched west along the quais; then, emerging from the Hôtel de Ville, there was Lafayette himself, looking grim.

In the evening the city was quiet with all the shops shuttered and so many people having left for Versailles. It was almost five months to the day since another such quiet evening when the carriages trooped to Versailles for the opening of the Estates. A different procession now, in October—first a horde of women, then the workers with their pikes, then the troops, and last of all, on his white horse, the general.

Everyone knows what happened in Versailles, or rather no one knows since the accounts are all so different. It rained all that night and all the next day. Late in the afternoon word had it that "the baker and the baker's wife" were indeed coming to Paris.

I went out at six; it was already dark, the rain continuing but the streets crowded. Near the Louvre I encountered the horde returning from Versailles with their precious captive. A more bedraggled and bizarre torchlight parade has never been seen. The Gardes led the way, their rifles decorated with poplar branches, yellow leaves fluttering, thick slices of bread stuck on the points of their bayonets. Then carriages crammed with deputies—as in July the escort for the king—then the royal coach with the king, the queen and the dauphin, a troop of mud-spattered but triumphant women on either side. After that, what appeared to be a population of refugees fleeing a beleaguered town. Every horse and cart in Versailles must have been pressed into service. Coaches, cabriolets and hay wains—all carried the rude women who had set out so noisily the day before, all of them now soaked and exhausted, their clothes clinging to their bodies, their hair wet and stringy, some nonetheless singing in a lugubrious manner.

At the Hôtel de Ville the Gardes mixed with the people. The royal family went into the building, then reappeared at an open window, the queen holding the dauphin in her arms, the king looking more portly than ever and a bit ridiculous with an oversized tricolor ribbon in his hat. There were some shouts but the rain continued to fall. I went straight home, afraid I was coming down with the grippe.

The next day, miracle! plenty of bread for everyone at the bakeries. Perhaps it was just a coincidence—the flour of the new harvest had begun to arrive—but who could fail to link it with the presence of the king?

In the afternoon I went to the Tuileries Palace where the royal family has been lodged. A large crowd in the gardens outside—not the market women who had brought the king to Paris but the well-dressed inhabitants of the Faubourg St.-Germain and the neighborhood of the Champs-Elysées. Insistent shouts of *"Vive le roi!"* and *"Vive la reine!"* until the king appeared briefly at a window. Then, delirium, of a special kind, the crowd trying to show the king that he was not without friends in the capital. Many had tears in their eyes; I heard an old man sigh, "That it should come to this!" . . . During the day the women of the grain market had carried fifty sacks of rotten grain to the palace to show the king what the people of Paris have been eating. The stink was so horrible that the king ordered the grain dumped into the Seine from the Pont-Royal.

Afterwards, the papers all full of contradictory reports. Was the queen's life ever in danger? It depends on which journal you read. . . . One sight I'm glad to have missed is the first women returning from Versailles; they carried, as trophies, the heads of two of the king's personal guards, each wearing a curled and powdered wig and a hat with the black Habsburg cockade; these delectable objects were displayed at the Palais-Royal. But for an event that again changed everything there were few casualties, only a handful. The Assembly also is moving to Paris; after weeks of stalling the king has approved all the articles of the Constitution voted so far: the Rights of Man, the decrees of August 4th—the Court plot (if there was one) has been foiled once and for all. And the whole thing began, they say, with a market girl beating a drum at the Halles at seven o'clock Monday morning! But who told her to do that?

It remained for one more murder to soil the "incomparable year," as Mercier terms it in his *Adieux à 1789*. On October 21st the baker François of the Notre-Dame district ran out of bread while a crowd of women besieged his shop. They accused him of reserving his loaves for the deputies of the Assembly—still meeting at the Archevêché, before their move to the Manège at the Tuileries. The women broke into his shop, found *three* loaves in a corner. The Gardes arrived, took the baker to the Hôtel de Ville for his own safety. By then a crowd of hotheaded idlers had collected; they snatched poor François away from the patrol, strung him up on the fatal lamppost.

This time the lynching was condemned by everyone. Martial

law was declared immediately, the red flag flown over the Hôtel de Ville; two men were hung the next day for the murder. The king gave a pension of 6,000 livres to the widow of François, mother of two children and pregnant with a third; he and the queen promised to be godparents to the unborn child. The Assembly created a new court for crimes against the Nation. There was only one deputy to object to the universal sentiment of disgust —Robespierre of Arras. (Even he did not approve of the crime, saying only that hunger was to blame, not the people. But haven't we lived with hunger for centuries?) The newspapers, royalist and patriot, all decry the lynching, with the exception, of course, of Marat. (That fanatic objects to the martial law because he wants *more* violence—public order, he raves, is desired only by "the timid, by those who want repose, by the privileged, the leeches of society, the scoundrels who live by injustice" —one sees his style, how the *timid* become *scoundrels* in the course of a sentence—he promises to continue to rub salt into the people's wounds, so they shall stay awake! Another MONSTER like the foul Augé!)

As for my own affairs, they remain troubled.

On October 28th at ten o'clock in the evening the patrol knocks on my door, says they have an order for my arrest—an order by accusation of the parricide MONSTER—I am taken to the police station at St.-Louis-de-la-Culture, shown three abominable pamphlets of which I know nothing, told I am the author of these works, and am interrogated three times in the course of a long and painful night! What a trial, good Lord, for a sick old man! Some justice still lives; my answers led to my release and the vicious defamer of my character was himself clapped in jail. I tremble still to think about it!

It was a Wednesday; I was at home and not feeling well, preparing to retire early. The Gardes arrive, tell me to get dressed and go with them; no explanation. I try to remain calm so as not to alarm my daughters, say there is some mistake but that I will go. (What choice have I?) My nephew Edmond offers to accompany me, but I tell him to stay with Agnès and Marion. The patrol takes me to the stationhouse. They were polite enough, but it is no picnic being arrested—I was shaking with fear. At the station the captain informs me that I am accused of having written and printed three anonymous pamphlets, two of them royalist tracts, the third pure trash. I ask who has accused me, and learn it is my son-in-law—or rather I inform the captain that Augé is my son-in-law and he is astonished to learn it, as well he might be.

The three abominations are as follows:

(1) *Sure means for the first two Orders to subjugate the Third Estate and punish it for its demands.* I told the officer that I had never heard of this tract if it existed, and that I was opposed to its sentiments, to judge merely by the title.

(2) *Domine salvum fac regem*—a Royalist tract that I have seen in several bookstores. I denied having anything to do with it.

(3) *Don Bugger at the Estates.* The nature of this work is apparent from its title. The officer had a copy that I scanned. Augé had apparently noticed that it contained a reference to a work of mine, *Le Pornographe,* published in 1770—that is all that could possibly link this piece of trash to myself. As for my having *printed* these sixteen pages of rot, there are a host of errors, typos, misalignments and omissions that I would never permit in any work that passed through my shop, trash or no! (Later I had a chance to examine this brochure. The author proposes that the king employ squadrons of whores who will be rushed to the scene of a riot to parade with uncovered breasts, thus distracting the agitators!)

I denied the accusations. Augé was interrogated in turn, while I waited in another room, under the eye of a sentinel. Then I was questioned again, this time about the situation of my family, my separation from my wife, my daughter's separation from Augé—all sorts of matters in which the police have no legitimate interest. But this interrogation worked in my favor, they grew more and more suspicious of the MONSTER who had accused me. To clear my name completely I demanded that a search be made of my quarters. This could not be done until morning. I passed a miserable night in a cell.

In the morning the patrol took me home, searched the apartment and my shop downstairs. They found nothing. On the advice of Augé they went so far as to search the room I had rented three years before above Duchesne's bookshop where I had written much of the *Nuits de Paris:* they even talked of going to the domicile of my wife, near the Châtelet, but by this time the officers were convinced that I was innocent and that this visit would not be necessary.

The tables were turned! Augé and I had seen each other once during the night, glared at each other through the bars separating the cells. At that moment I could have strangled him with my bare hands, except for the bars. In the morning I was freed; *he* was arrested for making a false accusation against an innocent man! False and absurd.

I would have left him behind bars for the rest of his life if I'd had my way! During the time he was in prison I breathed more easily. It seemed to me that was the right place for him. But it was not to be....

On the 31st I had dinner with Mercier, to whom I recounted the whole story. He advised me not to press charges against the MONSTER, saying it could only bring further disgrace on my family and myself. He assured me that if Augé were released he would be watched by the police and thoroughly discredited if he attempted to bring new charges; in short, that it was in my interest to let things stand as they were. The voice of reason, I suppose, but it went against the grain.

What really decided me was a long and difficult talk with Agnès the next day. The poor girl has always been unhappy—her mother never cared for her; she married out of desperation to escape the tyranny of her bigoted aunt Bizet and found a living hell instead of a home—and yet her soul remains so sweet and gentle that it is she who pleads with me on behalf of the man who has so abused her! Above all she talked of her son, her fear of what it would do to him to grow up knowing his father is in prison. In the end I gave in, even if it is to mean my death some dark night. Tears in both our eyes, we fell into each other's arms! How sad life can be, but sometimes how sweet when most sad. If only it had been my luck to marry someone like Agnès, instead of her mother!...

November 2nd I went to the Hôtel de Ville to sign a statement that I will not press charges of false accusation against Augé, preferring to leave him to the remorse and shame of his own crimes. However I demanded that a copy of Augé's deposition, my interrogation and his, the report of the police search of the premises, etc., be turned over to me in case anything of the sort occurs again. This was agreed to after some difficulty about the regulations—Revolution or no there will always be a clerk to find a regulation! I also asked to have testimony about Augé's threats on my life the night of October 1st put into the official record. My neighbors have all agreed to testify for me.

Augé was released November 3rd. We shall see if five days in prison have done anything to improve his character.

The *Thesmographe* is finished, printed, bound and available *chez* Madaran. More than anyone else, I am aware of the imperfections of this work, defects caused by its having been composed during a year of such violent change in the structure and life of the nation. Nonetheless I think there are parts that are of great utility, notably the review of the constitutions of all peoples about the globe, including the red men of the Americas and the empires of the Orient and Africa, of great importance at a time when our pamphleteers refer only to Greece and Rome for their examples, as if those two peoples of antiquity had exhausted the experience of the human race. . . .

Mercier and his friend Carra have begun a newspaper, *Les Annales patriotiques;* it has had a great success. The reason is clear: Mercier knows the value of the significant anecdote. An example: At a performance of *The Marriage of Figaro,* the actors sang the final couplets, which end, as everyone knows, with the line: *"And all finishes in chansons."* An aristocrat in one loge cried, *"Encore! Encore!"* meaning to remind everyone of the reputed frivolity of this country. At that a deep and sonorous voice sang out from the cheap seats, "And all finishes with *cannons."* The audience picked up this new finale and repeated it several times, clapping their hands. No doubt this new verse will be substituted for the original, throughout the kingdom. . . .

Charming young Camille also has his own paper, *Les Révo-*

lutions de France et de Brabant. The first number found the "district attorney of the lamppost" in a happy frame of mind. "*Consummatum est,* the king is in the Louvre, the Assembly at the Tuileries, the markets full of provisions, the Treasury filling up, the mills turning, traitors fleeing, the Clergy abased, the Aristocracy expiring. . . ." In short, the Revolution is over. Let us hope so.

MON CALENDRIER

1790

JANUARY 3: This first Sunday of the New Year, out with Marion for an afternoon promenade. Our destination was the Tuileries, but the gates were shut; the king was out taking a stroll. Along the Feuillant terrace we found a spot where we could look in through the grill. The king takes the air accompanied by six Grenadiers of the Gardes, behind him a group of notables, courtiers, members of the Assembly or others with special passes. Louis looked even more stout than at the Hôtel de Ville—they say his chief sacrifice in moving to Paris has been to give up the hunt—his complexion is sallow, his glance distracted, his walk almost a waddle. As soon as he reentered the Palace the gates were opened and the Sunday crowd streamed into the garden designed by Le Nôtre. The queen was still walking about with a lady of the court, surrounded by another detachment of the Gardes. The crowd pressed close about them; the men removed their hats as a sign of respect but everyone commented in loud voices about the queen's appearance, as if she were an animal in the Jardin-Royal. She did not look well; her face was blotchy and she seemed nervous. At the very least, this Parisian residence is a great comedown for the daughter of the Empress Maria-Theresa. When the queen also returned to the Palace the crowd thinned out.

Marion and I enjoyed the fresh air. There is a little garden that has been railed off for the dauphin, with a wooden gazebo for shelter when it rains. The little prince was hard at work with a hoe and a rake, playing at being a farmer as his mother had played a milkmaid in the Hameau at Versailles, two Grenadiers standing guard. He is a pretty lad of five or six, and paid no attention to the stares that followed his every gesture. It was a sight that touched my heart. Sad little prince, how I wish he could enjoy a childhood such as mine, with freedom to roam the fields and orchards, discover the wild creatures in the woods, be adored and caressed by all the girls of the village in their homespun dresses! It would be better training for the job of being king, than growing up in a palace with a little patch of earth for all of the great outdoors....

January 11: Regrettable anniversary! regrettable forever! the day when, for the first time, for one hard-earned écu, I bought the favors of a prostitute. Alas, she was neither the last nor the worst....

I expect that respectable citizens will be upset by this matter, in fact I ask that they skip ahead. Read no more! I want neither your approbation nor your indulgence nor your pity. I can think of nothing in the world more dangerous than a certain kind of respectable man, be he royalist or revolutionary; I place the prostitute far above him in the scale of human values. There are times when the whore can sell you an honest if desperate pleasure, but the sentiments of those who condemn her without knowledge lead only to bitterness, sorrow and cruelty. I detest all virtue founded on deprivation, inflexibility; all virtue that stems only from pride. I write only for those who seek to discover the workings of the human heart, for those who will weep with me, seeing how a man can be led astray, for those who seek the mirror of their own faults.

I was twenty-one. I had completed my apprenticeship in September, leaving behind Auxerre and the tender Mme. Fournier who had occupied my heart for three long years. I adored her still, not suspecting that I would never see her again. Boudard, whom I had known in Auxerre, had come to Paris several months before; he found me a job at the Royal Press at the Louvre. I earned fifty sous a day, *i.e.,* I was not rich. Boudard had a room on the rue des Poulies which he shared with a young watchmaker, also from Auxerre, Chambon; they asked me to move in with them. We split all expenses. Boudard went to the butcher; I bought vegetables, charcoal, firewood; Chambon did the cooking. We washed the dishes once a week, on Sunday, after our one decent dinner.

Two girls moved into the room across the hall. Chambon made their acquaintance, invited them to share our supper. Chambon was one of those weak men with a limited capacity for debauchery who make up for it by a continuous torrent of obscene conversation. Boudard, although a big man, had mediocre impulses; I was all fire and flame. At the first glimpse of our neighbors I could hardly control myself, although I suspected their profession. We invited them to join us and talked about this and that over the soiled dishes of our poor meal. Boudard and Chambon were quick with clever, if filthy, observations; I was mute.

The next evening, after work, I found the younger of the two in her room, her name Argeville. She guessed quickly what I was after; the bargain was made. What a difference from the experiences I had had until then! Argeville employed all the tricks of her trade, still new to me, but her evident coldness and the thought of paying her spoiled everything. Also, because I was kind to her, because I didn't try to kick her in the guts after I had taken my pleasure (such as it was) she decided I was only a *kid*. I crept into my bed, feeling like a fool and worried about my health.

What followed was even worse. The two girls were our neighbors for only a short time, but their arrival meant the end of our little society. Each of us wanted to have Argeville to himself exclusively, not that we were ignorant of what she did during the day. Argeville was clever enough to hide from each of us that all three of us were accorded her favors. But the truth came out because her companion became jealous. We made an agreement that both of them should share our bed and board and we would take turns with both of them. But immediately after Boudard's turn with Argeville, he refused to let her go to Chambon, claiming that the watchmaker had the clap. When Argeville heard that, she refused to leave our bed, placing herself between Boudard and myself so that Chambon had to be content with her companion, whom he would have all the time without sharing.

This agreement lasted only twenty-four hours; hostilities resumed the following night. Argeville got into our bed; Chambon wanted to have a go at her; I had to fight him off because it was my turn. Boudard took my side; he jumped on Chambon. "The ugly one is yours, the pretty one is ours, we've agreed to that!" Chambon said that he was leaving.

As it happened we all left. Chambon went back to Auxerre, where he advertised our libertinage to all the girls I had known. Fortunately for me he had the reputation of being a terrible liar and no one believed him, especially as the extent of our turpitude exceeded the provincial imagination of the Auxerroises. Boudard and I remained friends, but I quit my job and went to work for Claude Hérissant, rue Notre-Dame, where I was better paid, returning to my first Parisian lodging, *chez* Mme. Lallemand, rue St.-Julien-le-Pauvre.

I should like to report that this scene was either the last or the worst of such experiences but it was neither. Boudard became my companion in whoring, and as our purse was limited we often shared the same girl as we had Argeville. As I've explained, Boudard although strong had mediocre impulses; thus I was the witness to a host of practices that he used to excite himself, a knowledge that has permitted me since to comprehend the perversity of old men. He displayed an enormous attachment to me and I began to suspect after a while that there was something unnatural in this, especially as he could not arrive at satisfaction with a girl unless I was present during the act.

This was confirmed one evening in a violent fashion. I always took the girls first, since I could not bring myself to touch a creature whom I had just watched being screwed by another. (Observe here the peculiar mechanism of the human heart: I knew that these girls were whores, that they spent their days doing nothing else, I could have no illusion that they belonged exclusively to me, but once I had seen them interlaced with Boudard they no longer excited me, whatever their charms—we had tried it at first.) One evening while I was enjoying the quick favors of one of those *filles* on the rue des Mauvais-Garçons (well-named), Boudard was seized by a frenzy; he jumped on top of me as I was in the act and tried to sodomize me. I had

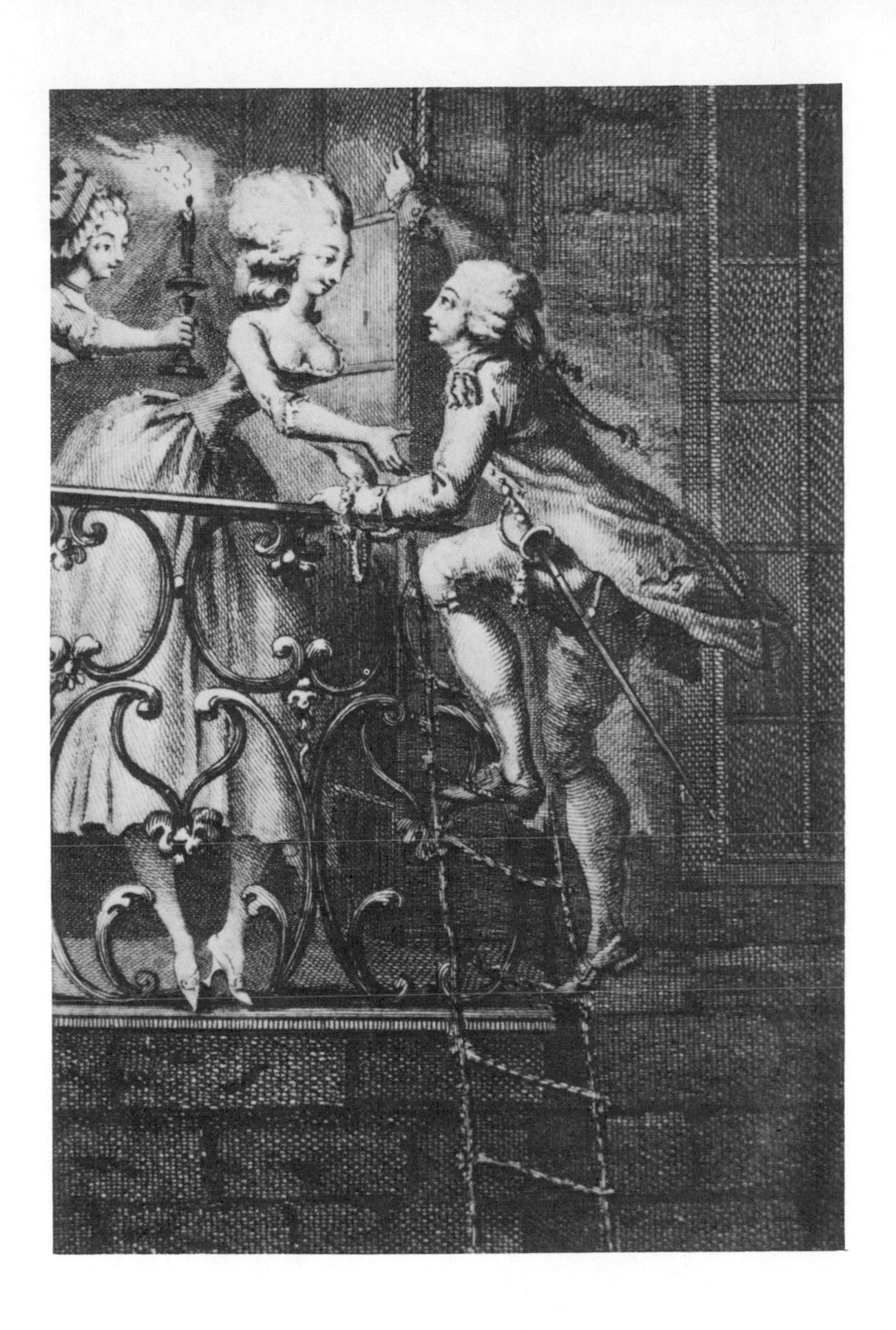

PLATE 8: Restif as a young man making an acrobatic assault on a young lady whose charms are well-lit by her chambermaid (The Bettmann Archive).

to defend myself with blows; I offered to cede him my place, but he would have nothing of it. As I've said he was a giant of a man and capable of killing us both in his fury; as a compromise I had to let him take the girl from behind while I screwed her. The next day he apologized but our friendship quickly cooled. Fortunately Loiseau arrived from Auxerre soon after and I began to live differently, still a libertine but with somewhat more feeling....

I write of the beginning of the twelve years of my youth that were entirely wasted, wasted both for the growth of my soul as well as for any ambition. And you, Reader, do you not have any wasted years?

February 4: A *Te Deum* at Notre-Dame attended by the entire Assembly and the king, a torchlight ceremony at the Hôtel de Ville, all streets illuminated throughout the city. The occasion: without advance notice the king dropped in on the Assembly to declare his fidelity to the Constitution, a sort of advance payment since that document is not yet complete and begins to seem a sister to the Dictionary of the Academy, in the works for over a century. No matter, the Assembly rises to its feet as one man to pledge allegiance to the unfinished document, the galleries join in the solemn oath; word of the great event is carried to the Hôtel de Ville, where Bailly leads the Electors in the pledge then goes out on the staircase and repeats the performance with the participation of a crowd on the Grève. For a week after that district after district is illuminated, with everyone, voters and nonvoters alike, gathering in a square or market place to join in the hopeful oath to the great work as yet incomplete, and the papers report that the scene is repeated all over France. After which everyone goes back to work.

The great unsettled issue is the property of the Church. The delegates of the left propose that it is the property of the Nation and want to sell it off to pay the debts of the state. The Clergy digs out all sorts of old parchments to prove that its immense wealth is *already* the property of the people and therefore cannot be sold. I not only scan the debates in the newspapers, but I profit from them; my friend Arthaud brought me a commission to print a series of pamphlets against the Abbé Maury, leader of the right, a commission that he hints comes from Mirabeau himself. I do the work gladly; my opinion of the priests is already known.

(I must explain the neologisms *left* and *right* as they are used here, since they may be out of fashion in a few years. In the Assembly the Nobility and Clergy have the place of honor, at the right of the President; the Third Estate sits on the left. As the Revolutionaries are almost all delegates of the *Tiers,* even if they are an Abbé like Sieyès or a Vicomte like Mirabeau, the word *left* has acquired that meaning, and *right* the opposite.)

Important things have been accomplished all the same. The courts are to be reorganized; the old hereditary *parlements* are no more. The *provinces* have followed them into history; we now have eight-three *départements.* Non-Catholics are now permitted to vote and hold public office; this is extended even to the Jews.

On February 19th there was a huge crowd at the Grève to witness the execution of Favas, convicted of a plot to assassinate Lafayette and Bailly, kidnap the king to send him abroad and have Monsieur his brother, the Comte de Provence, declared regent. The Comte de Provence protested that he knew nothing of the plot, and made his statement where? at the Hôtel de Ville! What a spectacle, inconceivable a year ago, the king's brother justifying himself to the Electors of Paris, now call the Commune. It was a long day for the spectators, the execution kept being postponed. (I report what I heard afterward.) Favas was in the Hôtel de Ville, writing his will; some say he had been promised a last-minute pardon by the king, but it never came. Finally the sentence was carried out by torchlight; the crowd was about to riot. Never before has a nobleman been hung.

March 7: Since November I often pass by Mérigot's bookshop while on my way to the Café Manoury. The reason: not Mérigot himself—he has done nothing to sell the fourteen volumes of the *Nuits de Paris,* piled up at the back of his shop—not

Mme. Mérigot, although she is a charming woman whose face and figure still display the debris of the beauty of her youth. No, the reason is their daughter Adèle, a girl of only fifteen but wise for her years, a lovely brunette with a wasp waist and tiny feet. Adèle reminds me of Sara at the time when I first knew her, with the difference that Adèle, growing up surrounded by books, has a culture that is surprising in someone unschooled, while Sara was completely ignorant. (But it is not Adèle's culture that attracts me to her. I've had a liaison with only one bluestocking, Minette de Saint-Léger, and she was more of a tease, more treacherous and more calculating than any of the others.) I pass by, drink some tea, and if Adèle is there pass an hour listening to her gossip about her friends, the boys in the district, the dress she is making, her dream of someday taking a trip to Italy.

On Sunday, the 7th, I was invited to dinner at Mérigot's along with Marion and Agnès. Agnès wasn't feeling well, but Marion accompanied me. During the meal I was persuaded to drink some wine, which I do rarely. But it wasn't the wine that made the thermometer of my heart shoot up, it was Adèle. She has two older sisters who are well-bred, good-looking girls, but they have no charms for me. I was troubled to the point of wondering if I had fallen in love again; I looked from Marion to Adèle, both across from me at the table, and it seemed that my feelings for them were similar.

After dinner I took Marion home, then went to my neglected isle to inspect my fading inscriptions, still troubled by the emotion I had felt earlier. The waters of the Seine were a turbulent milky blue, fed by the first thaws of the hillsides upstream after this kind winter. As I passed the Hôtel de Bretonvilliers the explanation of my emotion appeared in a flash—Adèle is my daughter! I dropped to my knees there on the quai, tears flowing down my cheeks, thanking Heaven for the fortunate revelation. Yet another fugitive moment of happiness! they are now few and far between. . . .

Mérigot himself has sparse gray hair; his wife and Adèle's sisters are all blondes, but Adèle is a brunette. Another proof: Adèle alone in that family has dark eyebrows, arching over her wide-set eyes, just like those of Marion as I observed that afternoon at dinner.

This is her story:

In her youth, Mme. Mérigot was one of the most appetizing blondes I've ever known, with a fine face and a flutelike voice. One evening in 1774 I was calling on Mérigot about some business concerning the publication of my *Paysan perverti*. As I came up the quai, unnoticed, I saw the couple at the door of their house and overheard Mérigot tell his wife he had some affairs that would occupy him for an hour; he asked his wife to leave the door open for his return.

As luck would have it there was another eavesdropper, a thief hiding in the shadows. Mérigot departs; Mme. Mérigot goes into her house—I am about to leave when I notice a young man going in the front door, left open by order of the master.

Curious as to whether Mme. Mérigot has a lover—I'd had my eye on her for some time—I follow the stranger. He goes up the stairs but pauses in an antechamber where Mme. Mérigot has left her candle.

The intruder waits until the bedroom door is shut, then looks around. He discovers that he is not alone and assumes that I am there with the same intentions as his.

"Comrade!" he whispers, "we can make a good haul in this house! Let's agree to split what we find!"

"Done!" I answer. "You watch the stairs and I'll do the job; I know the house!"

He agrees to stand sentinel, promising to warn me at the slightest sound. I waited a while until he had gone down to the front door, then silently made my way to the bedroom, to tell Mme. Mérigot what was going on. But she was already asleep. I was afraid to arouse her, thinking that the young thief might have accomplices in the street and that it would be dangerous for both of us if Mme. Mérigot began to shout. After a while I awakened her, gently. She turned over, murmuring "My dear friend!" and put her arms around me. And the thief, and all danger, were forgotten. . . .

A half hour later Mérigot returns; I hear the front door close. I leave immediately; the thief also, without giving the alarm (honor among thieves is an expression, nothing more). I crouch in a corner while Mérigot goes past, then descend the stairs and slip outside. The young intruder is waiting on the quai; he asks me what I got; I say that I had to drop everything when the master came home. I would have had him arrested, were it not for the explanation I should have been made to give of my own conduct, for which there was no excuse.

Did Mme. Mérigot ever suspect anything? I shall never know unless I can bring myself to confess my disgraceful conduct sixteen years ago. . . .

March 15: A letter from Augé *père,* saying that he is taking over the education of my grandson; the child is already living in his house. I had written him about this a month ago and his positive response is a relief. The thought of that child of eight growing up in the care of his monstrous father is horrifying. What brutality might he not suffer, what debauchery might he not witness at the most tender age! I will never understand why the magistrate who permitted Agnès to leave her husband also let Augé keep the child. Another instance of the arbitrary justice of the old courts. Augé's father is not an ideal parent, witness his son, but at least he has a good heart and the child will grow up in respectable surroundings. I sent him copies of the testimony concerning my false arrest in October; he answers that he was distressed to read them but asks me to excuse the MONSTER because he is sick. Does he mean mad? in that case he should be locked up! The five days in prison seem to have done him some good; I haven't heard anything from him since, aside from a letter that I returned unopened. . . .

April 7: To the Café Manoury, papers. The current president of the Assembly, Camus, a deputy of Paris, has played a wicked trick on the royalists. As chairman of the Finance Committee he had discovered that sixty-million livres of the Court budget were not accounted for. From the left, great cries that the king had sent the money abroad to subsidize d'Artois, Polignac, etc., all those *emigrés* who left the country last summer. Louis summoned Camus in secret, let him see the celebrated *Livre rouge,* list of all those who receive pensions from the Court. Camus at once had it printed and all the papers are full of it.

A hundred patriotic pamphlets couldn't do as much to show the need for change; for example:

To a German prince, four pensions, the first for his services as colonel, the second for his services as colonel, the third for his services as colonel, the fourth for his services as colonel; in all 40,048 livres not counting the sous.

To M. Andouillé, the king's barber and Grand Master of Barbering for France, 9,900 livres.

To a Mlle. Hué de Miroménile, "in consideration of her forthcoming marriage," 8,000 livres.

To a M. Blanchet, 4,727 livres for his past services and 4,727 livres "for his future services."

To Mme. la Marquise de Flavacourt de Mailly, 4,651 livres in three pensions, the first "to continue," the second "for no reason," the third, "for her appointments."

Also a number of pensions still being paid to persons who have died and a number to persons who do not yet exist, for example, 4,000 livres "to the man who will marry Mme. de Baschi" (mistress of the Comte de Provence). And a great many awarded to "worthy women," among them a Dame d'Avranches who collects 1,200 livres for having received a certain colonel at her table—it is specified that it was at her *table*.

Meanwhile an officer who lost an arm during the siege of Fribourg gets 4 sous a day, the pay of an ordinary worker.

When this fine book was presented to the Assembly the royalists hooted when Camus mentioned that it was covered with morocco leather with gilt edging. Later Camus introduced another such document, the *Livre des traitements*. A deputy of the right asked sarcastically what covered this one. A patriot shouted, "The blood of the people!"

April 22: Thirtieth anniversary of my marriage to Agnès Lebègue. For all that I pretend to unravel the intricacies of the human heart, I will never understand what it was that led me to tie the fatal knot. Desperation was certainly part of it. I had spent four miserable years of poverty and libertinage in Paris, years redeemed only by the love of two creatures whose memory

I venerate still. One was Zéphire; a whore when I met her but a whore who returned my love and abandoned her unfortunate life to share my poverty with me. I reproach myself still for the child she bore me, a child I had to abandon as a foundling. She was too young to be a mother and never regained her strength; she died in my arms in October 1758. Then there was Loiseau, my dear friend from the days of my apprenticeship in Auxerre; he died in 1759. Abandoning everything, or rather abandoned by these two who were all I cared for in Paris, I returned to Auxerre and there fell into the clutches of Agnès Lebègue and her mother.

But I was aware of what was going on, and should have had the sense to stay away. Agnès Lebègue was a flirt; her mother, usually drunk, seemed to compete with her daughter for my attention. The goings on in that house were a scandal and threatened to become monstrous on occasion—I found myself in a bed with the mother and daughter at the same time—but Agnès did not seem to mind. Mlle. Lebègue was clever in one respect; she reserved her ultimate favors for the wedding night. (A gift that, as it happened, was postponed by the intrusion of her mother, who wanted Agnès and me to return to the wedding dance—I had to threaten to hit her with a chair before I could get her to leave.) But if that one treasure was held back, everything else was offered, and Agnès had techniques to compensate for what she reserved that showed she was hardly new to the game. Her breasts were a bit droopy, unlike those of her mother, which were the best-preserved remains of a beauty now ravaged by age and alcohol. But aside from that Agnès was completely appetizing, tiny waist and feet, and perfection in between.

All the same, there were other girls in town, and given the nature of that household I should eventually have obtained the rest without marriage. My acquaintances told me that Agnès was known for her lovers, the mother for her scandalous life and drinking, that they had been deserted by M. Lebègue, a pharmacist ruined by a long legal action who had gone off to work for the army, that neither mother nor daughter had a sou. In other words I was hardly ignorant of the folly of what I was doing, but as soon as Agnès and her mother began to talk about marriage I agreed like someone in a trance, saying to myself, "This abyss is as good as any other!" It was as if I were throwing myself off a cliff.

The decision was made; my parents came from Sacy, glad that their erring son was ready to settle down at last; the contract was signed, the banns posted. My mother and father had such a respectable and grave appearance that no one in Auxerre dared inform them of what everyone knew about Agnès Lebègue and her mother, but they were a bit surprised when Mme. Lebègue asked if she could borrow the money to buy her daughter's bridal gown. Ten days later the ceremony took place. There I was, *married!*

My cousin Edmée, wiping the tears from her eyes as she stood on the steps of the church, caught my sleeve and whispered, *"There you are, tied!"* And so I was!

I have only myself to blame for my folly, but it is impossible to express how much I've suffered because of that woman. I know I had it in me to be an excellent husband; I am hard-working, sober and loyal. The first years were the most painful; Agnès Lebègue refused to keep house or care for our daughters; she ran off with lovers, then returned ever more bitter and cruel toward me because I was only a workman. But I don't accuse her of anything, I accuse only myself. Bred to have confidence, to be carefree, to work long hours, I let her go her own way until it was too late. I suffered but said nothing because I have a horror of scenes and quarrels. If I had treated her as she deserved she might have mended her ways, but I have never been able to strike a woman. A character like mine is good only for a woman who is already virtuous; thus the errors of Agnès Lebègue are my crimes. I took my revenge by returning to the debauchery from which I had hoped that marriage would rescue me and my years of nothingness were prolonged until the day when I became a writer.

May 6: Anniversary of my presentation to Fournier in 1751; I was sixteen. That afternoon, my first glimpse of Mme. Fournier, who shall be immortalized as the divine Mme. Parangon of *Monsieur Nicolas,* taking her place in the firmament of

Literature along with the Beatrice of Dante, the Laura of Petrarch, the Mme. Warens of Rousseau!

Two months after that first meeting I went to Auxerre to work for Fournier as an apprentice and learn my trade. It is the treatment I received in that printing plant, still as vivid in my memory as if it were only yesterday, that inspired my plan for a reform of the whole industry. But then, what aspect of life in France doesn't cry for reform? Our Revolution is long overdue. My father had to pay for my room and board so that I should have the privilege of being a slave. I had no salary, no rights, and was at the beck and call of the master, the foreman, thirty-two workers, two serving girls, the scullery maids, and even Fournier's valet, who made me do half his work.

The worst was being forced to clean up all the filth of the shop day after day, which included cleaning the latrines, a task made harder by the slovenly habits of the other workers. I was accused of neglect if anything went wrong. (My room was an unheated attic chamber directly over those latrines.) In addition I was forced to serve as secretary and messenger to the workmen, for whom I had to compose obscene *billets-doux* that I carried to their girl friends, at the risk of being punished if it was discovered that I was out of the shop. As an apprentice I was permitted to have neither a soul nor sentiments nor modesty; after my country childhood those four years were more an apprenticeship in vice, cynicism and bad habits than in the profession itself. . . .

I spent this anniversary at work, assisted by my nephew Edmond, finishing up the first proofs of *La Semaine Nocturne*. This despite a recurrence of the pain in my shoulders and a bit of a cold. But after the first hour my physical state was forgotten. I am never happier than when I work directly on the machine, breathing the heavy odor of printer's ink.

For me working at the case is the ultimate step in the process of writing a book; I've done this even when my works were printed by others since my handwriting is so crabbed and idiocentric that no one can read it. I love choosing the characters I employ to indicate the emotions I wish to convey, upper or lower case, italic or roman, Garamond or Janson.

At present I am frustrated by the fact that I have only a limited supply of type which I bought from M. de Beaumarchais, author of *Le Barbier de Seville;* many of the characters are worn or broken so that I am forced to mix different alphabets on the same page, a fault that would have been severely chastised in Fournier's plant, forty years ago. But by this time I don't care anymore; if an idea occurs to me after I have set a page in type I squeeze it in, using smaller letters.

How many of my readers will ever know, when they read one of my works, that the *original* is not some manuscript penned with a goose quill, but the book they hold in their hands, composed, corrected and printed by the author himself on his own press with his own hands?

La Semaine Nocturne, Part XV of *Les Nuits de Paris,* will appear with the name of the bookseller Guillot on the title page, rather than that of Mérigot, publisher of Parts I–XIV. And yet it was Mérigot who urged me to write *La Semaine,* which recounts the events of last year, all the important days of the Revolution. After the book was written, Mérigot cooled off. At the same time, *i.e.,* this past winter, I was writing *Les Filles du Palais-Royal,* a description of the various types of easy women to be encountered in the celebrated arcades, a bit of fluff that is frankly a potboiler. I ran into Guillot at the Palais-Royal one afternoon—he had published *Les Françaises* and *Les Parisiennes* five years before and made a lot of money from both of them—and when I mentioned *Les Filles du Palais-Royal* he insisted that I give it to him. In the end I did, on condition that he take *La Semaine Nocturne* also.

To tell the truth, *Les Filles du Palais-Royal* is pure fantasy. If I recounted the true story of the sad life of those girls no one would want to read it. My head spun with my own inventions as I wrote: the thirty-two delicious creatures of the *Allée des Soupirs,* the brothel where one is passed from one girl to another, each more appetizing than the one before; the *Sunamites,* specializing in the arts of restoring the vigor of old men, the *Converseuses, Berceuses, Chanteuses, ex-Sunamites,* etc.—I kept getting them all mixed up. No doubt the book will have a great success, especially among men coming to Paris from the provinces, or rather the *départements,* leaving their wives behind. I end with a moral epilogue: "And thus, a new Petronius, we have tried to depict the bad habits of all sorts that the reign of privilege had introduced before the Revolution. In our own way we have shown how much that Revolution was necessary, for moral as well as political reasons." Ha! what would we do without Petronius, what would we do if there were not at least one pornographer of antiquity who has attained the rank of a classic? I've read those fragments collected under the title of the *Satyricon* and I doubt that that Latin libertine had any intention of turning into a classic text; he would have paid more attention to his grammar and his slang. But if he didn't exist, we should have to invent him to legitimize our more salacious productions. . . .

June 10: Last year we had a revolution; this year is to be devoted to celebrating it. The Assembly has decided that the anniversary of the fall of the Bastille is to be a holiday, dubbed *Fête de la Fédération,* with delegations from all over France joining the people of Paris to celebrate the great event. The proposed fête is already an object of criticism and complaints; where will all those people be housed, how will they be fed? This will be a true holiday for thieves and pickpockets; the whores also will have their bellies full. At my shop the men complain that they would rather have a raise than a day off; Daniol mutters darkly that the whole thing is a royalist plot. (Of course for Daniol *everything* is a royalist plot—one wonders how the Revolution could have occurred in the first place, since the Court is so clever.) Many Parisians are planning to go to the country that week, to avoid the whole thing.

Meanwhile the Bastille itself is only a ruin, and will soon be nothing more than a hole in the ground. By now every city in France must have one of its stones as a souvenir of that memorable day, cannonballs also are highly prized. The new religion of Liberty is fortunate to have such an immense corpse from which to quarry relics; no one has to be content with a few hairs or threads. Lafayette had one of the blocks carved into a model of the fortress and sent it off to his friend Washington in America. There are all sorts of proposals for the site, a Palace of Liberty or a magnificent Hall for the Assembly, but for the moment it is only a vacant lot.

June 15: Passed by the ancient Café Procope in the district of the Théâtre Français, spot hallowed by the memory of Voltaire; surprised to find it draped in black, with a banner over the door reading, "FRANKLIN IS DEAD." Inside I learn that Franklin is indeed dead, has been dead in fact for two months (but the news has just crossed the Atlantic). The banner is the work of a club that meets in the café, "Friends of the Revolution and of Humanity." In addition to the black hangings there is a bust of Franklin crowned with oak leaves and surrounded with cypress branches, all about it maps of the world, globes, and other emblems of Science and Enlightenment. . . .

June 22: Stranger and stranger! The reports of Saturday night's session of the Assembly read like one of dear old Cazotte's visionary tales. First it is decided to remove the chained figures of conquered provinces from the base of the statue of Louis XIV, Place des Victoires, so as not to offend the *fédérés* arriving in Paris. Then a bizarre delegation is given the right to appear at the tribune, men from all over Europe in peasant costumes, plus a couple of Malays, Chinese, and even an American red man, feathers and all; they call themselves "Representatives of the Human Race" and ask to join with the people of France in celebrating the birth of Liberty. This group is led by one Anacharsis Clootz, a German baron who has lived in Paris for years; he turned up once at Mme. de Beauharnais's, where he amused everyone with his Utopian ideas.

Inspired perhaps by this picturesque vaudeville, the Assembly suddenly amazes everyone and no doubt most of all itself by voting nothing less than the ABOLITION OF THE NOBILITY IN FRANCE. There are to be no more titles, distinctions, grades, etc.; all liveries, armories and escutcheons will be banned! With which they adjourn, well after midnight on a soft June evening, just a day before Midsummer's Eve when fairies dance on moonlit cobwebs—which is perhaps the explanation of the entire event. . . .

July 3: The *fédérés* have begun to arrive; I saw several groups descending the rue St.-Jacques, each with a homemade banner inscribed with the name of their village or town. For many, I am sure, it was the first time they had left their own corner of France. They seemed tired but happy, also bewildered by the sights of the capital.

I remember my first voyage to Paris when I was only twelve and had never been further from my native Sacy than the villages of Nitry and Joux, both within walking distance; my father was taking me to the seminary at Bicêtre. We rode, first to Vermenton, then to Auxerre. At my first glimpse of that town, its red roofs climbing the hillside with the river below, I was overcome with wonder. The cathedral seemed a vision from a fairy tale, also the clock tower with its revolving sun and moon and especially the quais—I had never seen a bridge or a ship. I was seasick on the boat that descended the placid Yonne; we had to get off and take the stagecoach, but I found that just as bad; in the end we made most of the journey by foot. The fine houses, the châteaux, the cathedrals of the towns we traversed astonished and frightened me, as if I were a savage who had never left the primeval forest.

As we were leaving Villejuif we mounted a crest and in the distance I saw a huge mass of houses with a cloud of smoke hanging over them. I asked my father about the strange sight.

"It's Paris, at least the beginning of it; we can't see all of it from here."

I was terrified. And yet when we got into the city itself all my fears suddenly vanished; I was enchanted by all the shops, the markets, the pretty girls shouting their wares at the corners; I found myself in my natural element and decided I wanted to live there forever. . . .

July 8: A kind of fever pulses through the city with the approach of the Fédération. Three days ago the papers reported that the work was delayed at the Champ-de-Mars where the festivities are to take place. They asked for volunteers. Since then the holiday seems to have begun already, at least in this district. The ports are deserted, many shops closed and those open are understaffed. A little sign is tacked up: "We have gone to assist our brothers at the Champ-de-Mars. Vive la France!" . . .

All day one sees groups of workmen, armed with shovels and pails, heading west. An improvement, to be sure, over the muskets and pikes of last summer. Groups of women also, all decked out with tricolor ribbons to make a *"coiffure aux charmes de la Liberté."* As they march they all sing a banal ditty that rings in one's head like an obsession, an air with the slangy refrain, *"Ça ira! ça ira!"*

Ah! Ca ira! ça ira! ça ira!
La Liberté s'établira!
Ah! ça ira! ça ira! ça ira!
Malgré les tyrans tout réussira
Celui qui s'élève, on l'abaissera!
Ça ira! ça ira! ça ira!

(It'll be all right, all right, all right!
Freedom will come at last!
Despite the tyrants all will succeed,
If one pops up we'll mow him down!)

To be sure, that also is preferable to the words of last summer, when the song was first sung

Les aristocrates à la lanterne!
Les aristocrates on les pendra,
Et quand on les aura tous pendu,
On leur fich'ra la pelle au cul!

(Aristocrats, to the lamppost!
Aristocrats, we'll string them up!
And when we've hung them one and all,
We'll stick a shovel up their ass!)

This afternoon I followed the quais to the Champ-de-Mars, to see what all the fuss was about. Astonishing spectacle. A vast sea of mud, from the Ecole Militaire to the Seine, swarming with thousands of people, all hard at work. Someone looking down from the heights of Chaillot would think he was watching a colony of oversized ants, building a new nest. The old mix with the young, women work alongside their husbands or lovers, there are men in rags and men in silk, equally covered with dust. Banners, here and there: TREMBLE, ARISTOCRATS, HERE ARE THE BUTCHERS!—THE PRESS, GUARDIAN OF LIBERTY! (Despite the banner I saw neither Mercier, Desmoulins nor Marat at work with a spade.)

I'll admit I came to scoff and stayed to marvel. A man had a barrel of wine on a cart. I thought him a clever fellow who had found a way to make a few francs until I saw that he was *giving it away*. In Paris! "You're welcome, brothers, if you really need it!" The only men I saw drinking were those truly exhausted from their labor.

On my way back I passed a number of menageries and sideshows on the esplanade of the Invalides, the gypsy wagons parked on the lawns with dark-haired women stirring black caldrons over charcoal fires. There you have to pay to see the show. . . .

July 12: Out late, a warm evening; I wore my threadbare suit with its faded braid, walked along in a sort of dream. On the rue St.-Honoré, I am awakened from my reverie by the touch of a stick on my back; turning around I see a young man running away. A minute later I am beset by five thugs who mutter, "He's marked!" In a twinkling they frisk my pockets, my vest, even the gussets of my jacket.

"Young thieves!" I shout, "I have nothing!"

An old woman is selling papers before a haberdasher's shop.

"Respect his robe, if nothing else!" she cries, taking me for an abbé. My assailants run off.

"A pack of thieves!" I shout. "They respect nothing!"

"Thieves, I thought them young gentlemen."

I ask her to look at my back; she finds a chalk line, rubs it off; that was their mark. . . .

The Palais-Royal is busy with merrymakers. It is the anniversary of Camille's green cockade, but the orators have vanished; I see only visitors from the provinces, out for a lark, and gamblers, libertines, pimps, streetwalkers. Pickpockets everywhere, enjoying the crush. I feel a hand on my thigh. "Go to it!" I shout, "I have nothing, my pockets are unpickable!"

July 14: Last night to the Champ-de-Mars, now called Champ de la Fédération. Here and there, clusters of men and women camping out to be sure of a place the next day. Torches sputtering in the night air, flickering campfires, the scent of sausages roasting over the flames, the murmur of talking and singing—all subdued, expectant; the bivouac of an army the night before a battle. In the shadows the immense works accomplished in the past two weeks are even more impressive than by day. A huge amphitheater, partially earth, partially wooden scaffolding, with benches for spectators. A bridge of boats across the Seine to Chaillot. An Arc de Triomphe. In the center of the arena the Altar of the Nation at the summit of a newly created mound of earth, the Mountain of the Fatherland that in the trembling light of the torches appeared a veritable Alp. . . .

Say what one will, and all Parisians are scoffers, what has occurred in the past year is astonishing. The spectacle at the Champ-de-Mars is worthy of ancient Greece or Rome. I found myself kneeling in the mud and praying for my country. A sentinel approached, asked what I was doing. "I am praying for France as Horace prayed for Rome in the days of its glory!" He asked no more questions.

This morning, as early as five, the streets were crowded with troops of Parisians and *fédérés* assembling to march to the ceremony. On the Place Maubert I saw the market girls handing out sacks of provisions. On the rue St.-Jacques people hung ropes out their windows with smoked hams and bottles of wines swaying above the crowd like the bait of the anglers of the quais, but they weren't trying to catch anything, they shouted that the marchers should take what they offered. Unfortunately it is raining; spirits remain high but people joke that the sky is an aristocrat. A carnival of a new sort; may the spirit of the Revolution always remain as generous as it is today! Having performed my devotions last night I decided to stay home. . . .

July 17: Reports in the papers of Wednesday's ceremony. Everyone and everything was there: the king, the queen,

Lafayette on his white horse, the entire Assembly, two hundred priests wearing white sashes, an orchestra of twelve hundred musicians, a salute by forty cannon, the oath of fidelity sworn in unison by two hundred thousand spectators, and the new flags of the eighty-three *départements* blessed by the Bishop of Autun, M. de Talleyrand—nothing missing but the sun. . . .

August 9: In the papers, discussion of the decree of June 19th, its consequences; the question of names, for example. Shall the great Mirabeau now be called *M. Riqueti?* Shall Lafayette, dropping the title he made illustrious, begin again as *M. Motier?* If Voltaire were alive, would he now became *M. Arouet?* When the Countess de Beauharnais returns from Italy, will she find herself Mme. Fanny Bouchard? (Under whatever name, I wish she *were* back.) Will I be forced to drop *de la Bretonne,* which comes from no title but might be taken for one? It is easy for the United States to ban all titles; their great men are simply FRANKLIN or WASHINGTON, but in an old country like France things are more complicated. . . .

Out yesterday, a fine Sunday, with Agnès to the Champs-Elysées. Instead of my usual route by the quais we took the rue St.-Dominique and the rue de Bourgogne. Above the portes cochères of the Faubourg St.-Germain signs of a grudging compliance with the new rules—the shields of the noble proprietors of the great houses are indeed obscured, but only by a thin coat of plaster that will wash away in short order.

On the Champs-Elysées the parade of carriages was as brilliant as ever. Since servants are now forbidden to wear livery, one wag had dressed his coachmen as Harlequins, his footmen as Pierrots; this carnival apparition was hooted as it went by. The escutcheons on the carriage doors are covered by a thin coat of paint, often in the form of clouds. One coach, whose owner thought the clouds alone too subtle a symbol, bore the motto, "This storm will pass!"

August 21: Everywhere in Paris, for the past few years, certain houses have these letters over the front door: M.A.C.L. for *Maison assurée contre l'incendie* (house insured against fire). This afternoon, rue St.-Honoré, I overheard one delivery boy tell another that they mean, *"Marie-Antoinette cocufie Louis"* (Marie-Antoinette makes a cuckold of Louis)....

September 15: Out at five, to my isle by the Cité and the Pont-Rouge, then along the quai d'Orléans. The day foreshadowed autumn, gray but luminous, neither sun nor rain; a light that insinuates a sweet melancholy into one's soul that is hard to define. Never have I experienced a sensation more innocent and more delicious all at once. The air was soft; it was the hour of vespers; the bells of the churches on both banks of the Seine rang all at the same time, each with a slightly different tone; the trembling of the atmosphere set off by their vibrations caressed my ears and seemed to awaken my soul. Life is so short and precious, and at times it can be so lovely. This great city, which I have seen so cruel, felt tender and loving, the great gray mother of all the poor creatures that live out their lives under her sooty roofs....

A complete circle of the isle, past the inscribed memories of all my joys and sorrows. Why do I persist in this mania for commemorations? Because there is no one with whom I can share these thoughts except my readers. With the passage of time one becomes one's own best friend, remembering that other self of the years that have passed with interest and indulgence, and by those memories resuscitating that other self with the feeling that there is finally someone who truly understands.

Afterwards my annual pilgrimage to the rue Saintonge in the Marais. It was there that I made my first inscriptions in stone, years before I began to note my *dates* on the Ile St.-Louis. There are only two: *8 7bris, Victoria visa* (8 September, saw Victoria) and *14 7bris 1769, felicitatem Vict. ineff.* (14 September, ineffable happiness, Victoria), both scratched on a garden wall across from No. 14, her house.

What struck me today, twenty-one years later, is the nature of the emotion I feel now at the sight of those words, still dimly visible, if only to my eyes. And not only the words; there is a fountain at the corner of the rue Vielle-du-Temple that I pass on my way to the rue Saintonge; at the sight of that fountain

I am filled with Joy, I rediscover the emotions of my thirty-fifth year; it is as if I am about to see Mlle. Victoire again. And yet that was hardly a great passion; I spent only two nights with the girl. . . .

It occurred to me today that when one is in love, or even when one only makes love, it is not really the woman who is exciting, but rather the enchantment that she casts on one's entire existence; that all love, be it trivial or profound, is really a romantic, magical love of oneself! . . . Is that the truth? have I done nothing but love myself in loving Jeanette Rousseau, Mme. Fournier, Zéphire, Sara, Louise and Thérèse? This would explain how one can fall in love again and again. But it would mean that we are all Narcissus!

Returning, an idea for a useful supplement to *Monsieur Nicolas:* a CALENDRIER, that is to say my own personal calendar, a list arranged by the days of the year of the commemorations I observe, recalling each of the women I have known and loved, a sort of index to the main body of the work, according to the chronology of my heart. I do believe that brief encounters are as revealing in their way as the grand passions, at least for the dissection of the human heart, which is my purpose. For example: Mlle. Victoire of the rue Saintonge, muse of those first *dates.* There were only two nights and yet the experience was extraordinary, especially the second time. Victoire was perfection itself in all the arts of love; she made the instant of the most acute pleasure last for three hours! The gods in Olympus may have known the sensations I enjoyed that night, but surely nothing better. The final spark before the extinction of consciousness was unique in my entire life.

I can't work all those girls into a straight narrative; it would seem like boasting, which I don't mean to do, since I have so often been unhappy. Yet what a pleasure for me to gather all those beauties into an amorous garland, each with her own day, like the saints of the church! (But some days will have more than one patron; the year is only so long. . . .)

October 5: letter to Grimod.

I first became acquainted with the young La Reynière in November 1782; he was then only twenty-four but already celebrated for his plays and even more for his circle of friends. It was a cold afternoon; I dropped into Duchesne's bookshop, rue St.-Jacques, and noticed an elegant young man warming himself at the stove. When he heard my name he jumped up and put his arms about me, assaulting me with compliments so extravagant that I thought they must be flattery with some hidden motive. But I soon learned that he was perfectly sincere and that his spontaneous enthusiasm was characteristic. At a time when it was the fashion to be scornful and insolent young Grimod was affability itself, caring for no distinction but personal merit. We quickly became fast friends.

Was this good nature the result of his disability? I prefer to think not. But perhaps that malformation accounts for certain odd quirks of his character. La Reynière was born without hands, only webbed paws at the end of his truncated arms. A celebrated physician constructed steel fingers that were attached to the incomplete limbs Nature had provided. Grimod always wore gloves and even those were usually hidden in the sleeves of his jacket. He managed somehow to write and even draw. On occasion, to shock the ladies, he would touch a glove to a red-hot stove and then smile at the squeals of horror.

The La Reynières were a family of tax collectors, excessively wealthy but with no other accomplishments. His grandfather made a fortune under Louis XV by graft, as was the custom; he died before Grimod was born—of suffocation after choking on a mouthful of excellent *pâté de foie gras*. The tradition of gourmandize was continued by Grimod *père,* known for his lavish table, his superlative cook, and his lack of wit. It was said that he was "edible but not digestible." The family owns a magnificent mansion just off the Place Louis XV; the house is now closed, they may have emigrated.

Grimod's luncheons were celebrated in their time, a time that now seems terribly distant although it was only seven years ago. The guests were chosen purely for their accomplishments, with no regard for title or wealth. You could bring two or three friends along and no questions were asked. The hours were eleven to four. When everyone had assembled the doors were locked and no one could leave until the session was adjourned.

There was an immense round table in the center of the room with one chair raised on a platform for whoever presided that afternoon; the post changed by rotation. You drank coffee or tea and ate buttered toast with anchovies; the coffee was weak and hot milk was offered with it, so you could take all you wanted without risk. Everyone had to drink twenty-two cups, that was the rule. The sessions began with general conversation; then authors read from their manuscripts, poets recited their verses and dramatists declaimed speeches from their plays—a true Academy. Afterwards there was an immense roast beef, washed down with cider, never wine.

His father made Grimod study law and bought him a judgeship when he was only twenty-one. Grimod refused it out of pique, preferring literary society. His allowance was cut off; Grimod retaliated by renting out the family coach as a hack. After that there was no restraining his prodigality. But the ax descended when he fell in love with a cousin, Mme. Mitoire. He didn't bother to conceal their affair—she was present at all his luncheons, dressed as a man. In April 1786 Grimod's father procured a *lettre de cachet* which exiled him from Paris. I haven't seen him since and I miss him cruelly.

It was on March 9, 1786, at one of Grimod's magnificent suppers, a true Roman *coena,* that I had the inspiration for *Le Drame de la Vie,* the work that has occupied most of my time of late. Since 1783 I had been writing *Monsieur Nicolas* and although I was pleased by it I felt it needed a complementary work, in dramatic form, to convey the immediacy of the living experience, rather than experience remembered. At that epoch I was possessed of a dramamania; I wrote play after play, hounded the directors of all the theaters of Paris with scripts, inserted dramatic scenes and even entire comedies into the middle of novels, tales, even essays (where, to tell the truth, they had no reason to be at all, except to pad out the volume). But, enchanted as I was by the theater, I felt its form too restricted to depict an entire life.

Because I had a beastly cold, Grimod permitted me to wear my hat at table as protection against drafts (see the engraving by Binet in *Les Nuits de Paris,* where I am shown seated next to Mercier as one of the courses is carried in by eleven waiters led by a master of ceremonies in Roman armor). The precaution proved unnecessary; the three hundred sixty-six candles made the room so hot that the windows had to be opened. There were twenty-eight courses, one for each guest. The collation terminated, Grimod announced a "shadow play" to be executed by the celebrated Italian, Signor Castanio, an expert in electrical phenomena, the sort of display I usually find a bore.

To be sure, it began with the usual tricks, glowing bottles, sparks jumping from table to table. But then the play itself began; a platform was erected, a curtain lowered, illuminated from behind by a flickering white light—and, as if by magic, figures, houses, forests, ships, horsemen, palaces, came and went on the white screen (shadows, of course, but what shadows!), growing larger and smaller, following each other with an incredible rapidity, all arranged to tell a story. Hidden actors projected their voices so they seemed to come from the shadows themselves. What the play was about I cannot remember, but almost from the start I had realized that this magic lantern spectacle was the form I needed for my Drama. It was the words I was to write that filled my ears as I watched the flickering scenes, beginning with the announcement: "And now, my dear friends, you are going to see me as a child!"

A month later Grimod was gone. I'm afraid that his years in exile have changed him, and for the worse. Instead of returning to Paris—there are no more *lettres de cachet*—he writes that he is staying in Béziers with his aunt, Mme. la comtesse de Beausset (they don't seem to have heard that titles are abolished in Béziers). Ever a gourmet, he describes the dinners of the "society" of that town, the melons, fish, pheasants, wines; he suggests I spend next summer there for the climate and the food. Affectionate recollections of our walks on the Ile St.-Louis and of mutual friends, but all of it spoiled by politics.

Grimod, who once was proud to have the son of his candlemaker to dinner while excluding anyone with the title of Chevalier de St.-Louis, Grimod who found there were too many courtiers at the salon of Mme. de Beauharnais, Grimod has become a fanatic Royalist!

PLATE 9: Supper at Grimod de la Reynière's, March 9, 1786. Restif is the guest wearing a hat. The La Reynière mansion was on the site of the present American embassy. From Volume VII of *Les Nuits de Paris,* 1789.

He asked me to break with Mercier because of the "radicalism" of the *Annales Patriotiques* (someone should tell Marat); he speaks of our "execrable Revolution that has returned France to the age of the Goths and Vandals . . . that has destroyed literature which flourishes only under despots such as Pericles or Louis XIV." (Pericles a despot? and if it were so, wouldn't despotism be too high a price for a few verses?) He complains that my *Semaine Nocturne,* which I sent him when it was published, is much too "liberal." No mention of the *Fédération,* that joyous ceremony uniting all of France, no mention of so many humane reforms that once would have gladdened his heart, including the abolition of these *lettres de cachet* that so abruptly cut off his Parisian career. Until the end of '88 he was confined in the monastery at Domèvre; I'm afraid the monks have corrupted his heart.

This morning, a reply to his latest letter, as gentle as possible since I hope that despite all we can remain friends. Told him to come to Paris to see for himself that the city has never been more splendid or more civilized. Sent him a copy of my portrait as a present for his aunt, the one engraved by Binet, with the verses that had appeared in 1785 in the *Journal de Genève:*

Restif de la Bretonne

Son espirit libre et fier, sans guide et sans modèle
Même alors qu'il s'égare, étonne ses rivaux
Amant de la nature, il lui dut ses pinceaux
Et fut simple, inégal et sublime comme elle.

(His spirit proud and free, with neither guide
nor model,
Even when he wanders, astonishes his rivals,
Lover of Nature, he learned from her to limn
And like her was simple, uneven, and sublime.)

October 17: Returning from the Palais-Royal by the rue des Lombards I am seized by that emotion that used to be a daily experience and now, alas! has become rare—my heart skips a beat at a glance from a young girl. She is decently dressed, her auburn tresses tied by a tricolor ribbon, her feet marvels of lightness and delicacy, encased in graceful pointed slippers. I smile at her; the smile is returned with, I thought, nothing more than the frank good spirits of youth. Enchanted, I follow her. At the corner of the rue St.-Denis she stops to scan the latest papers at a newsstand. I could see that she was reading nothing, did not even know how to pretend to read and probably couldn't read at all. . . .

I approach her; to my astonishment she immediately takes my hand, whispering, "Come along!" She leads me up to the third floor of a nearby house. Startled to find myself there—the room was simply furnished and clean; there was nothing in the girl's manner that marked her as a professional—I was even more startled when I found myself face to face with a fine-looking buxom woman whom I guessed, from a similarity in their expression, to be the girl's mother. She was not at all surprised at my presence, but I was embarrassed. I said I had offered to escort her daughter home; she laughed in my face. The conversation that followed was singular, worthy of an episode in *Le Drame de la Vie:*

LA MÈRE: Do not pretend with me, monsieur; I know why you're here and I've come to fix the price, since my daughter is too thick to do it herself.

MOI: You shock me, madame.

(To tell the truth, I *was* shocked at the appearance of such bourgeois virtue speaking so frankly of vice.)

LA MÈRE: My excuses, monsieur, if my daughter was in error.

MOI: Your daughter is charming. With her face and figure surely you could find something better for her than——

LA MÈRE: A face and a figure aren't all it takes. My daughter has beauty and youth but she lacks talent, wit and any aptitude for vice.

MOI: You certainly express yourself well—but do you really mean that you wish she were proficient in vice?

LA MÈRE: I know what I'm saying. As it is now she'll never amount to more than a streetwalker, which is a sad life.

MOI: How can you say that?

LA MÈRE: Because it's true. She can't do anything else, would look like a goose up on the stage, can't even sew. She doesn't like to work, won't pay attention, she's fussy about what she eats; there's nothing I can do about it. So one day I said to her, "All right, Robertine, you'll have to be a whore." And that's that. I stay with her to take care of her because after all she's my child and I can't abandon her.

MOI: You are frankness itself, madame, but you are ruining your daughter.

LA MÈRE: *Basta!* What do you call *ruining?* Wouldn't she be ruined as a lazy working girl, dragging around in rags? Wouldn't she be ruined married to some good-for-nothing, some streetsweeper or water carrier, beaten every evening, bearing one child after another that she'd have to give away? Wouldn't she be ruined if she became a beggar? Because that is the alternative for us, *monsieur le philosophe* who isn't above following a child up to her room! Don't preach morality to poor people who have nothing—we can't afford it! Everyone talks about Equality and Fraternity—when the talk turns into facts everyone will be virtuous. But until that day, I'd rather that my daughter be a whore!

November 13: Paris is changing, but then Paris is always changing. In the thirty-five years I've lived here I've seen the Montagne St.-Geneviève crowned with the noble dome of the church of the same name, the bare field at the start of the Champs-Elysées become the magnificent Place Louis XV, the houses on the Pont-au-Change torn down to make way for the heavy traffic of modern times (it is fortunate that so many bridges were constructed to hold houses, or they would all be too narrow for today's traffic), the Mint constructed on the quai de Conti, facing one of the choice prospects of the city, and of course the new Palais-Royal. The boulevards, once the site of the walls of the new capital, are now tree-lined promenades, well within town, even if the districts beyond are still called *faubourgs.* This year the Bastille has been demolished—Baron Clootz predicts that the Tower of London will suffer the same fate when the Revolution becomes universal—and a new bridge almost completed at the Place Louis XV with some of the stones of the prison serving as material, the Pont-Louis XVI. But what are monuments, compared with other things? Paris is now truly the capital, the king in the Tuileries, the Assembly in the Manège, newspapers sold at every streetcorner, bread at last cheap and plentiful, the theaters crowded, and, of course, the *filles* never more abundant. . . .

The great rage of the moment is to belong to a club. (I regret having to use this word borrowed from English, but that is the style.) At the Palais-Royal the Club '89 meets in a splendid apartment above the arcades, the club of Bailly, Lafayette, Mirabeau, Sieyès; from time to time these luminaries appear on a balcony to salute the crowds in the gardens below. There is the Cercle Social that meets on Friday in the horrible wooden *Cirque* that disfigures the gardens, a building that I hope is only temporary since it destroys all the charm of the spot. On the Left Bank the Cordeliers meet in the church of the same name, not far from the Café Procope. Both the charming Camille and the fanatic Marat belong to that group, a strange combination, since they so often attack each other in their respective journals, but then both of them live close by, so it is easy for them to drop in for the debates. The society includes also the "representative of the human race," Anacharsis Clootz, who has found a forum more suitable to his talents than the blue-and-silver salon of Mme. de Beauharnais. I wonder at the effect of his ravings on the skeletons of the monks under the paving stones.

But the foremost club of all, and the most powerful, if not at the Palais-Royal itself, is at least in the neighborhood. I mean of course the Friends of the Constitution, known to everyone as the Jacobins, from the church they have rented for their deliberations. Foremost because there are at least two hundred deputies among its members and because the real work of the Assembly is often accomplished there at night, after the legislature has adjourned. It is not only a Parisian club; there are hundreds of them all over France. Not at all aristocratic, but restricted nonetheless; distinguished foreigners plead for tickets to the galleries, but when I tried to enter one evening I was turned away at the door by no less a person than M. Choderlos de Laclos, author of the scandalous novel *Les Liaisons Dangereuses.*

This afternoon I went to see Guillot to find out how *Les Filles du Palais-Royal* was selling. While I was there, a friend of Guillot's arrives, M. Saurade, member of the Jacobins, a rich merchant like so many of that fraternity; he says that something interesting is taking place in the rue de Varennes, at the house of the duc de Castries.

When I left Guillot's I went to the spot, and the sight was indeed interesting. One would have said that a band of brigands was pillaging one of the finest mansions of the Faubourg St.-Germain while the police stood by and pretended to see nothing. And yet the brigands were not brigands, and the police not police; the pillagers were Jacobins, respectable citizens all, the watching battalion Gardes of the section, also respectable citizens, who refused to intervene.

What happened is this: one of the founders of the Jacobins, Charles de Lameth, had been provoked to a duel by the young duc de Castries, like Lameth a deputy in the Assembly. The subject: insults by royalists in the corridors of the Manège, the latest of a long campaign of provocations by the gentlemen of the right—Mirabeau himself had been struck by a cane just a week before. Lameth and Castries met in the Bois de Boulogne; Castries was untouched but Lameth received a scratch on his left arm. Word spread that Castries's sword was poisoned and the wound was fatal—the sack of the Hôtel de Castries was the Jacobins' revenge.

Lafayette himself arrived from the Hôtel de Ville and was forced to stand by helpless when the Gardes would not obey his orders to intervene. The Jacobin band slashed the paintings, axed the furniture, shattered the marble stairs and paneling, chucked the debris out in the courtyard. The only thing spared was a portrait of the king; a sentinel was posted to protect it. Shortly after I arrived the "brigands" marched away, with their pockets turned inside out; nothing was stolen, but nothing remained to be stolen.

To the king, the Assembly, the Commune, one must now add the Jacobins; they have become a power. . . .

December 31: A year that began with such high hopes ends with a sort of lassitude. Perhaps that's only normal, perhaps it is precisely the *normality* of the present moment that produces a sense of fatigue, even if it is a new sort of normality that has never been seen before. Rome wasn't built in a day . . . France is not to be rebuilt in a year. There are events I haven't mentioned, the massacre of Nancy, the revolt in Santo Domingo, but this is neither a newspaper nor a history. In Paris the Assembly continues its work, despite the opposition of the *Noirs,* who would like to set the clock back; the king has finally approved the reorganization of the clergy.

Two weeks ago, an evening at the *Théâtre des Italiens* with Mercier, Carra, Camille Desmoulins and Camille's young fiancée, Lucille Duplessis. I hadn't seen the charming "district attorney of the lamppost" since the fall of '89 at Mme. de Beauharnais's (he seems to be a bit ashamed of the title just now—one of the errors of his youth that he will have to live down). Lucille is his childhood sweetheart; they met when she was twelve, he seventeen.

The theater was packed with a well-dressed audience. If many aristocrats have been leaving Paris for the dubious delights of some German town, their place has been taken by curious foreigners who come to see what is happening in the capital of Europe after an unprecedented revolution. I heard English, German, Spanish, Italian and I think Russian in the lobby during the intermission. Mercier, Carra and Desmoulins were of course beset by a host of acquaintances or would-be acquaintances, as one would expect when three of the foremost journalists of Paris appear together, especially at a time when the press has become the Fourth Estate. All this bright and fashionable crowd looked at my old clothes with distaste and I kept being shoved aside; there were startled and curious expressions when I rejoined the party at our seats. The opera was *La Villanella Rapita* by Bianchi, a delicious composition, playful and airy and beautifully sung. It seems strange that at a time when everyone is so patriotic the Italian opera should be so popular; the quality of the music is the explanation.

Afterwards to a restaurant at the Palais-Royal where we had supper in a private room. Some talk of politics, especially as it affects the press. Camille's wit and malice have earned him many enemies as well as many readers. In July there was a motion of censure against him in the Assembly itself, brought by a Royalist deputy, Malouet; Desmoulins was defended by the Jacobin Robespierre, who had known him at school. Camille had made fun of the actor Dessarts because of his great bulk; when they met in a restaurant Camille was challenged to a duel. He refused, saying they would both have "more useful and glorious occasions on which to die." Carra was recently cuffed by some young aristocrats at the Palais-Royal; Camille said he also had been threatened one afternoon—fortunately he was carrying a pistol which he showed his assailant before driving him off with a cane.

But most of the evening was devoted to Lucille, a dazzling blonde of a well-to-do family. Her father approved the match only a few weeks ago. The young couple seemed very much in love; they kept exchanging tender glances; Camille has lost his stammer. Laughing at his own confusion, he told how he had written to his father to ask for his consent to the match, received an answer that his parents were delighted at the news but would he please tell them the name of his betrothed. They were having great trouble in finding a priest to marry them, because of Camille's well-known anticlerical opinions.

The marriage took place on the 29th, at Saint-Sulpice. Mercier was one of the official witnesses, along with Robespierre and Brissot, yet another journalist. In order to get permission to use the church, Camille had to swear to the curé that he was a good Catholic and promise to print a profession of faith in his journal (will that promise be kept?). The ceremony was conducted by the Abbé Bérardier, who had taught both Desmoulins and Robespierre at Louis-le-Grand. (So many of our Revolutionaries are lawyers who were educated by priests!) Mercier reported that when the benediction was pronounced Camille's eyes filled with tears; Robespierre whispered to him, "Cry if you must." . . .

DECEPTIONS AND SHAMS

1791

WE enter the age of deceptions and shams. Everyone whispers of plots and schemes, evasions and lies, flights and treason; everything is denied and in the end everything proves to have been true. The powerful continue to think that the people can be fooled forever, but the people are not taken in.

I read the papers at the Café Manoury; I have dinner with Mercier who knows everyone in Paris, the members of the Assembly, the Electors of the Hôtel de Ville. In the end it is the gossip of the housewives at the market on the Place Maubert that proves to be sound.

For example, February 20: the two old aunts of the king had left Paris for Rome, with the intention of celebrating Easter in the Holy City where they could receive communion from the pope himself instead of from the hands of the Constitutional Priest at the Tuileries palace. Their presence in Paris meant nothing, but their departure was a sign that the royal family had its misgivings about the Revolution, whatever their public stance. The fear that the king and queen might make a similar voyage was already widespread.

This at the Place Maubert: "What, those two old bags couldn't say their rosary in Paris? Paris is as good as Rome! ——Let them go! What good are those two old bigots to anyone? —— But what if the king should want to join them there? We need our king in France. —— Our little father wouldn't do that to us! I believe that he loves his people, whatever they say! —— Yes, but the Antoinette might talk him into it, the Austrian, she doesn't care anything about France. ——Bah! she's too busy giving Louis horns with all those young aristocrats. Let her take her ass back to Vienna if she wants but leave us our king! —— Let her take Mirabeau also, they say he's been bribed, and not just with money. —— Who, our Mirabeau? don't talk about him, he's a great man! —— Great man or not, he likes wine and women. ——Well, why shouldn't he, since he's got a gullet and balls? I'll take a real man like that before some of these lawyers who do nothing but make speeches no one can understand! ——All the same the aunts should stay here in France, it's their country the same as it's ours. ——Let them go! good riddance to all those aristocrats who want to live in places where they don't even talk French! Let them go!"

And they went. Merely a private visit, said the Court, no political implications whatsoever. Meanwhile the roads to the frontiers remained busy with the carriages of noblemen who had suddenly decided to take a trip, a long voyage by the look of it, since the springs groaned under the weight of the linens and silverware, jewels and wardrobes. But once out of France the carriages did not go on to Rome or Venice, Berlin or Vienna, but instead stopped at Kehl or Triers, Bonn or Coblentz, little German towns just over the border that had never before attracted so many elegant French visitors. Once there the visitors showed no appetite for further travel, at least not with Paris at their backs. They rented houses, on a quarterly basis only, unloaded the linens and the silver, arranged for loans with the bankers of Frankfurt, using their jewels as collateral, and washed off the clouds that covered the coats of arms on the coach doors. But that also, of course, was only a private matter; in the era of Liberty, what was to stop a Frenchman from passing a while in a quaint town on the Rhine, if the fancy so took him?

A week after the departure of the king's aunts, we had the day of the Knights of the Daggers. To the housewives of the Place Maubert the story was simple: the king was ready to take a trip abroad, or perhaps others had decided for him that he should leave (that was the only disputed point). Under cover of darkness hundreds of noblemen had gone to the palace, armed to the teeth, preparing for the departure that they had planned. The people had wind of the plot, ran to abort it; the Knights of the Dagger were arrested, the king remained where he was.

Too simple, no doubt, but were they wrong?

On the day itself it was much more confusing. I was working on the proofs of *Monsieur Nicolas,* Fourth Epoch, when a drummer came by, beating the *générale,* a sound we hadn't heard for some time. Agnès, returning from the bakery, reported having seen several battalions of the Gardes going east. All seemed calm, but in the afternoon, when I went to Mérigot's to see Adèle, I heard reports of an insurrection in the Faubourg St.-Antoine. What would have been terrifying only two years ago is now almost expected; the only question is the outcome. But as it happened the events in the Faubourg St.-Antoine that day came to nothing. The people who see a conspiracy behind everything that takes place think it was all part of a *plot,* but it may have been only a coincidence. When the reader finds that a story turns on a coincidence he thinks he has been cheated, but in real life they happen every day.

I learned later that the Conciergerie and Châtelet prisons were overcrowded with the usual run of criminals; some of them were to be transferred to the Château de Vincennes. A rumor spread in the Faubourg St.-Antoine that Vincennes was to become a new Bastille. The morning of February 28, a Sunday, columns of workers converged on Vincennes shouting they were going to demolish the château. (We have insurrections on Sundays or Mondays because no one is working.) The *générale* was beaten, the Gardes called out, the workers persuaded to disperse. . . . Meanwhile one of the servants at the Tuileries sent out word that the palace was full of armed men; an aristocrat, trying to leave, was searched and found to be carrying two pistols (he tried to explain the weapons by saying he was an American, but the Grenadier was not fooled). Lafayette is informed; a courier races to Vincennes; the Gardes march to the Tuileries.

Knowing nothing of all this, I left Mérigot's for the Palais-Royal. As I pass the Tuileries, I see the palace surrounded by troops, behind them an angry crowd, shouting that "they" are trying to make off with the king. I have no idea who "they" may be, until I see a long file of men wearing black emerge from the palace, passing between a double line of the *Gardes.* Each one is searched, then they are taken away. The crowd hoots. I had a few difficult moments because of my old-fashioned coat—fortunately a patrol from my section was stationed nearby, the same men who had arrested me in October '89; they assured the crowd that I was all right.

For a month the papers are full of the affair. The incidents at Vincennes are declared to be an aristocratic plot, their authors labeled "counterrevolutionary brigands" (which seems unlikely). The king disowns the "Knights of the Dagger" and for that is called a coward by his own partisans. (These "Knights" are soon released.) There is a furious debate in the Assembly; Mirabeau's enemies try to fix the blame for the affair on him; he replies by attacking the Jacobins as a group of conspirators, although it seems unlikely that either Mirabeau or the Jacobins had anything to do with the matter; such is politics. For the moment the prestige of Lafayette is greatly enhanced. . . .

Is the complete liberty of the press to be desired? As a matter of principle I would say it is. But I find that that is comparable to saying that in a state of nature men would find nothing offensive about a belch or a fart. When I was a child I noticed that the donkeys grazing on the hilly pastures of Courgis never seemed to notice each other's little explosions. But men are not donkeys. All the same there are circumstances in which it is dangerous to inhibit these natural functions. There is the tale of a woman who died because she was ashamed to let the vapors formed in her intestines take their natural course—unless the report is mistaken, and it was rather the necessity of holding her tongue that was the cause of the fatality, instead of the inhibition of the nether orifice. There is the story of an abbé, downing his soup at his Bishop's table, who could not hold in a sonorous belch. "By all the saints!" he exclaimed, "the little devil did well to fly off! I was burning him alive!" (There is one useful effect of this civilized prejudice: how many people could never support finding themselves alone if it weren't for the pleasure of being able to indulge in those two private fireworks without restraint!)

What have we seen this year? The journalists Royou, Durosoy, Fontenay and other supporters of the Court demand a *counterrevolution* while the Assembly is still at work on the Constitution. But a counterrevolution can be accomplished only by a civil war—shouldn't the state have the right to protect itself against those who threaten the very principle of its existence? The situation in France isn't comparable to that in England, where the opposition argues about policy, but never questions the fundamental law of the kingdom. Why should the Assembly shelter those who demand its extinction? In the name of Liberty, of course—but the royalists are opposed to that liberty by whose tolerance they are permitted to publish and speak! What are *Le Contre-Poison, L'Ami du Roi,* the *Gazette de Paris* but so many daily appeals to betray that Constitution to which all of France swore fidelity last summer, including the king himself?

On the other side we have Marat, bribed or perhaps mad, who loses no occasion to destroy all confidence in the Assembly as well as the king. He asks his readers to fill their pockets with stones to lapidate the deputies of the right; he advises the women of the Halles to castrate Lafayette; he suggests that the counterrevolutionists be locked in the Manège and the place set on fire! One day he says that six hundred heads must roll for the Revolution to be safe; a week later it is twenty thousand. In *his* paper, Camille asks, "My dear friend, to be serious, of those nineteen thousand four hundred heads that you added to the six hundred, can't one be spared? Are they all really indispensable?"

Camille makes a joke out of everything, but Marat is no joke because he is so popular. A partisan of Lafayette dares summon Marat to appear at the Palais de Justice for one of his more outrageous slanders. The yellowed skeleton emerges from his catacomb to face the court; the chamber, the corridors, the streets of the Cité are packed with the admirers of the popular divinity. The Gardes are out in force and it is all they can do to protect the person of the plaintiff. The case is dismissed to avoid a massacre.

On March 30 we learn that Mirabeau is gravely ill; immediately there is no other subject of conversation and all of Paris holds its breath. Aside from the king there is no other man whose disappearance would leave such a void; this is recognized even by his enemies. At the Place Maubert many women have tears in their eyes. The papers forget all other events and again there is talk of a *plot,* either by the Jacobins or the Court. The king sends a messenger to inquire of the condition of the great man; *Les Révolutions de Paris* rejoices that the monarch didn't decide to go himself, since that would have made him too popular. Indeed it would, but Louis seems incapable of the simple gestures that his ancestor Henri IV performed instinctively. Agnès asked me what would happen if Mirabeau died, but I couldn't answer; Mirabeau was the only man to represent both the Revolution and the king.

Death seized the giant on April 2nd. The next day, a Sunday, the whole city was draped in black. But in Paris everything turns into theater almost at once; people rented places at the windows that overlooked the route of the funeral procession. An autopsy was performed, witnessed by eminent surgeons; they found no trace of poison. The great man of the Estates and the Tennis Court Oath now appears the last hero of the old regime. "Surround me with flowers and music, so I can slip sweetly into that sleep from which no one awakes." The priest at his bedside was Talleyrand, and I doubt that they spoke of the fires of hell.

The Assembly decreed that the church of Ste.-Geneviève was to be renamed the Panthéon and become the resting place of the great men of France. Mirabeau was buried there on the 5th. I saw the torchlight procession that mounted the rue St.-Jacques at ten in the evening; the night was cold and wet but the crowd was enormous. All day long the city had been noisy with the clatter of mounted troops and the sound of drums. Nothing so grandiose has ever been seen in Paris, even at the death of the old king.

The royalists could hardly conceal their glee at the disappearance of the great man, even while decency demanded at least silence. They were joined by Marat, who asked the people to rejoice that their greatest enemy had fallen. But the rest of the press was filled with stupefaction, even those who had accused Mirabeau of being bribed by the queen, even *Le Père Duchesne,* a new paper that tries to rival Marat in the violence of its sentiments with the added attraction of the most vulgar style imaginable. ("How happy they are, those John-fuckit aristocrats, what a holiday for those buggers of royalists, this day of universal dismay! Is it true, fuckit, he is no more, that intrepid bugger who pulverized them with a single word so many times? How many fools, how many useless souls, are alive to bother their fellows, while that bitch death has struck the greatest of men without pity!"—ten days before, the same paper had called Mirabeau a traitor.)

Two weeks later I learned at the Café Manoury that the king was planning to spend Easter at St.-Cloud. Fabre, our Jacobin, was playing the *enragé;* "This voyage shouldn't be allowed! it's all a plot and Lafayette and Bailly are both in on it!" A stout merchant objected that the king ought to be able to spend Easter wherever he wished, since he was king. Fabre is one of those thin men who grow pale and choleric when they have had too much wine; he turned white as a sheet and shouted that once out of Paris the king would go on to the camp of the regular army at Metz, call the emigrés and the Austrians to his side, then march back to the capital to reverse the Revolution. The merchant, who wore a hat like a Quaker, declared the king had shown his good intentions in dealing with the Knights of the Dagger. "That was before the death of Mirabeau!" Fabre shouted, "Now he has lost hope that he can control the Revolution!" One of our chess players told him to pipe down—a man who can sit for hours staring at the board, sucking on a pipe that never seems to go out, I'd never heard him speak before. Fabre called the man a royalist. "I am indeed a royalist in chess, I intend to keep both my king and my queen." With that he moved one of his pieces, adding, "But I don't mind sacrificing the Austrian Lady when necessary." Fabre's response was lost in the general laughter. . . .

On the 17th I went out early to see if the king would depart as planned. In my neighborhood it was an ordinary Sunday morning, but as I approached the palace by the rue St.-Honoré there was an unusual number of people in the streets. The Gardes permitted everyone to enter the Place du Carousel, which was already crowded. The grille before the palace was lined with Grenadiers, their bayonets in place. A crisp, fresh day; it seemed the most reasonable thing in the world for the king to want to go to the country.

Here and there in the crowd, clusters of men who look

organized. At one o'clock the royal coach clatters across the cobblestones toward the palace gate. It is immediately surrounded by the crowd. The bells of St.-Roch begin to peal in the crisp air. I am reassured when I see Lafayette, accompanied by Bailly, but not for long—the general mounts on a platform to address the crowd, but his voice is drowned in hostile shouts.

It looks as if there will be violence; the huge square seems a vast trap. It is impossible to move; the press of the crowd is too great. Nonetheless the Gardes manage to clear a path from the palace to the coach. Louis emerges with the queen, the dauphin, and two ladies of the Court; I lose sight of them as they pass the grille but apparently they get into the coach. Many people are yelling, especially the groups I had remarked earlier. Near me a real harpy is shouting her lungs out, an old witch of a woman in shabby clothes, "His aunts are in Rome, let him stay here in Paris!"

Some men try to unharness the horses. Lafayette is furious, his face red under his blond hair; he tries to give orders but no one listens. The crowd is chanting, "The king won't go! The king won't go!" The noise is deafening. Some of the Gardes have broken ranks and are shouting along with the mob; their officers talk to them, then converge on Lafayette, who is as helpless on his platform as if he were a statue.

Stalemate. Lafayette descends and goes to the coach. The queen puts her head out the window and receives a hail of obscenities. Oh daughter of Maria-Theresa, have you ever heard anything like this! Discordant voices chant, "NO! NO! NO! NO!"

Then it is all over. The king and his family get out of the coach and walk slowly back to the palace talking with Lafayette. The gates are closed. I wonder who will explain to the little prince why he can't go to the country. . . .

The papers reported the fine remark of the king: "If it will cost a single drop of blood, I shall not go." But I believe it was that day that finally turned Louis against the people of Paris.

If so, the sentiment was well concealed. For two months the royal family gave every sign of devotion to the eternally unfinished Constitution. Instead of attending Mass in the palace chapel, they went to the parish church where the priest was, of

PLATE 10: An argument at the Café Manoury. Restif, in the background, wearing his hat as usual, is reading the newspapers.

course, one of the constitutional clergy. Marie-Antoinette wore a tricolor cockade; Louis had the windows of the carriage lowered so the people could see him, saying he didn't want to be taken for an aristocrat. There were cheers along the route, but who was cheering? The people were not fooled.

Meanwhile other cares demanded my attention. . . .

I've already written something of the horrors endured by Agnès. As for Marion, her life has been less dramatic, but hardly gay. Born in Sacy in the same fieldstone house where I saw the light of day, she remained there for three years, nursed and tended by a peasant woman of the village. I wish now that she had remained there among the fields and orchards, even if her sweet presence has often been a consolation to me. Instead she joined our tumultuous household in Paris, or rather that of her mother, since there were long periods when we lived apart, Agnès Lebègue kicking me out each time she took a new lover.

(Shameful epoch! I accepted everything because of my poverty, living alone in garrets and or as a boarder, taking my revenge where I found it—which was not difficult, the women of Paris are so available! As for my wife, she did not even have the good sense to get any money out of her paramours. One even ran off with our valuable furniture, that had been given us by one of my mistresses! When A. Lebègue wanted me back she would turn up coiffed and rouged and displaying a pretty slipper that always made me succumb, furious with myself each time. It was after one of these conjugal episodes that I nearly died of the shameful malady whose lingering effects are still with me. Hardly an edifying tale, but the truth. All those elegant gallants who think they have invented immorality should learn something about the life of the poor.)

Along with her sister, Marion spent several years of her childhood in the gloomy house of Mme. Germain, rue de la Montagne-Ste.-Geneviève. She returned when Agnès Lebègue and I were again living together, but she and her mother scrapped like alley cats and there was no peace. When she was fifteen she was put *en pension* with the pious and bigoted demoiselles Garnier, rue Mouffetard.

What a time! My wife had two young literary puppies yipping about her skirts, Joubert and Fontanes; both of them have since acquired a certain reputation. *That* nasty situation began with those two aspiring writers posing as my friends. We had dinners, outings, long conversations about my works. Then they paid court to my wife. What hurt me was not so much the betrayal but their lack of taste. Against my will, but with the approbation of those two butterflies, my daughter Agnès was married to the MONSTER, Augé. I was then caught in the net of my passion for Sara, who proved to be a whore.

My wife and I separated again, this time for good, and Marion moved in with me. Although she was my daughter, I found the presence of this young girl disturbing in the most intimate way. After all, I had hardly known her when she was a child. One afternoon she read my play *La Prévention Nationale*. As her father, nothing should have interested me but the joy of sharing the production of my pen with the production of my blood; instead I found myself fascinated by her black shoes with high heels.

It became a veritable obsesssion, which I did my best to control. For example, one day I find in my journal: "*Sem.ej.vid.* (ejaculation at the sight of) Mar. with her pretty leg . . . and two hours later, thinking about her . . . then in the evening in my bed, after she talked with me."

There are other items of a similar nature. I find that as a man gets older there are fewer obstacles to his recognition of his sexual feelings. Fortunately, as a compensation, they are easier to control. I doubt that Marion has ever had the slightest suspicion of what I went through at that time, despite the accusations of her mother, who guessed correctly about my sentiments while accusing me of actions that I never attempted.

I had then a well-placed acquaintance, the Chevalier de St.-Mars, who adored both my daughters and had helped Agnès obtain her separation from Augé. I thought he would be a good husband for Marion even if he was a bit old; he was very rich.

We had a number of pleasant dinners in his garden at Le Roule near the Etoile and I could see that he was becoming attached to Marion. But my plan was thwarted by a scheming flirt, Mlle. Félicitte Mesnager who also had her eyes on the Chevalier.

Ten years older than my daughters, she became their confidante and learned of my projects. To keep me from any suspicion of her true motives, she pretended to an attachment to me, praising my books, receiving me in deshabillé, showering me with attention and eventually offering the pleasures of her bed, crying, "I am going to make you immortal!"

At the same time she secretly told St.-Mars that Marion had several lovers, persuading him that he had no chance of obtaining her hand. In the end St.-Mars married neither Marion nor Félicitte but a rich widow; I didn't learn of the marriage until 1789.

In the meantime a young man, Morel de Rosières, who (as it happened) had met Marion at one of St.-Mars's dinners, had fallen madly in love with her. Marion was not indifferent to this young gentleman, who sighed for her affection. Thinking that she still had a chance with St.-Mars, I told her that Rosières, who had a title but no wealth, would have to marry someone who could bring him a fat dowry. This was probably true. As a dutiful daughter Marion discouraged the young man. He retired to his country home, languished and died of a broken heart in '88. What a subject for a novelist of the English school! Never a complaint from Marion, even when she learned of the secret match of St.-Mars. . . .

In the hard winter of 1789 my nephew Edmond came to Paris, following the death of his father, my brother Pierre, known as Pierre le Paysan because he had stayed at Sacy to work the family farm. Edmond was frail and tubercular, a young man of nineteen who seemed younger because of his small stature and his innocence. I found a corner for him, and asked only that he assist me from time to time at my press. I still had to do the most demanding work myself, because Edmond wasn't up to it. A pale skeleton, I would see him sometimes wandering wide-eyed along the quais, with that timidity that marks the country boy in

Paris. I thought of him as a child and was delighted when Marion and Agnès showered their affection on him. Since he hardly ate at all, I thought that he needed a bit of love to keep him alive. (As it happened I was right, but not in the way I had planned.) Aside from that I didn't think about him.

One morning in April Marion took me aside to say that she wanted my permission to marry Edmond. I'm afraid that I was beside myself as well as astonished and said some very cruel things in my anger. I shouted that he was too young (five years her junior), without a sou, likely to die any minute, also that he was her first cousin and the union would be unnatural and incestuous (I will admit the words sounded a bit strange on my lips as I said them).

For answer Marion only patted her belly and said the marriage must take place soon if she were not to be dishonored. For the first time, as I looked at her cherubic face under her dark curls, I noticed a resemblance to her mother. If the conversation had continued I would have struck her; instead I bolted out of the house to seek consolation from my *dates* on the Ile St.-Louis.

What made me furious was the sense that I had been deceived and betrayed, my kindness taken advantage of, the wool pulled over my eyes. How long had the affair been going on and how long would it have been kept secret from me if Marion had not become pregnant? Why hadn't Edmond asked my permission to marry Marion before this and why did he leave it for her to do for him? I thought of sending him back to Sacy, of letting Marion have the child and giving it to the foundling hospital, of kicking them both out and letting them see how they would fare without my help.

Fortunately for everyone, Mme. de Beauharnais was in Paris for a short visit. As soon as Marion realized the violence of my reaction she ran to see the countess, told her the whole story. I had a note from Fanny in the morning, on her old stationery but with the crest crossed out, written in affectionate terms but more or less commanding me to pay her a visit. She received me in her boudoir in one of those charming *deshabillés* of which only Fanny has the secret, chatted a bit about her travels before getting down to the subject. Marion, she said, was twenty-six and without any fortune, which is to say in great danger of ending up an old maid. The chances were, therefore, that if she did marry, it would be someone without a situation. While Edmond's poor health was a drawback, at least I knew that he came from an honorable family (my own), was not an adventurer and not likely to waste whatever he did make on drink or other women. In short, a known quantity. Besides, she doubted that I could keep the pregnancy a secret—I had said nothing, but she had read my thoughts—and once it was known, another match would be impossible. Therefore, she concluded, I should swallow my pride and give the young couple my blessing and my help.

What else could I do? They were married May 21st at St.-Séverin; we were myself and Agnès, Mercier and Mme. de Beauharnais, also my wife, who has suddenly aged into a vision of respectability, gray-haired and plump. The young couple found two rooms in the rue du Fouarre, just around the corner from me. Edmond still helps me at my press, which is clanking away with the first two volumes of *L'Année des Dames Nationales* (new title of *Les Provinciales*); Marion and Agnès still go to market together, Place Maubert, and we all have dinner as before, in my apartment on rue de la Bûcherie. But Marion no longer brings me breakfast, her peach-like breasts seeking escape from her nightgown. I am less troubled, but all the same I find that I miss that vision at the start of my days.

Decidedly Grimod is out to pick a quarrel with me. Several long letters this spring, growing more and more bitter. He continues to ask me to spend the summer with him and his aunt in Béziers, promising that I shall have the best bed in the house, exquisite dinners, promenades in the countryside—all preferable to my life in Paris, "that city of mud and blood." Then he heaps reproaches on my head for my politics. His aunt, Mme. de Beausset, has read *La Semaine Nocturne* and removed my portrait from her wall because of my "democratic" opinions. Grimod *excuses* me by telling her that I have merely adopted the fashionable opinions of the day and do not believe what I have written. The old lady, to her credit (and mine) cannot accept this.

I answer as circumspectly as I can and receive a furious reply. "May your execrable philosophers all perish . . . they will pay dearly for their infamous triumph; their blood will be the first shed on the day of expiation and *I shall dip my hands into it with joy*."—Does Grimod remember that he has no *hands,* only those metal hooks?—"A curse on all atheists, deists, unbelievers, heretics. . . . I would gladly light the fire that will consume them, *even if those whom I have loved are among the victims*. Yes, I am *thirsty for the blood* of all those who have led us to where we are now, etc. . . ."

Could Marat himself be more violent? I tremble when I read such words because I believe that words are a serious business and will eventually be translated into actions. Grimod finds that in the *Semaine* I "attack without shame the most sacred institutions," that I "recount massacres and cannibal actions with a kind of delectation," that I have become one with the "detestable Mercier" (once La Reynière's good friend), the "disgusting Carra" (his one-time guest), the "infamous Desmoulins and other supporters of popular despotism" whom the once-gentle Grimod says he would see "quartered and burnt alive on the Place de Grève with the greatest joy!" Shouldn't I conclude that I would share their fate if he had his way? There, in black and white, is what piety and fanaticism can lead to.

But then the royalist papers are all full of the same sentiments, encouraging their readers either to emigrate or else show their disdain for the present state of affairs with a redoubled insolence. The Church and the aristocrats will never accept the fact that there has been a profound change in France; they are encouraged by the English and the Austrians, who would like nothing better than to see France destroyed by a civil war, after which it will be carved up like Poland. One would hope that Louis would have the sense to recognize that his "friends" abroad are not eagles but vultures, awaiting the moment to gorge themselves on his blood.

Working in bed the morning of June 21st I hear a great cackling of washerwomen in the street; the sounds float in the open window "... ran off last night, and monsieu' and madame and the little prince!"

I go out at once, run to Duchesne's for the news. But there's no need to go so far; the news is shouted at every corner, cried by the peddlers, shrieked by shopgirls, bawled by fishwives, exchanged by friends, muttered by coachmen, sung by streetsweepers, announced by the Gardes, gossiped by scullery maids, whispered by streetwalkers, grunted by porters, posted by booksellers, chattered by housewives, sputtered by merchants, bellowed by horsemen and howled by the dogs. Paris has become a single voice repeating over and over with the same astonishment, "THE KING HAS FLED!"

So it has finally happened, what was so long suspected, so often denied; what some hoped for, others feared; a marvel, a catastrophe, a crime or perhaps a blessing: THE KING HAS FLED. . . .

I wander here and there. On a notary's shingle the words, "by order of the king" have been crossed out. The word *Royal* is erased from the notice of a lottery vendor. In the Théâtre-Français district, at the door of the Cordeliers Club, a huge placard reading:

> *Si parmi les* français, *il se trouvait un traître*
> *Qui regrettât les rois et qui voulû un maître*
> *Que le perfide meure . . .*
>
> (If among the *French* there is found a traitor
> Who regrets our kings and desires a master,
> Let the scoundrel die . . .)

The verses are by Voltaire, with the word *français* substituted for *romains*. I cross the Pont-Neuf, go on to the Café Manoury.

The newspapers are as out of date as the annals of Babylon; no one talks of anything but the news and no one knows anything. I continue along rue St.-Honoré. All the fashionable shops that boasted of the patronage of the king or the queen have blacked out the signs that announced that honor; wherever a fleur-de-lis has served as a decoration it has suffered the same fate. I pass the Tuileries. A wag has posted a hastily scribbled sign on one of the palace doors: FOR RENT—A LARGE HOUSE, FURNISHED. . . . At the Palais-Royal the scene of June '89—crowds, orators on café tables, reports of German troops moving on Paris. The difference: every speaker declares that France must be a republic. One speaker demands: "If Louis decides to return he should be certified as an imbecile, in the name of humanity."

For two days everyone waits for news but there is no news. The Assembly does nothing, even the papers are reticent, with a few exceptions. *La Bouche de Fer* notes that the duc d'Orléans appeared at the Tuileries, advises against any move to declare him regent, opts for a republic. *L'Ami du Roi* is certain that Condé's troops will soon be in Paris, opens a register for all revolutionaries seeking amnesty. *L'Ami du Peuple,* Marat, of course, calls for a military dictator, demands the heads of all traitors beginning with Lafayette and Bailly, whom he holds responsible for permitting the king to escape. Then on the morning of the 23rd we learn that the king has been arrested at Varennes, just a few miles short of the Belgian border, where he would have joined the Austrian troops; he is being brought back to Paris. But after that? Nobody knows. . . .

The details of the flight became known later, that voyage that was a miracle of imprudence; Louis, it seems, cannot do anything right, not even flee.

Instead of using an ordinary coach, the king commanded an enormous and slow-moving berline, vast enough to hold all the trunks, wardrobes, cases and supplies thought necessary for the royal progress. This land-locked galleon was painted chocolate brown with bright-yellow decorations. The couriers who trotted at its sides wore uniforms of the same color, livery of the duc de Condé. The royal family was provided with false passports identifying them as the household of a fictitious Russian Baroness de Korff, returning to St. Petersburg. Louis himself was dressed as the valet of this lady, wearing a gray suit and a small wig. (His brother, Monsieur, Comte de Provence, took a different route and crossed the frontier without difficulty; but then he went alone and quickly.)

As the royal caravan lumbered along the routes of Champagne, the news of their flight preceded them. The countryside was alive with the local Gardes Nationales and bands of peasants. Louis, glutton that he is, had to stop to eat. In the evening they arrive at Ste.-Menehould where they were to be met by hussars sent by Choiseul; no one is there. Louis puts his head out the carriage window and is recognized by the postmaster, his identity confirmed by a glance at his portrait on an *assignat*.

The royal coach moves on, but the postmaster takes a back road through the woods to the next town, Varennes; alerts the Gardes. The famous berline waits half an hour outside the town for Choiseul's troops, who do not appear; finally they move on. It is eleven-thirty at night. Horsemen block the road, the cry is, "Stop, in the name of the Nation!" The king is arrested by the officers of that little town; his first prison was the back room of a cabaret.

Paris waits for the return of the prisoners. The Assembly debates, the Jacobins debate, the Cordeliers debate; no one can decide what is to be done with this embarrassing captive. Many wish that he had succeeded in his flight, both the royalists and those who would be happy to see the last of the king. The Faubourg St.-Antoine assembles, calls for a republic, marches to the Place Vendôme. Lafayette puts himself at the head of the parade, assures the Assembly that the workers have come to swear fidelity to the Constitution (again!), which is untrue. The rude throng parades through the Chamber; the Assembly applauds the people but decides nothing.

The return from Varennes is slow; 500,000 troops line the route. Announced for the evening of the 24th, the king does not arrive until the morning of the 25th. A solemn day, and strange. . . .

Forgetting about work, I went out early. Placards everywhere: "Whoever salutes Louis shall be beaten; whoever attacks him shall be hanged." I found a vantage point on the terrace of the Orangerie overlooking the Place Louis XV. The statue of the old king had been given a blindfold—either to spare him the spectacle of the shame of his grandson or else to symbolize the blindness of the monarchy. The crowd immense and solemn, like the congregation at a funeral, which indeed this was. Everyone wore a hat as a sign of *disrespect*. Apprentices and young lads who are always bareheaded at this season sported kerchiefs or at least a ribbon to show that they had become peers of the realm. The heat was intense. The sun shone down on the silent throng from a cloudless sky, a sun without pity or shame worthy of an ancient tragedy.

A double row of Gardes lined the route, their rifles held upside-down. The wait was long but no one joked, no one shouted, and if any flirtations took place I did not see them. Some boys had climbed the trees for a better view, but they too were silent in their high perch among the green leaves.

Finally a murmur sweeps through the throng, like a breeze rippling a field of wheat, "They are coming!" Three carriages descend the Champs-Elysées under a cloud of white dust. The first is the lumbering berline with its yellow decorations, the second an ordinary coach, the third an open carriage filled with Gardes, one of them the officer who had arrested the king at Varennes.

The crowd presses forward; I heard someone say that the coachmen are aristocrats who have been taken prisoner (false). There are neither cries, insults, nor cheers; nothing but an ominous hum. The carriages turn at the blindfolded statue, take the quai. The royal berline is accompanied by a troop of Grenadiers, its shades are half-drawn. I thought at first that it was empty, a decoy vehicle, but as it passed not thirty feet from where I stood I caught a glimpse of a face at the window surmounted by childish curls, the face of the boy I had pitied as he raked the sand in his little enclosure at the Tuileries. He was waving at the crowds as no doubt he had been taught to do—

no one had had the heart to tell him that on this occasion the gesture was a mistake.

When Louis was back in the palace he dropped into an armchair and sighed, "Voilà! here I am. . . ."

Indeed, there he was, but no one knew what to do with him. The difficulty was the almost finished Constitution, to which everyone had sworn fidelity so many times. The powers of the king had been debated, defined, discussed, again and again; it had been a difficult task each time to find a compromise on which a majority could agree. But without Louis the task will have to begin all over again, and will there be a majority, not only in the legislature but in the nation to agree on anything?

Before his death Mirabeau declared, "We live in a time of great events and little men." Now it seems a prophecy.

The Assembly begins by *suspending* the power of the king and his controversial veto, alerting the troops at the frontiers. We are on the verge of a republic and of war, foreign and perhaps civil at once. The abyss is frightening.

Voices on the left demand that the king be tried for his flight —Marat would skip the trial and proceed immediately to the execution. But the lawyers ask if under its own Constitution the Assembly has the right to judge the king. The Assembly is full of lawyers, as are the Jacobins; they dispute, invent, twist words around as if words could alter facts.

The real question, as put by Barnave in the Assembly: "Are we going to be finished with the Revolution, or are we going to begin all over again?"

Then, gift of the Gods, a communication from Bouillé, General of the Emigration, asserting that *he* is responsible for the king's hasty voyage. A great sigh of relief from all the attorneys, the formula has been found! The Assembly declares that Louis has been *captured,* has been *carried away;* there is certainly to be a trial, but its object will be to discover who was responsible for this strange *abduction* (which did seem more like an *elopement* at the time). Meanwhile Louis is to remain king, for the moment a king who can command nothing, in reality a hostage to Austria. The question of his ultimate fate is postponed, perhaps it will be forgotten; the lawyers will run the country and we will all pretend that the journey to Varennes never took place!

But will this legal fiction suit the workers of St.-Antoine and the fishwives of the Place Maubert? Their common sense tells them that Louis *fled* and was not abducted, that he fled a traitor and returned a prisoner. I fear our lawyers are King Canute, ordering the tide to recede. . . .

While all this sophistry was in progress, we were offered the distraction of a grand ceremony transferring the remains of Voltaire from their original resting place to the Panthéon. I saw part of the procession on the quai des Théatins, now renamed quai Voltaire. (July 11th.) There was a bit of everything: uniformed battalions of the Gardes, cavalry, students carrying banners, besiegers of the Bastille, some stones of the fortress (it is lucky there were so many), plaster medallions of Franklin, Mirabeau, and Rousseau, a flock of vestals who may or may not have been virgins, a float displaying the cadaverous statue by Houdon, deputies from the Assembly, and a team of twelve white horses dragging the exhumed bones of the great skeptic in a magnificent coffin—nothing lacking but candles and incense. The sky was heavy with clouds and the distant thunder seemed the laughter of the sage of Ferney himself at this ghoulish consecration. . . .

A few days later another ceremony. This one ended in a massacre instead of an interment.

At the Café Manoury, Saturday evening, July 16, I learned that the Cordeliers Club had passed a resolution protesting the actions of the Assembly, condemning the king for his evasion, and demanding a Republic. A petition to this effect was to be presented to the people the next day at the Champ-de-Mars, where a great crowd was expected to celebrate the anniversary of the *Fédération* of last year. The project seemed bold, but hardly dangerous; nonetheless I decided to stay home. On the 17th, about noon, I heard the *générale*. M. Frazé, my landlord, reported that the red flag was flying at the Hôtel de Ville, martial law proclaimed—no one knew why. Paris is so large that what happens in one district can remain a mystery to all others for the longest time.

That morning, as I learned later, two young wigmakers were discovered hiding under the stands of the Champ-de-Mars. (All the temporary structures created last summer are still there, if a bit weatherbeaten.) They were arrested as troublemakers even though they assured the police that they had nothing more wicked in mind than looking up under some skirts when the crowd arrived. Some people of the neighborhood were already there; the women declared that they considered themselves insulted by these servants of the aristocrats. Some workers who had stayed up all night drinking in a *guinguette* made a grand fuss, shouting that the Altar of the Fatherland had been desecrated—they seized the two imprudent *voyeurs* and hanged them from a convenient tree.

Word of this incident was passed on to the Hôtel de Ville, and by the time it had crossed Paris the lamentable stringing up of two *voyeurs* by a gang of toughs had become a popular insurrection. Martial law was declared, which shows how nervous the authorities were. Was the case of the wigmakers but a pretext? No one will ever know. . . .

People continued to arrive at the Champ-de-Mars, an ordinary Sunday crowd, ignorant of what had passed, knowing nothing of the red flag floating at the other end of Paris. The sponsors of the petition set up a booth and collected signatures; many people signed but there was no disorder.

At seven in the evening, when the crowd was enjoying the lingering sunlight of a long July afternoon, many sitting on the Altar of the Fatherland under which the lecherous wigmakers had been discovered *twelve hours earlier,* the commander of the Gardes gives the order that everyone is to leave immediately.

Some young hot heads at the edge of the crowd throw some stones. That's it—the Gardes open fire on the Altar of the Nation, that scaffold where only a year ago Louis had sworn to uphold the Constitution, now covered with women and children, mothers and fathers, a Parisian Sunday crowd. No one knows how many were killed, but all were innocent. . . .

Oh Lafayette! oh Bailly! how you have fallen, shown yourselves weak, heavy-handed and guilty! A massacre of the people of Paris, unarmed, defenseless! And by whom? the Gardes, created but two years ago to defend the capital from its enemies!

The next day, patrols everywhere. They have become enemies in the eyes of the people and for good reason. Near the Halles I saw a young man in the uniform of the Gardes escape with his life only by chance. He had become separated from his patrol and was beset by an angry crowd of herring peddlers and apple vendors; a pockmarked lad with a butcher's knife threatened to cut him up. A plasterer, a magnificent figure of a man with white dust all over his shabby clothes, strode through the throng and took the knife from the stripling's hand. I thought at first that he had decided to do the deed himself, but instead he turned to the crowd and ordered it to disperse, then threw the knife into a cellar window. The young Garde escaped with nothing worse than hearing himself called a "cornflower," an insult derived from the color of his uniform. . . .

The red flag of martial law flew over the Hôtel de Ville for three weeks. At the Café Manoury, Fabre claimed that the Jacobins were in danger, Robespierre forced into hiding. If so, it was but for a moment; the Jacobins sent a letter to the Assembly applauding its "wisdom." Astonishing development, the royalist press became even more vociferous than before Varennes in calling for a counterrevolution. Meanwhile Louis sits in the Tuileries, as restricted as a king on a chess board. The lawyers are in charge.

Returning one afternoon from chatting with the adorable Adèle *chez* Mérigot I take the rue de la Huchette. At the corner of the rue Zacharie a toothless old hag suddenly jumps at me, throws her arms about my neck. The foulness of the breath issuing from the yellow gums is nauseating. At first I thought that I was assaulted by a madwoman, then I looked for an accomplice who would pick my pockets. The old witch cried, "Madame said you were dead but I see you are alive!" I stepped back for some fresh air but remained as bewildered as ever.

"You don't recognize me, monsieur, but I am Mlle. Mauviette!" The name meant nothing until she added, "The midwife." Then I remembered Agnès Lebègue shouting, "Go get Mauv'ette!"—in 1763 this old hag had brought our daughter Elise into the world, an adorable child who died while still a baby.

Mauviette had met my wife in the street in December '90. She had inquired about me. The MONSTER replied, "M. Restif is dead to me." Mauviette had taken her literally, which explains her pestiferous greeting.

We exchanged information about our lives in the abbreviated fashion of two people who haven't seen each other for decades. She asks if I know the hosiery shop on the rue de l'Egout. "My daughter, or rather *our* daughter, is mistress of the establishment. She has two children, a boy and a girl. I am a grandmother!" I congratulate her on that estimable condition and bid her good-bye, delighted that at least one of my natural daughters hasn't ended up walking the streets.

The explanation of this fatherhood is singular. Before the birth of Elise, Mlle. Mauviette often dropped by to check on the health of the mother, who hated being pregnant and would not take the most elementary precautions to assure a normal delivery. (There were lovers who found her attractive in that bloated state; she inspired only repugnance in me.) If it was late I would walk Mauviette home. One evening, to my surprise, she squeezed my hand as I said adieu on her doorstep. I went up with her. Mauviette explained that it was a professional matter.

"I have very few clients; women don't trust me because I've never had a child myself; they think I don't understand their condition. You seem like a reliable young man—make me a mother!"

The man who could refuse such a proposition would lack something essential, unless he were a newlywed or the woman who addressed him was an absolute horror. As for me, I performed on the spot.

"The task was well done," Mauviette observed as I was buttoning my breeches. "We shall see if it is successful. If not, we shall try again."

She waited two months, then said, "Let's try again, if you don't mind."

We tried again. Six weeks later Mauviette informed me, "It took."

She gave birth to a daughter, had a large clientele, and never again spoke of trying. To hear her thank me for my services, you would have thought that I had been put to a great deal of trouble with no pleasure at all. It is true that Mlle. Mauviette procreated as if it were a surgical operation.

In the *Annales Patriotiques* dated September 13, a review of *Les Nuits de Paris*. From the style, I should guess it was written by Mercier himself. When we had dinner the week before he hadn't mentioned the notice; perhaps he thought it would be a pleasant surprise for me to discover it myself. To be sure, the review couldn't advise the public more directly to purchase the work, which is gratifying. But how is the book recommended? "In these times when the imagination absorbed in politics needs a bit of rest, readers should be offered a few more pleasant images. Those contained in *Les Nuits de Paris* are of an infinite variety; their originality is refreshing; they illustrate the cause of the Revolution in the countless examples of corruption collected by the author during thirty years." And that's all! No mention of the grand design of the work, its poetry, its prophetic visions, its pleading for reforms, many of which have yet to be accomplished—no mention of part XV, *La Semaine Nocturne!* And for that notice, which is but a paragraph, I am expected to be grateful!

But all my affairs are in a bad way, aside from the work itself. At my press I am reduced to the help of one or two occasional workers plus Edmond. And most of the time that ancient press is stamping out my own works, which is to say I have no immediate profit, only expenses for labor, ink and paper. Nonetheless I continue, encouraged by the fact that the work I am doing now is superior to anything I have done before, including *Le Paysan*.

The first two volumes of *L'Année des Dames Nationales* are almost completely printed, with the sketches I wrote for *Les Tableaux de la Vie* added to the original tales. And, most important, the first epochs of *Monsieur Nicolas* are in the works. For any author, no doubt, it is a proud moment when the words that had existed only in manuscript finally appear in print, all marching in proper order, each sentence led by the sturdy UPPER CASE, the sentences marshaled into paragraphs, the page enlivened by the divine *italics,* with punctuation marks setting the pace like drummer boys and titles and numbers like battalion flags! . . . But so much more so for myself, who am typesetter, printer and publisher as well as author. . . . I sent Grimod some of the proofs of the first epoch, hoping to rekindle our friendship by a work that has nothing to do with politics.

The Constitution is finally complete; it is entirely favorable to Louis. All of September was given over to celebrations and the elections for the new Assembly, from which all deputies of the original Estates have been excluded. This means that now the king will confront a chamber without experience and elected by the suffrage more limited than that which chose its predecessor. The popularity of the monarch at this moment is unbelievable to anyone who remembers Varennes. One Sunday the king went to hear Mass in the palace chapel and found himself cheered by a close-packed crowd; he seemed surprised himself. Marie-Antoinette held up the dauphin and all the women were misty-eyed at the sight.

I have become a grandfather for the second time. On the 18th, Marion and Edmond brought the baby to dinner, the first time they have taken her out. At the first sight of that adorable blue-eyed child—all Restif since Restif from both her father and mother—my heart melted; whatever rancor still remained against the young couple for having deceived me was no more! I feel more strongly than ever that the notion that incest must be a crime is merely a superstition that will some day be swept away. . . . Marion insists on nursing the child herself, but it seems to do her no harm; her cheeks are rosy, her breasts round and firm as melons. Poor Edmond, unfortunately, has never looked more pale; the baby keeps him awake at night. . . .

Afterwards out with Agnès. There were ceremonies at the

Hôtel de Ville, the Place du Carrousel, the Place Vendôme and the Champ-de-Mars, where the altar was purified of the blood of July 17—if a ceremony can accomplish that. Agnès and I went to the Champs-Elysées, which were a vast fair; bands everywhere, people dancing on the greens. The only discordant note, and that a mild one, a placard reading:

VIVE LE ROI
S'IL EST DE BONNE FOI!

signed, "A shoemaker." Children played in the groves; a puppet troop enacted the loves of Harlequin and Columbine; in a solitary corner a young man practiced the flute. I saw a young Italian beauty with her *ciscebo;* her husband held the hand of an elegant lady with one of those extravagant coiffures decorated with tricolor ribbons that are called *"coiffures de la liberté."* They spoke the language of their nation; but for the coiffure one might have been in Venice.

The sun descended; all became rose-colored, a vision of Arcady. We started home in the twilight, pausing on the new Pont-Louis XVI. A string of paper lanterns hung from the trees all the way from the Tuileries to Chaillot. The twilight deepened; the lanterns grew brighter. The noble façades on the north side of the Place Louis XV were a soft orange. Surely that square is one of the most majestic sights of Europe! From the Champs-Elysées a Montgolfier balloon rose into the air, its basket decorated with tricolor bunting. As it sailed over the Seine, almost directly over our heads, two stones were dropped into the soft-flowing water, to permit the aeronauts to rise even higher.

Another day I took a long promenade alone. Instead of my usual route, I chose the rue St.-André-des-Arcs through the Odéon quarter, now Section du Théâtre-Français. Each neighborhood of Paris now has acquired a political tone, and this is the most revolutionary of all, home of Desmoulins and Marat, site of the Café Procope and the Cordeliers where Danton thunders (he also lives nearby). What is strange is that you can feel all that just walking through the streets; there is something in the stride of the rudest worker that proclaims, "I AM YOUR EQUAL!"

COËFFURE A LA NATION
Se trouve à Paris Chez Depain. Cœffeur de Dames, et Auteur de cette Cœffure
Rue St. Honoré au coin de celle d'Orleans, au 1.er au-dessus du Caffé au Grand Balcon.
AVEC PRIVILEGE DU ROI.

PLATE 11: A *"Coiffure aux charmes de la Liberté"* (The Bettman Archive).

Afterwards along rue St.-Dominique, where more and more of the noble *hôtels* are shuttered or for sale. But what is not for sale in Paris today? convents, parish houses, even churches! I crossed the river, went up the Champs-Elysées. A pretty nursemaid was taking her charges home. Her waist called for an arm about it; the shoes under her white skirt were delicious, pointed, with high heels; the feet they enclosed must be marvels.

"Hola ma petite!" I cried. "When the children are in bed we can have supper together."

"Alas! my masters are away; I must stay in the house."

"I could keep you from being bored if you'd like a visitor."

"You are very kind, Papa, but I expect a friend to keep me company."

The word *friend* was masculine; at least I hope so, such loveliness shouldn't go to waste; it doesn't last long. . . .

I passed the majestic garden that had belonged to Pompadour in the days when the chief minister of France was the king's mistress, went on past other great houses hidden behind the trees, all shuttered and dark. At the Chaillot gate I lost myself in memories of my youth, recalling Zéphire and Virginie, a delightful dinner in the Bois de Boulogne with my friend Boudard and three actresses of the Opéra-Comique. Say what one will about the corruption of the old regime, there were times when I was happy.

It was dark when I started home, taking the back road bordered with garden walls. Shortly before the rue de Marigny I heard voices; a man and a woman were talking on the other side of a hedge that hid them from me. The softness of the night, the charm of the place, the solitude, all suggested they must be lovers. But they were speaking of other things.

"Who knows how far this Revolution will go? To emigrate is to abandon the field to the foe, to stay is to be dishonored. I've had threats from our partisans, but I said that I was needed here."

"You must leave, monsieur, there is no compromise with honor. What can anyone do here, with that weak king who does us more harm than our enemies? After Varennes I hoped that they would kill him; all of Europe would have come to help us!"

"Oh, madame, you are mistaken!"

"I know the Powers better than you. So long as Louis is alive they will do nothing!"

"Calm down, madame! If Louis were dead they would turn on France to destroy us all, nobles and commoners alike. Our situation is desperate, and if I were guided by reason instead of hatred I would become a Revolutionary!"

At this the woman ran off; the man followed. I heard her cry, "No! No! I never want to see you again!"

Acting on a sudden impulse I shouted in their direction, "Whatever your reasons, monsieur, become a patriot!" Then I slipped away.

Returning home I took the rue St.-Honoré, passing by Grimod's house near the Place Louis XV, site of his famous lunches and *coenas*. The moon was just rising in the east, and by a peculiar reflection of its light the high windows of the dining room seemed illuminated from within by a spectral glow, as if coming from the ghosts of the 366 candles that were consumed at his most famous dinner. Despite myself I found that I was weeping; I could do nothing to stop the tears, the emotion was too strong. Ah my friend, why don't you return to Paris and learn that there is still a *douceur de vivre* in this city that even your promenades in Béziers cannot match! I do miss you and have been very hurt by your letters. One makes so very few real friends in even the most crowded lifetime. You were the only one who ever shared my promenades on my isle, understanding what I felt. Read *Monsieur Nicolas* and learn that I am still the same man with whom you shared those moments! Some things change but others remain the same. . . .

Another evening as I went by the Tuileries the fancy took me to stroll alone in the royal garden. I followed the quai to the center of the terrace, then scaled the wall with the help of the iron tool I use to inscribe my *dates*. But I wasn't alone. Various groups were seated under the trees, talking quietly. Remaining in the shadows, I approached and listened.

A woman's voice: "Ah, monsieur le duc, what will become of

us?" Another's, louder and sharper: "We must risk everything, sacrifice everything!" A man answered: "Prudence, mesdames! His Majesty has regained more than we would have thought possible with this new Constitution. Our turn will come in time."

A heavy-set man stood up and walked directly toward the tree where I was hiding. Luckily for me a woman called, "Don't go too far, my friend!"

The man turned around, "My dear countess, do you want me to piss under your nose?" Laughter from the company; I managed to slip away unnoticed.

In a more solitary grove a couple embraced. "This is no time for love," the woman protested. "You must get away and fight!"

"Without you, never! But if you depart I'll follow, to the end of the world."

He kissed her; they sank down on a chair. The chair cracked; they stretched out on the grass. . . .

But I report only what is unusual, and what followed could not have been more expected, even among the peasants of Sacy. . . .

One destination of many of my promenades remains the Palais-Royal, that incarnation of the Chimera of myth whose head has the smile of an enticing whore, whose eyes dart flames, whose tongue is a serpent, whose mouth distills venom and heroic words, whose hands are clawed, whose heart is empty, whose cunt is a bottomless well of disease, whose thighs are as hairy as a ram's, whose legs are those of a buck, whose feet are squat and heavy with pig's hooves. So be it!

If the arcades no longer ring with the voices of orators on café tables there are other distractions. Speculators gather in the passage that leads to the rue Montpensier to seal transactions that are illegal at the Bourse. The number of gambling houses has doubled, which one would have thought impossible. Young aristocrats make a little Coblentz of the garden and the streetwalkers continue their eternal rounds. But there are more exotic spectacles from time to time.

At a doorway near the passage that leads to the rue des Valois a short, dark-skinned man is barking a show. He has the accent of Marseilles.

"Who wants to see the *for-r-r-midable* savage? Enter, messieurs, for the *gr-r-reat* ballet of the wild men!" I ask what sort of ballet this may be; he answers, with a knowing wink, that it is truly, *"extr-r-raordinary."*

I pay, I enter, and find myself in a dimly lit room that is bare; some curtains at one side indicate a small stage. I wait for ten minutes, am about to leave, thinking I've been gulled, when an obese old man with an old-fashioned wig comes in, tells me that the spectacle begins only when there are at least four in the audience, but that it is worth a wait.

He sits down on a bench that cracks under his weight, takes a pinch of snuff and starts to sneeze. Two more spectators arrive, both middle-aged men with a furtive air. When they are seated the curtains part.

There is a tiny stage with a candle on a stand. A drum in the wings beats softly. Two performers come out together, one a tall man with the build of a blacksmith, the other a girl who must have been stunning ten years ago, but now is beginning to show her age. Both are scantily clad in rags, their bodies partially blackened with burnt cork. After a few ludicrous imitations of dance steps, accompanied by a few grunts, the drum grows louder, the two savages discard their rags and are revealed as Nature made them, which is to say well-endowed, especially the smith, who is on his way toward being a monster.

This proves pertinent to the chief business of the spectacle, which is to copulate on the floor, assuming the position that is considered primary for beasts but secondary for men. They go at it with gusto. Considering that it is a show, the smith's performance would seem to refute St. Augustine's contention that the organ of generation is controlled by the will of the devil rather than that of man. The girl's breasts swing this way and that; the smith grunts; the obese snuff-sniffer has a sneezing fit. Soon it is over; the "savages" collapse on the floor; the curtains shut. On leaving I ask the barker how many of these "ballets" are presented each day. He answers as many as nineteen when the public is willing. . . .

That spectacle was soon shut by the authorities; the performers and their employer clapped in jail. But there were others that remained, more horrifying because less natural. The Palais-Royal seems always to have been destined to be the theater for all that can incite young and old to vice. Before the Revolution the duc d'Orléans had a secret apartment where the notorious thirty-seven postures of the engravings by Arentino were represented by life-size wax figures. The duc would show them to his favored guests, among them, on one occasion, Mirabeau.

One evening, in the furthest arcade, at the passage that leads to the rue de Beaujolais, there is a young girl just at the point of nubility. She is accompanied by an old whore who offers the guaranteed virginity of her charge to whoever is willing to pay the price. In the shadows, a greater horror: two children, a boy and a girl, still at the age of innocence. They are in the care of a woman who is obviously a professional, although less ravaged than most whom one sees in that place. Then I noted others, girls who were but children, their cheeks ineptly rouged, inviting me to join them in high piping voices. It was as if they were playing at being prostitutes, as children play house—but I could see it was not play at all.

I was about to flee when I was accosted by the guardian of the boy and girl, the youngest of that infantile gathering. Taking me for a modern Tiberias in search of a new thrill—and there are many such—she invites me to go up to her rooms. In my role of Nocturnal Spectator, who must know what takes place during the hours when honest folk are all asleep, I consent.

We take a small staircase to an *entresol* that looks out on the arcade. The door is shut, the procuress details the lubricious talents of her charges, then asks me which one I want. This takes some time and as she is speaking the two children undress. They pretend to play with each other, miming an entire catalogue of obscene acts and couplings that they are physically unable to accomplish. Never have I seen anything more piteous than those two frail, pale, naked waifs simulating the utmost depravities.

It was obvious that the two poor creatures weren't playing at all; they had done the same thing many times and were bored, tired and unhappy.

When the whole menu had been detailed and illustrated, the woman asked what I desired. I answered that I was a writer and wanted only to pose a few questions about her affairs. I promised to pay for that as if it were what she had originally offered. To my surprise she agreed readily. She sent the children away, saying that she had recognized me as the author of *Les Filles du Palais-Royal* and knew that I would not denounce her to the police. After a few remarks about the unreality of my book (perfectly justified), she explained the workings of her infamous profession without further prodding.

First the supply: There is a woman who lives by picking up unwanted babies, sending them off to be cared for by peasant girls until they are the right age, then selling them to pimps searching for new talent. There are midwives who refuse abortions to chambermaids and other servants, sometimes even girls of good families, but who assist at the delivery for nothing on condition that they are given the baby, which they then sell. There are others who buy children from poor couples with large families who can't make ends meet, going into a tenement where thirteen people live in a single room, picking out the prettiest child. There are wet-nurses who tell the mother of their charge that her baby has died, arrange with the village priest for a death certificate, pay for a funeral at which a bundle of rags is buried, then sell the child. There are disreputable women who sell their own children, whose presence interferes with their mode of life.

As for the demand: certain high-class courtesans use the children only for show, to give themselves the appearance of respectable women, so that they can promenade in elegant districts where otherwise they would be barred by the police. But most are put to more demanding work, offered to old men with limp pricks whose performance is dependent on the spice added to familiar pleasures by the innocence of childhood. Boys are as good as girls for this function, the choice being left to the client. The mouth is the only orifice that can be utilized, since the others are as yet closed by nature. Occasionally one of these aging monsters forces a girl; if the child dies they pay for it, as one pays for an overworked animal. The price for this eventuality is fixed in advance and the procuress always stands to gain if it occurs, so that this sacrifice of the innocents is in her interest. If a child proves too delicate or recalcitrant in performing the ordinary services, he or she is fattened up, then sold to a particularly demanding client, who covers the cost. . . .

I could listen to no more. Giving my informant the three livres she had demanded, I left, sick to my stomach. The hour was late, but there were other children waiting in the peristyle.

After these details it may seem strange to say that the worst depravity I encountered at the Palais-Royal was printed on the pages of a book. But I am not speaking of the run-of-the-mill pornography found in the bookstalls of the arcades—the cheap editions of erotic novels (such as I myself have written in my time), paintings taken from private collections belonging to emigrés, libertine engravings destined for the boudoir whose delights they depict—so many temptations served up for curious adolescents or tired husbands which serve, so to speak, as publicity for the horde of prostitutes lodged in the garrets under the mansards. No; the book of which I speak, *Justine ou les malheurs de la vertu,* is something in a different class altogether.

Put a pen in the claws of Satan, and he could do nothing worse. This anonymous work, widely sold since it appeared in June, is reputed to be the production of a nobleman who spent several years in the Bastille for his perverted crimes and vicious practices, monstrous satisfactions of a twisted lust that caused the death of several young persons. The reader will know of whom I speak; his name has become legendary. His years in prison, for the misfortune of the human race, were spent in the transformation of his fantasies into literature, the elaboration of a complete philosophy of evil, all the more dangerous for being clever and well-written. The prostitution of several hundred children in the cloaca of Paris is wicked enough, but if *Justine* ever falls into the hands of the army it will mean the cruel death of twenty thousand girls. But there is no restriction on its sale because the liberty of the press is considered sacred.

My own theory about all these horrors is based on my study

of the mechanisms of the human heart. Now that I have reached the age when my own desires have begun to wane, I begin to understand the cause of the atrocious tastes of certain old men and I find that it is their impotence. I wouldn't claim to have been an angel all my life, but I've always loved with tenderness, with delicacy and respect for women, whatever their position in life; at times I've even loved platonically. But now I realize that if we are to speak frankly, the source of tenderness is not the heart (which is nothing but a muscle that pumps blood about the body), but rather the secretions of the organs of physical pleasure, however strange or even repulsive that idea may seem.

Our prudes and puritans should take notice of this fact. When the organ of generation ceases to function, tenderness vanishes along with desire.

To regain the excitement of their youth certain old men develop a taste for the most obscene expressions, and the most revolting practices. Corrupted and blasé, the old monster no longer wishes to share his pleasure with a woman; he wants her to suffer, to tremble, to moan, to shiver at his touch, to fear his approach, and all this in proportion to her youth and beauty. If, in addition, she is well-born, delicate and helpless, he wants her to perish from the tortures he inflicts on her frail body. The more she seems destined for happiness, the more he wishes to make her miserable, out of compensation for his own failings. That is the explanation for the practices described in *Justine*. But the memory of tenderness, if not its presence, restrains most men, as well as the precepts of humanity. *Justine,* with its philosophy of cruelty, destroys all restraint, and that is what is so dangerous in the work.

This year ends with a new fad, a silly toy that has become fashionable and is seen wherever young elegants promenade: two disks of wood or ivory, held together by a pin; a string is attached to the pin, the other end looped about a finger of a glove; the string is wound up, the toy released, it bounces up again. At the Tuileries, on the Boulevards, in the garden of the Palais-Royal, on the Champs-Elysées, one sees all the young bloods playing with these bagatelles. Many of them have become quite proficient. They toss them at the girls, then pull them back, make them loop and spin. All are decorated; some are quite expensive, ivory encrusted with gems. Their name: *emigrants* or *jeu de Coblentz*—they depart, but then they come back. An appropriate ensign for the year of Varennes.

BONNETS AND PIKES

JANUARY–JULY 1792

THE last time I ordered a suit was in '86 at the insistence of Mlle. Mesnager. Félicitte (or Infelicity, as I called her afterwards) cajoled me into this purchase between two false kisses and other favors. The tailor, a scoundrel named Leroi, proved as false as the flirt who sent me to him. I paid him 165 livres in advance and after several fittings he turned out a garment that was so ill-cut and poorly made that I refused to accept it. I still wear some honest clothes that I bought ten and even twenty years ago. My friends accept my shabby appearance for what it is and I am indifferent to the opinion of the rest of the world.

My interest in fashion, as this demonstrates, is hardly personal. But as an observer there is much that I find fascinating. Of late, like everything else, clothes have become political. It began, I suppose, with the tricolor cockade of the patriots and the black dress affected by aristocrats as a sign of mourning for the state of the nation. Then a royalist journal, attacking the revolutionaries as rabble, dubbed them all *sans-culottes,* thinking it would be an insult. But the left found it useful to be identified with the workers who wear pants instead of breeches and took the name as a compliment. Some of them even began to adopt the garment, if in a modified and more elegant form, and one began to see shops displaying fine suspenders for the "well-dressed *sans-culottes,*" a phrase that would have been unthinkable because self-contradictory some years ago.

The patriots of '89 found it embarrassing to denounce the shortage of bread while wearing wigs powdered with the very flour that was so scarce. They therefore stopped whitening their wigs, and some gave up wigs altogether. Women stopped using powder on their faces, and if that gave an undue advantage to the young, that was, after all, as it should be in an era of change. Jewelry became unfashionable after patriotic women deposited theirs on the tribune of the Assembly as a gift to the nation. Shoe buckles also vanished, for both men and women, to be replaced by rosettes, often tricolor like everything else. The old usages, skirts with panniers, white wigs, powdered faces, silver buckles, were retained only by the Court, and then only for state occasions, as a matter of ceremony. But even that last bastion eventually succumbed. This March, when the new ministers were installed, Roland arrived at the Tuileries for his presentation to the king wearing plain shoes. The Master of Ceremonies, who had to announce him, was horrified. But since even a Master of Ceremonies accustomed to the etiquette of Versailles cannot refuse entrance to a Minister of the Interior, all he could do was sigh under his breath, "No buckles! No buckles!" The Foreign Minister, Dumouriez, replied, "Alas, monsieur! All is lost! . . ."

I heard that anecdote in Mme. Beauharnais' blue-and-silver salon, rue de Tournon. She has been back in Paris since January and her Fridays have resumed. Fanny the divine is no longer the *countess,* in deference to the new style. She has dropped the *"de"* from her name, but otherwise everything is the same. The first gathering was a true reunion of the faithful. Cubières, of course, who accompanied the *ci-devant* countess in Italy, Mercier, white-haired Cazotte, in from the country, even Baron Clootz, the "Orator of the Human Race." I went with the proofs of the first epoch of *Monsieur Nicolas* in my pocket, in case I should be asked to read, but it wasn't the night for it. I gave them to old Cazotte instead. He asked me, "What would you do if you had your whole life to live over again and were master of its events?" I answered, "Just what I have done, except for my marriage."

(Clootz was teased on the subject of his opposition to the decree of May 15, 1791, granting full civil rights to all freed blacks in the colonies, a position that astonished everyone from this German dreamer. The columns of the *Moniteur* had printed a letter of protest from the colored "representatives of the human race" whom he had led to the tribune of the Assembly on the eve of the *Fédération.* Clootz justified his stand by the massacres last fall in Haiti, saying the blacks were an inferior race. Throughout this winter the gentle Prussian has been one of the most ferocious of warmongers, calling for a universal *Jacquerie* of the peoples of Europe against all tyrants, led of course by the armies of France. One never knows.)

A new style of hat is gaining popularity this bellicose spring, the *bonnet rouge* or Liberty Cap, guaranteed to make the wearer look ridiculous. This headgear is a knitted drooping woollen stocking, derived from someone's conception of antiquity, in this instance the cap worn by freed slaves in ancient Rome. Combined with pants, suspenders, and a short Italian vest known as the carmagnole, it forms the costume of the perfect Jacobin of the left, especially if its wearer is on parade with a pike to indicate his ferocious patriotism. The workers of St.-Antoine can carry this off pretty well, since they have the proper swagger and dustiness, but fresh and clean on the head of a lawyer or notary it seems to denote nothing but an emptiness inside. This bonnet has been seen everywhere since the Fête de la Liberté, April 15th, when it was worn by the forty amnestied Swiss Guards, whose pardon was the occasion for the celebration. But it was worn even earlier. Whatever its Roman origins, it is basically the cap of peasants and fishermen, useful on cold days because it covers the ears and will stay on in a gale. In Paris in May it looks odd.

Women also use their heads to make themselves silly. What strange contructions of the straw and ribbons haven't been seen sailing along the boulevards and the Champs-Elysées, extravagant bouquets of flowers and plumes that would blow away in the slightest breeze if they weren't securely attached to the frizzed wig that serves as their foundation? But one can pardon this caprice as natural to the weaker sex.

A style that is unpardonable, however, because contrary to all grace and beauty, is that of *flat shoes* or slippers, especially those with rounded toes! I hold the *Journal de Paris* responsible for this horror, because of its articles, no doubt the work of a pederast, advising the fair sex that high heels are unhealthy, the cause of bunions and corns. The scoundrel went so far as to declare that the footwear natural to women is the cause of abortions and miscarriages! And the slaves of fashion hastened to obey, despite the mud of the streets of Paris, despite the loss of height and delicate stride that are the happy result of high heels.

And then, as one would expect, taking for themselves what they had stolen from women, our young elegants began to wear pointed shoes. The result: go to the quai des Augustins, in the shadows cast by the poultry stalls, and you will see the parapet lined with pederasts impudently displaying their perverted charms, all with the pointed shoes that used to be worn only by effeminate dancers.

It is horribly immoral for the dress and style of the two sexes to resemble each other's in any way. Since the human race is always clothed, dress has become a second nature and one of the principal means of sexual attraction, replacing the plumage of birds or the scents emitted by wild animals. This is so true that if you dress an adolescent boy in girl's clothes you will find yourself attracted to him. I learned this in 1764 or '65, at Carnival time. I was strolling on the rue St.-Honoré. At the corner of the rue de Champfleuri I encounter a pretty girl of fifteen or sixteen, charming! A pretty mouth, a provocative air. I was all excited and wanted to kiss her. The pretended young girl lifted her skirt and showed me a pair of breeches. The attraction ceased immediately, but I had been caught....

I believe that the chief cause of the spread of pederasty among the Greeks and the Romans was the resemblance of the dress of young people of both sexes, their flowing robes, their sandals, their hair that boys wore long until the end of puberty. This resemblance, plus the freshness of youth, made handsome boys look like pretty girls; and the boys had a touch of vigor that made them even more attractive to men who were less tamed by civilization than we. If either sex was disadvantaged it was the girls, because of the grave consequences that could result from commerce with them. The results are well known to anyone who can read Latin and Greek.

Women should not be allowed to wear men's hats, as they do at certain times. Men must never be permitted to wear pointed shoes and especially—as has been seen in these degenerate times —shoes with high heels, stealing from women that charm that is like a talisman of the delicate sex. If you examine the individuals who try to confuse the two sexes you always find vicious creatures: a woman who is hard, imperious, unlovable, antisocial; a man who is a fool, or trivial or a pederastomaniac!

If I am so furious on the subject of women's shoes, it's because they've always been the first incitement to desire for me. When one sees a woman fully dressed, no matter how lovely her bosom or narrow her waist, one knows nothing about her. But a delicate foot, well arched, is a sure sign of the nature of the most intimate attractions, especially that which is the ultimate goal of the enterprise. Far be it from me to depreciate the delight of delectable breasts, crinkling with desire, be they peaches or apples; the man who neglects to offer his devotions at that altar is cheating both himself and his companion. Yet the path that leads from the foot to the essential shrine of love is more direct and less deceptive. Besides, there is a Latin proverb that I have found fairly reliable when put to the test: *Parvus pes, barathrum grande.* (Little foot, big cunt.) For someone built as I am, it is a useful guide, since what I seek is always pleasure, never pain, in the act of love. The reference to my own anatomy isn't boasting—that would put me into the category of the pederasts I so despise. It is tenderness, not physical qualities, that makes love worthwhile. But a physical compatibility can smooth the way.

It was in the summer of 1748 that I first experienced the impression of a pretty shoe. I was living in the vicarage at Courgis in the care of my half-brother, the abbé Thomas. Not quite fourteen, I was fully formed; my voice had changed and I had learned how to use a razor. That Easter I had fallen in love with Jeanette Rousseau (and I still love her, forty-four years later!) but that was a moral passion. The modest Jeanette never troubled my senses. But my encounters with other girls of the village had other results. I resisted, as well as I could, the temptation of solitary vice; but at times I succumbed.

My brother had a housekeeper, Marguerite Paris, forty years old, it must be said, but as untouched as a nun, or rather as fresh as a woman who has never needed anything. Besides, as everyone knows, middle age represents no obstacle for pubescent young men; it would seem rather that Nature leads them toward experienced women. Marguerite and I had become good friends; I had confided to her my love for Jeanette.

On Assumption Day, August 15, I returned to the vicarage after vespers, and sat down at the kitchen table to study. Marguerite was preparing the salad, not far from me. It was a hot afternoon; Marguerite was wearing a light housecoat with a skirt that floated above her ankles. We were alone. My schoolmates were playing; my brother Thomas was busy with something or other. I was sitting near the window; she in the shade. Marguerite had her legs crossed; I could see her well-formed calf. Marguerite was always fastidious about her person; her shoes came from Paris; even when she wore sabots they were delicate with high heels. That afternoon she had new mules of black morocco leather, a narrow heel, and white stitching. She dangled one of these enchanting shoes on the toes of a delicate foot, revealing a well-turned leg, covered by a white stocking with blue embroidery. Like a bird charmed by a viper who feels the danger but cannot flee, I couldn't take my eyes from the sight.

The shiny black slipper swayed on the toes of Marguerite's foot. My imagination was inflamed, my senses on fire. I began to jiggle my leg and the rubbing of the fabric of my pants produced a sensation that the action of my hand under the table reenforced. I must explain that until that day I had never had an ejaculation without fainting. Terrified, but unable to resist, I jumped up and ran to Marguerite.

"My dear child," she said in a sweet voice, "what is it?"

I couldn't answer, but I grabbed her hands, moist from the fresh-washed lettuce, and squeezed them.

"Monsieur Nicolas, you look sick—let me get you some water."

She tried to get up but I put my arms around her and held her tight. With a sublime understanding of my plight, Marguerite pressed me to her ample breast.

A mist covered my eyes, my legs grew weak; I would have fallen if Marguerite hadn't held me up. But I remained conscious and experienced the full sensation of the shock that passed through my body. Delighted at what I felt, I said to myself, "At last I am a man! I could be Jeanette's husband!"

I calmed down and Marguerite asked me what had come over me. I answered that I didn't know, but that it was the sight of her slipper and her leg that had put me in that state where I couldn't control my actions.

"But you love Jeanette Rousseau!"

Her words were a dash of cold water. I began to shiver and blush for my actions, for all that they were involuntary.

After that, to calm the excitement occasioned by Marguerite's voluptuous feet and slippers, I made use of my horror of the sight of blood, imagining a furious soldier passing his sword through her whenever my imagination began to lead me astray. But what happened on that day changed my whole life.

Must I repeat the story of Mme. Fournier's slipper? I think I must if I am to be honest.

We are five years after the episode with Marguerite; I am nineteen, living in Auxerre, apprenticed to the gross Fournier and in love with his wife, the angelic Colette. I could never believe that she had any dealings with him other than those imposed by her situation as mistress of his house. (From the gossip at the shop I knew that Fournier preferred the favors of the girls of Auxerre, and I had observed that the couple rarely shared the same bedroom.)

Colette had rescued me from my garret over the latrines when she returned from Paris, and taken me into her household as a member of the family, out of affection for my parents and respect for the learning which set me apart from the rest of the workers. But this proximity was a constant torment as well as bliss. I saw Colette at every meal; I listened while she discussed the affairs of the household with her servant, Toinette; I saw her in deshabillé in the morning and in the evening; I held the skein of wool for her as she wound it into a ball. For her I was nothing but an amiable young man whom she respected because he spent most of his free time reading. For me she was a goddess!

Her image was constantly on my mind during the long solitary nights I passed in my room, unable to sleep. The fury she aroused led me to chase after the girls I met through the other workers, but at the same time her superiority made them repugnant to me. My companions arranged sordid little orgies in a garret with two compliant chambermaids. I was invited to join the party because one of the girls had found me handsome, but my obsession with Mme. Fournier kept me virtuous, at least for a while. When I found her linen in the clothespress I would touch my lips to it, her chemise, her corset and that garment which I imagined in contact with the most intimate part of her body. (May what I write here be useful to others! I thought at the time that my obsession was unique, which made it all the more painful.)

Colette had perfect tiny feet and exquisite taste in shoes, which she ordered from Paris. One Sunday, returning to the house after Mass, I found her elegantly dressed, wearing pink pumps with pointed toes and tongues, with green heels and stitching, pretty rosettes with tiny diamonds. Apparently these pumps were uncomfortable, because new, or else after returning from church she wanted to keep them clean, because a few minutes later she exchanged them for a pair of green mules, no less provocative, with pink heels and ruffles. I kept very still, devouring her with my eyes. Toinette put the pink shoes on a small table, beside the door. The two of them went upstairs, telling me they would be busy for a while. The house was silent; I was alone. Carried away by my idolatry for Mme. Fournier and everything that related to her, I thought that I could touch her by means of the shoes that had just left her feet. I picked up the glittering objects, pressed one to my lips, while the other, by a deviation of nature and a mockery of its most sacred rite, replaced that treasure that I so ardently desired. There are no decent terms that are more clear. . . . The warmth that her foot had communicated to the shoe still lingered in its lining and gave it a soul. . . . A cloud of ecstasy veiled my eyes. . . .

Calm again after a while, I removed the traces of my shameful action. I picked up a pen. In tiny letters I wrote, *"I adore you!"* in the toe of the shoe I had just soiled. Then I returned the two elegant slippers to their place beside the door. But I was observed by Toinette, who at that moment was descending the stairs. Pretending not to see her, I fled. But I knew from that day on that my passion for Colette had been revealed. And strangely enough my bizarre and frenetic use of the pink and green shoe seemed to smooth the way toward that shrine whose place it had taken.

What followed occupies an entire epoch in *Monsieur Nicolas. . . .*

When I left Auxerre two years later, I took a pair of Colette's slippers with me as a souvenir. The only feet they ever graced were those of Zéphire. I still have them and should like them to be buried with me in my grave.

The first of my novels to have any success was *Le Pied de Fanchette,* published in 1769 and reprinted in 1776 with the subtitle, *"Or the Pink Shoe"* (one can imagine what pink shoe that was). The book was inspired, as usual, by a woman, a Mme. Lévêque, wife of a silk merchant of the rue St.-Denis, whom I had seen one afternoon wearing white mules with silver lace and fringes on feet that were marvels of delicacy. I wrote the first thirteen chapters in two days. Although I was cheated out of the profit I should have made from the book's success by the rapacity of the booksellers, it did establish me as an author who could win the favor of the public.

Since then I have encountered a number of women, proud of the form of their nether extremities (and often with good reason), who thought that the author of *Le Pied de Fanchette* would be an easy conquest. Among them were a few who were all the more eager to arouse my attention because they imagined that I was one of those men who are satisfied by a pretty foot and nothing more. I never took long to dissipate this false impression, starting indeed with the foot but then moving onward and upward. There was none who regretted her disillusionment.

For a long while I paid little attention to politics. For one thing there were no striking events of the sort that have you eagerly awaiting the papers, and then many of the cast of characters had been changed and those in the new roles were a dull lot. The grand outlines of the plot remained the same: the tug of war between the Assembly and the king, those who wanted the Revolution to move forward and those who wished it to retreat; the resistance of the Clergy; the flight of the emigrés; the menace of the coalition of crowned heads. But lacking incident and personality the play suffered.

The new Assembly was composed largely of lawyers, especially the delegates from the southwest, who formed a party known as the Gironde. Bailly was no longer mayor of Paris; the austere Pétion now held the post, having defeated Lafayette in a close election. Robespierre swayed opinion at the Jacobins, Danton at the Cordeliers, Marat and Desmoulins in the press; none of them was in the Assembly.

Among a host of lesser actions, there were two decrees of substance; one demanding that all priests (now employees of the state) take an oath to uphold the Constitution; the other declaring all Frenchmen living abroad (*i.e.,* the emigrés) were considered under suspicion of treason. Both of these were vetoed by Louis, and these vetos became the great issue for those who refused to trust the king. Meanwhile prices had risen to new heights, especially the price of sugar, rum and coffee, because of the revolt in Santo Domingo.

In January and February we had riots at grocery shops, especially in the *faubourgs,* mobs of women forcing the proprietors to sell sugar at last year's price, sometimes simply looting. Again there were grain riots in several towns, again châteaux were burned by bands of peasants, again there was talk of speculators and hoarding, the familiar symptoms of the crisis of '89, as if calculated to prove that the Revolution could not be over.

But the great question, the great issue that dwarfed all others, was the threat of war. In August '91 the emperor of Austria and the king of Prussia had stated that they would send their troops into France to reverse the Revolution if any harm should come to the royal family. The threat had not materialized, but the troops were still there on the frontiers, joined by the forces of the emigrés. In Paris there were many who preached immediate hostilities, saying that France should strike first and spread the Revolution to all the peoples of Europe. Oddly enough the royalists also seemed to be in favor of war, perhaps because they hoped for a defeat.

The leader of the war party was Brissot, formerly a journalist, now a deputy of the Gironde. The chief proponent of peace was Robespierre, no longer a deputy but the soul of the Jacobins. The debate had for theater the Jacobin club, rather than the Assembly.

Robespierre maintained that it was necessary to complete and consolidate the Revolution in France before trying to spread it to other nations. He was suspicious of the Army, disorganized by the emigration of many of its officers, still staffed by the aristocrats who had held all commissions before '89. He saw danger even in victory, the specter of a military dictator.

Like everyone else, I had read a great deal about Robespierre, "the Incorruptible" as he is called by his partisans, but I had never seen him. One evening in March I was teased by Fabre, our Jacobin at the Café Manoury. He said that the Nocturnal Spectator should be acquainted with what takes place in his club, according to him the most important spot in Paris. I answered that I pretended to observe only what happens in the streets and alleys, leaving to others the Court, the Assembly, the clubs and the salons. But finally I agreed.

The next evening I met Fabre at the Café M., then walked with him down the rue St.-Honoré to the seat of the "Mother Society." He gave me a ticket for the gallery, leaving me at the entrance to take his seat on the floor. This arrangement was to my liking. I don't know exactly what I expected, but I was surprised. The place itself was formerly the chapel of the Jacobin monastery from which the club takes its name. A plainer church cannot be imagined; it might be a Quaker meeting house. A rectangular room, white walls, two iron stoves in the center aisle with pipes rising to the vault. The members sit on benches facing each other; the galleries are at the ends of the room. A tribune of wood, a simple table for the speaker's notes; behind it a pedestal with a bust of Mirabeau. The members all soberly dressed and quite respectable; the galleries also filled with a serious and attentive audience, some of them foreigners.

The meeting began with communications from affiliated

clubs in the *départements*. After that, a résumé of the proceedings of the Assembly that afternoon. I was in luck; Robespierre took the floor.

Again I was surprised. Instead of some sort of demagogue, which is what I had expected he was, a good-looking man in his thirties, dressed in the most conservative fashion, silk suit with breeches, an embroidered vest and powdered wig. I would have taken him for a royalist had I seen him in the street. A handsome and amiable face that inspires confidence, but none of the bravura of the chair-climbers of the Café de Foy. He did not *orate;* he spoke in the most simple fashion, addressing himself directly to everyone in the room, not very loud, although I heard every word. Certain mannerisms that marked the provincial lawyer that he is, a certain stiffness, as if he valued dignity above all else. That made me think his conservative dress might be a compensation for his youth.

Having come for a show, I was disappointed—until I realized how attentively I was listening. Actually that realization came only upon reflection, after I had left. While I was there—and once I had swallowed my disappointment—I ceased to listen to *Robespierre* but I was absorbed by what he *said*. And every word seemed irrefutable, not by his personal authority but because it was self-evident; he seemed the voice of Reason itself, worthy heir of the century of *les lumières*.

He denounced Brissot, Dumouriez, all those who say we must have war to spread the Revolution. As the thought of war horrifies me, I was disposed to agree. But later I realized that the men he denounced did not seem merely mistaken, but odious, perfidious, treacherous. The man is so convincing that while you listen you are sure his opponents must be evil.

When the meeting was over I waited downstairs for Fabre. To my astonishment Camille Desmoulins was there and made a point of saying he was glad to see me again. (Our last meeting was that evening at the Théâtre des Italiens in December 1790, just before his marriage.) I was surprised that he remembered me and made a point of renewing our acquaintance, but then the man has always been charming, and a flattering attention to others is the chief ingredient of charm. We spoke briefly of Mer-

PLATE 12: Robespierre. An idealized engraving based on a contemporary drawing (Granger Collection).

cier and Mme. de Beauharnais. Fabre arrived as we were chatting; he was astonished to see me on familiar terms with one of the luminaries of his club, delighted when I introduced him.

There had been a series of debates between Robespierre and Brissot on the question of war that threatened to split the Jacobins in two. That society was now more powerful than ever; it had become, so to speak, the Church of the Revolution. In fact its authority had received a *cachet royal* when it was denounced by Leopold, emperor of Austria, brother of Marie-Antoinette, as "that pernicious sect which is the principal enemy of the monarchy." Now entirely devoted to his college chum Robespierre, Camille had written a pamphlet, *"Brissot Dévoilé"* that many in the club found gossipy and unjust. It contained many absurd accusations: that Brissot had proposed a republic after Varennes to pave the way for the massacre of the Champ-de-Mars, so that the people would be disgusted with the idea of liberty, that he had proposed freeing the slaves in the colonies to set Santo Domingo on fire, knowing that the massacre of the whites would discredit the Revolution. But it was written with Camille's customary verve, and in journalism style and wit count for more than logic or truth.

Nonetheless it was Brissot and his party who triumphed, although Robespierre remained the chief leader of the Jacobins. Austria and Prussia had signed an offensive and defensive alliance aimed at France. On March 1, Leopold suddenly died and was succeeded as emperor by his nephew, Francis, whom the papers all proclaimed an even more ferocious enemy of the Revolution, perhaps because he had less concern for the safety of the queen of France, his aunt, Marie-Antoinette. When the Girondin ministers took their portfolios later that month the die was cast.

All the same, I believe that the decisive factor was neither the intrigues of the Court, nor the debates of the Jacobins, nor the maneuvers of the Assembly, but the bellicose reaction of ordinary people when they learned that the Revolution was threatened from abroad. Everywhere people began to procure arms, and their favorite was the pike, an ineffectual weapon in this era of rifles and artillery, but one which had the advantage that it could be manufactured by everyone. Besides, Austria and

Prussia were not the only enemies of liberty; there were many at home, and against those the pike might again serve as well as it had in '89. The Faubourg St.-Antoine became an armed camp, as did the others. But the movement was not limited to the *faubourgs,* it spread all over Paris and indeed all over France, encouraged by the Girondin press. Danton, leader of the Cordeliers, was converted to the cause of war, and Robespierre himself was forced to trim his sails, walking alongside Pétion at that Fête de la Liberté in April, where half a million Parisians took to the streets despite the opposition of the Court and Lafayette, so that there were no Gardes to assure order.

War was declared April 20th. It was immediately followed by disasters that justified all of Robespierre's forebodings. But by then it was too late to turn back.

April 14: Passing by the rue de la Huchette at about five I hear shouts and see people running. I follow the crowd by that alley with the charming name of rue du Chat-qui-Pêche and arrive on the quai just in time to see a punt pull ashore with a wet and bedraggled youth whom the boatmen had fished out of the Seine. A young girl fights her way through the crowd—a true nymph, fair-haired and delicate—takes the youth in her arms and covers his wet face with kisses. Neither of them could have seen twenty summers. Embarrassed by the attention of the onlookers, the shivering young blade attempts to explain: he had been paying court to his sweetheart in one of the chambers that gives on the river; she resisted his advances; in despair he threw himself from the window into the Seine. A touching sight, this young lover, hollow-cheeked and pale, unhurt but very shaken, his clothes soaked and dripping, his hair plastered over his ears. The idlers listening could believe neither the reluctance of the girl nor the ardor of the youth; they shouted gross wisecracks that the lovers did not seem to hear. One of the Gardes took them off to the section to have the incident recorded, although what the section will make of this amorous contention I can't imagine.

April 24: At the Grève, a gang of workmen setting up a

curious sort of machine, mostly of wood but with a large metal blade, the whole mounted on a platform, quite sturdy and well built. One of the Gardes explained that this was a device for mechanical decapitation that will replace the headsman's ax and its grisly errors. Now that beheading, formerly reserved for the nobility, has become the fate of all who are sentenced to die, the Assembly has ordered the use of this new machine as a humane measure. Its inventor—or rather its adaptor, since the machine has been used in Italy for some time—is one of the Parisian delegates to the first Assembly, Dr. Guillotin. One of the onlookers complained that this device would take the *sport* out of executions! . . . Its first victim, the next day, a thug who had killed an old woman to steal her purse.

May 25: At the Tuileries, on the Feuillant terrace, a red-faced officer of the regular army suddenly jumps up on a chair and shouts: "Long live the queen! Long live the king! And SHIT ON THE NATION!" A patriot demands that he retract his words, the officer answers with insults, the patriot knocks him off the chair, the officer draws his saber, a spectator throws a stool at the sword, the patriot's pregnant wife tries to shield her husband, the officer grabs the poor woman's hand and bites it, then gives her a kick that knocks her down—the enraged beast is about to stomp on her when he is seized by several men at once and led away, still shouting obscenities.

The Girondins had promised a quick victory, the occupation of Belgium and the Rhine, destruction of the emigrés as a threat, removal of Austrian troops from the frontiers of France. Instead the war began by a series of retreats. As there were no battles, the blame could only be placed at the doors, or rather the tents, of the generals. The troops themselves drew this conclusion. General Dillon was killed when he gave the order to turn back. Rochambeau resigned; he had won his marshal's baton in the American Revolution, but that of France could not command his loyalty. Lafayette, commander of the Army of the Ardennes, set his sights on Paris instead of Brussels, declaring himself ready to march on the capital to disperse the Jacobins.

We learned all this little by little, but it did not take the patriots long to realize that they had been duped. If there was treason, its source must be the Court. In the *Annales Patriotiques* Carra denounced the "Austrian plot," claiming that Louis and Marie-Antoinette were in league with the enemies of France. Brissot took up the charge in the Assembly, accusing the Court of ties with the aristocrats of Coblentz, and, through them, Vienna.

In two months there was a paradoxical change. It was Brissot, Roland, Dumouriez, etc.—the Girondins—who had pleaded for war *in alliance* with the royalists, opposed by Robespierre. But now that all of Robespierre's suspicions of the generals were proved well founded, it was the Girondins who led the attack against the Court, and became the heroes of the people.

The Assembly, led by the ministers, decreed that all priests who refused to support the Revolution should be deported, ordered the King's Guard dissolved, called for a camp of twenty thousand Gardes Nationales at the gates of Paris as a wartime successor to the civilian *Fédérations* of '90 and '91. Louis vetoed these decrees, but under the Constitution his veto had to be countersigned by the cabinet and the cabinet refused. The king decided to dare all, dismissed the ministers whom he had called to power in March. Six thousand royalist troops, vowing fidelity to the king, menaced the Assembly. Paris was alarmed; the sections rumbled; the people demanded arms. Instead of a war at the frontier, it seemed that the streets of the capital would be the theater of operations.

The 18th of June I went to supper at Mme. de Beauharnais's. Politics is again in fashion in that salon, where several of the company are in the circle of the cashiered ministers; they spoke with indignation of the king's veto, the inaction of the generals. Their great hope: the people, their patriotic fervor, their attachment to the Revolution. If one read a transcript of some of the conversation one might imagine a gathering of *sans-culottes* with red bonnets and pikes, or at least a meeting of the Jacobins. But what was the scene? the latest fashions, coiffures, jewelry, silks, satins, and servants providing all that one might desire in the way of food and drink. I did not feel at ease, knowing the people too well to believe they really cared about the veto or

Roland, that they can be aroused again as they have been before merely to keep a number of bourgeois politicians in office. . . .

The next evening I went out at nine, passing by the rue St.-André-des-Arcs and the rue Mazarine. Although the sky remained bright with the afterglow of a magnificent sunset that did not want to end, the streetlamps were already lit. Patrols everywhere. I crossed the Pont-Neuf to the Café M. We have a new regular, Fragnières, of a Swiss family but born in Paris, a curious little man who always seems to know everything that is taking place in his section, one of the liveliest in Paris, that of the Théâtre Français. He was at his usual table, smoking his pipe. As I entered I said that his district seemed agitated this evening.

"Who do you think is agitating?" he asked with his sly grin. "You should go to St.-Antoine or St.-Marceau if you wish to see some *agitating* that deserves the name. There is to be a petition tomorrow, presented to the Assembly, perhaps even to the king."

I observed that a petition didn't sound violent. A red-faced man at another table spoke up: "It is to be a petition with arms!"

"You mean an insurrection?" I asked. Everyone laughed and said I must be a royalist to use such a disgraceful word.

"Many workers cannot write even their names," Fragnières explained. "Their pikes will mean more than another *X* on a piece of paper. Besides, they have friends."

"Where?"

"In the Clubs, in the Assembly, but especially in the Hôtel de Ville. M. Pétion is not timid."

Preferring, as always, not to commit myself, I sat down and read the papers, all full of the letter from Lafayette to the Assembly blaming our defeats on the lack of discipline of the troops, the scheming of the Jacobins and the Cordeliers, the anarchy reigning in France—it was like reading a letter from Grimod. Does our blond hero on his white horse imagine himself a Cromwell, or perhaps even a Caesar?

Afterwards along the quai to the Tuileries. It was surrounded by troops. A year ago the king slipped out a back door to take the ill-fated brown-and-yellow *berline* on his aborted journey. Where would we be now if he had succeeded in his escape? Less confused, in any event. . . . Returned by the quais. All seemed quiet.

The next morning, Sunday the 20th (anniversary of the flight to Varennes and the Tennis Court Oath), Agnès returns from the market and says that the streets are full of armed men. I go out. On the Place Maubert I see a raggle-taggle mob of workers going toward the river. This troop was rather cheerful, calling on the pretty girls to come along. A patrol of the Gardes watched carefully but let them pass, pikes, red caps, wine sacks and all. I noticed Rollin, now captain of the patrol; he said that they had orders to let the "petition" proceed, so long as it was peaceful.

It was a lovely June day, the sky clear. No drum rolls, no tocsin, no musket fire, no cannon, i.e., none of the usual signs of a violent event. I returned home to work, not going out again until the middle of the afternoon. All was quiet. I went to the Tuileries.

On the quai, a mixed crowd leaving the gardens. I assumed that the petition had been received by the Assembly and that the petitioners were going home; I joined them to learn what had happened. At the Palace, a rank of Gardes; the crowd trudged past without incident, a Sunday throng, men and women of all ages, a sprinkling of children.

Someone was carrying a tattered pair of breeches at the end of a pike with a crudely lettered sign reading, "VIVENT LES SANS-CULOTTES," but this was the only indication that there was anything political about the occasion.

The head of the crowd arrives at the passage that leads through the Louvre to the Carrousel, then stops. The mass thickens; I am caught like a raisin in a pudding. Because of my old clothes I am easily accepted; pushed against a pretty girl, I excuse myself—"We are all friends, Papa!" she laughs.

The way finally opened, the crowd surged forward, I found myself in the Carrousel. It was April '91 all over again, the Gardes before the palace, the square filled with humanity, a good-natured crowd that made jokes about Monsieur Veto and

PLATE 13: The people break into the Tuileries palace, June 20, 1792. From *Tableaux Historiques de la Révolution Francaise.*

Madame the Austrian while passing wine bottles from hand to hand, or rather mouth to mouth.

Suddenly people began to shout. I looked up and saw that a cannon at the side of the square was being turned away from the crowd and *toward the château.* Proof enough that the demonstration was sanctioned, if not planned, by the Hôtel de Ville. As if to confirm this the Gardes placed their hats on the points of their sabers, raised them over their heads, and shouted, "VIVE LA NATION!"

The palace doors were opened. I glimpsed a small artillery piece carried inside at the head of the crowd. By the time I was at the doors, carried along by the throng, the cannon was at the head of the grand staircase, apparently caught in an archway. A group of men held it on their shoulders shouting at each other all the while as if they were furniture movers having difficulty with an oversized wardrobe. In the end the gun was somehow or other taken back down the stairs, against the flow of the crowd. "You see what they keep here to massacre the people," one housewife said to another. Right or wrong, every Parisian is an expert.

The way at last clear, the human stream mounted the marble stairs. I had read that the Tuileries is old, ill-furnished and dilapidated in comparison with Versailles. If so I regret never having seen Versailles. As the motley throng trooped through the royal chambers it grew quiet, like peasants in cathedral, except for a few who had had too much wine. Everywhere one glanced there was something to delight the eye—marquetry, brocades, embroidered silks, gilt, bronze, paintings, parquets, marbles. The crowd maintained perfect order—nothing was touched, nothing damaged, nothing stolen. Finally I arrived at *l'Oeil de bœuf,* the chamber of royal receptions, where a reception such as this palace had never before seen was in progress.

Louis was standing in the bay of a window, with an inlaid table between himself and the crowd, protected only by four unarmed guards, his wig and face powdered, his suit a pale blue with an embroidered vest, a polite smile on his lips. He seemed very sure of himself, every inch a king, his obesity a mark of dignity and power. One of the leaders of the demonstration addressed the king. I was at the side of the room and could catch the word "veto," nothing more. Louis responded; the only words I heard were "duty according to the Constitution." Those few words told the whole story.

Someone offered the king a red bonnet. To my surprise he accepted it, plunked it on his own head. It was too small for him and sat perched on his powdered wig like a toy. A young man handed the monarch a bottle of wine; Louis raised it directly to his lips and swallowed a swig of the sour stuff as if that were what and how he always drank. He asked for a cockade; a pretty girl offered hers; Louis stuck it on his Punchinello stocking cap which became more ludicrous than ever.

If he was acting, it was a good act and it conquered his audience. There were shouts of "VIVE LE ROI! VIVE LA NATION!"

The crowd moved on, sluggishly, the leaders pleading with the people to let those still waiting have a chance to see the king. As I left the room I saw that Louis had climbed up on the table, so the people could get a better look. The man has courage; anyone with a pistol could have finished him off with no trouble.

In the king's bedroom a stout charlady poked the royal mattress and muttered to her husband, "Big old Veto has a better bed than the likes of us, God bless him!" In another room the queen sat behind a massive desk, her cheeks flushed. She looked at no one and bit her pale lips. The dauphin stood on the desk and smiled at the crowd. (It was reported that someone gave the prince an enormous red stocking cap. One of the organizers of the demonstration snatched it from the dauphin's curls, shouting, "Can't you see that this child is too hot?")

Such was the scene that was presented to all of Europe as a scandal and the triumph of barbarism. To read the royalist papers you would think that the queen had been raped, the king slaughtered. And yet what really happened? The crowd shouted, "Recall the ministers, take back the veto!" Louis did neither; in fact he issued a proclamation insisting that he would continue to do his duty as prescribed by the Constitution, which meant that he would stick to his present course. And yet here were many simple folk that day who entered the palace believing themselves republicans and left convinced royalists. The king had come out ahead.

July 4: To the Café M. The papers report new reverses in the North. Fragnières asks if I've been to the Tuileries in the last two weeks. No, I've been too occupied. He proposes a stroll. We take the quai but the gate to the garden is shut, we have to go all the way to the Place Louis XV. Even then we can't use the main entrance but have to circle around to the gate of the Feuillant terrace, near the Assembly, the only one open.

Aside from the terrace, the royal gardens have been closed to the public since June 20. The terrace was excepted because the Assembly declared it to be under its own jurisdiction. After seeing the Swiss at the other gates, I was astonished to discover that the stairs that led down to the main part of the garden were protected by nothing more than a simple ribbon strung between two trees. But it was clear that this ribbon had a power greater that that of iron bars. It has been dubbed the *barrière de faveur* and sags with the weight of bits of paper tied to it on which the most violent slogans attacking the king there have been scribbled.

The gardens are deserted, the terrace crowded. An old man, who seems distracted, walks around the silken barrier, starts down the stairs. The promenaders on the terrace shout that he is going to Coblentz. He retraces his steps. Fragnières reports that two days earlier a woman of fashion had done the same thing. She was jeered and tried to come back. The crowd on the terrace wouldn't let her pass the ribbon; she had to go down again and ask one of the Swiss to let her leave by one of the other gates.

We walk past the Manège, well protected by Gardes. A man whom I have never seen before darts out of the crowd and takes hold of my sleeve. "I know you have a printing press," he whispers, "I have some interesting matter that I wanted printed at a good price."—"Monsieur," I answer, "there are many flourishing journals that will print whatever you wish. My press is a private affair."—"That is just what I want. Shall we go down to the garden to talk about it?"

I move on without answering, but keep my eyes on the stranger. He rejoins a group of men sitting in a circle; among them I recognize Daniol le Manceau, my former employee. I tell Fragnières to try to eavesdrop on their conversation. He slips away without further explanation, delighted to have a role in an intrigue.

A few minutes later we meet in the shadows. "The man who approached you said to the others, 'He wouldn't fall for our trap!' A man with red hair (Daniol): 'He must be an aristocrat, he used to dine with a countess. Besides I have an informant.'—The other, 'We have nothing against him.'—Daniol, 'We'll get him another time!' "

I ask Fragnières to remember everything he has heard and make him promise that he will report everything that has happened, if ever it should be necessary.

Was I too suspicious? There is an atmosphere of suspicion abroad in Paris today.

July 6: To Guillot to check on the new edition of *Les Filles du Palais-Royal,* but find the doors locked. On to Mérigot, who informs me that Guillot has been arrested for trafficking in counterfeit *assignats.* He and two other criminals had a clandestine press in a barn in Passy where they printed the notes which they mixed with others and then sold at the Bourse for hard currency. Ha! not content with cheating writers and the public, the scoundrel also has to cheat the Nation! The charge is capital, but Mérigot thinks that Guillot will manage to get off with some time in prison; he has friends connected with the ministry and even the Court. Meanwhile I find myself out of pocket, although I suppose that if I had been paid it would have been with counterfeit bills. But Guillot's shop is under seal, which means that what remains of the edition of the *Palais-Royal* and *La Semaine Nocturne* cannot be distributed.

July 14: Third anniversary of the fall of the Bastille. Paris again full of *fédérés,* but this year it is only a way station; they are volunteers, departing for the front. (But that front threatens to be Paris itself; the news from the North is all bad.) Another ceremony at the Champ-de-Mars; I stayed at home and worked. The papers report that it was a sad event; the king looked like a debtor being taken to prison. There is no "federation" of sentiment; everyone is suspicious of everyone else despite all appeals for unity. . . . Reports of royalist insurrections in Provence and Brittany, led by aristocrats and anticonstitutional priests.

July 22: Awakened at six by the sound of cannon; one shot from the east, one from the west. Nothing more. The street outside is quiet. At seven again the two ominous reports. I dress and go out. On the rue St.-Jacques none of the normal traffic of a Sunday morning, instead a noisy procession coming across the Petit-Pont and ascending the Montagne-Ste.-Geneviève. First a detachment of the Gardes on horseback, then a military band, trumpets and drums, six fieldpieces, four mounted officers with placards reading "LIBERTE—EGALITE—CONSTITUTION—PATRIE." After that a group of notables with tricolor sashes, more cavalry, and, most important, an immense tricolor banner inscribed with the words: "CITIZENS! THE NATION IS IN PERIL!"

So the Assembly has finally triumphed over the resistance of the Court with the call for mobilization. There have been reports of volunteers from all over France preparing to march to the front, but the royalists seem to regard them as more of a threat than a shield, citing the complaints of the generals about undisciplined troops, agitators, etc. And to be sure, arming the people is a threat—to the Court. . . .

I followed the procession to the Panthéon, where it halted. The drums rolled; an officer mounted the steps of the church and proclaimed, with great solemnity, "The nation is in peril!"

All day, every hour on the hour, the cannon sounded their dull and ominous signal. I wandered about. On the Pont-Neuf, by the statue of Henri IV, a huge flag. Another at the Hôtel de Ville. Returning, I find an unusual sight for a Sunday afternoon at the Place Maubert. A hastily erected platform in the center of the square; on it a tent surmounted by two tricolor banners, each flagpole decorated with a red stocking cap, between them a strip of bunting again proclaiming, *"La Patrie est en Danger!"* Inside the tent officers of the section are enrolling volunteers.

A circle of Gardes in uniform protected this station, and the Gardes were necessary because of the press of those waiting to enroll. It was announced, from time to time, that the minimum age for volunteers was sixteen, but I saw the son of the baker of the rue Galande in the line (he is fourteen), also the apprentice to the tailor across from my house (he is only twelve although mature for his age); also a number of gray heads who have no more business in the army than I.

When I was a lad the news that the king's officers were coming to Sacy or Vermenton to conscript men for the army sent all the young bucks off to the hills until the danger had passed. But that was before the Revolution.

July 31: The papers all print the manifesto of the Duke of Brunswick, Supreme Commander of the Armies of Prussia and Austria, addressed to the people of France, telling us what to expect from the forces of the Coalition.

Any town or village that puts up a resistance to the invading armies will be demolished. All members of the Assembly, all officials of the *départements,* the municipalities, all troops of the Gardes Nationales, will be court-martialed. If any harm is done to the king before the arrival of the German troops, Paris will be burned to the ground.

Every line of this document rings with the spirit of Prussia, that nation of soldiers where every order is obeyed instantly and the notion of liberty does not exist. It would be hard to imagine anything better calculated to make Frenchmen forget their differences, to turn every farm lad into a volunteer, to inspire each raw recruit to fight like a veteran. It is one thing to fight for the Constitution, the Declaration of the Rights of Man, the spirit of '89; it is another to fight for your home, your soil, your wife and children.

The volunteers from Marseilles have arrived in Paris after a month of marching north. These five hundred men have already become a legend, a symbol of the volunteers from every part of France marching to defend the Nation. There is a patriotic song that has been popular since May, *The Song of the Army of the Rhine;* it has replaced *Ça Ira!* as the anthem of the Revolution.

The music is stirring and the verse well-turned, if somewhat bloodthirsty. Nonetheless, even after repeated hearings, I find that I am moved every time a deep-throated voice sings out:

"Allons enfants de la Patrie . . ."

The song is now called *La Marseillaise.*

AUGUST AND SEPTEMBER

AUGUST–SEPTEMBER 1792

WAS there ever an insurrection so widely heralded before the event as that of August 10th? Was there ever an insurrection so logical and necessary? For over a year the king had been in a false position maintained by a fiction, Chief Executive of a nation he had tried to flee, swearing fidelity to a Constitution he at heart opposed, Commander in Chief of the Army while hoping for its defeat. If there were any doubts about the king's sentiments, they had been removed since the Declaration of War, by his vetoes, his dismissal of the ministers, his opposition to calling up the volunteers. Now that the Nation had been declared "in peril" and the Coalition had declared its intention of invading France to reverse the Revolution, the power of the throne was not only false but absurd.

During the first week of August, Mercier spoke to me in guarded terms about the activities of his associate Carra; the cofounder of the *Annales Patriotiques* and one of the chief conspirators plotting to get rid of the monarch. Mercier's secrecy hardly seemed necessary. Since July 25th the forty-eight sections had been meeting every day, their debates open to all citizens, whether qualified to vote or not; they were forty-eight permanent centers of agitation; forty-seven voted for the deposition of the king. This activity was directed by the Hôtel de Ville, especially by Danton, leader of the Commune and the Cordeliers. The Marseilles regiment and many of the *fédérés* remained in Paris instead of leaving for the front, considering that the first decisive battle would take place in the capital. On August 3rd, Pétion, speaking for the Commune, demanded that Louis be deposed. On August 6th a huge assembly of the sections and the *fédérés* at the Champ-de-Mars demanded the same thing. All this was published in the press, known to every chair-mender and knife-sharpener. The clubs seethed; the blacksmiths made pikes instead of horseshoes. The machinations of some conspirators in the back room of a café hardly seemed to make a difference.

The only question remaining was how bloody the event would be when it occurred, and whether the king would be killed. (The date had been fixed in advance when Faubourg St.-Antoine declared that there would be violence if Louis was still in place on August 9th.) Several battalions of the Gardes Nationales were known to be commanded by royalist officers; young gentlemen from the fashionable quarters had volunteered to defend the king at the Tuileries; Louis had his devoted Swiss Guards at the Palace. Many of the *départements* had protested the insult to the king on June 20. The Prussian and Austrian armies were poised with little between them and Paris; there were rumors that the Assembly was planning to flee to the south at their approach.

And how far would the popular fury go once it was unleashed? Duval of the Parlement of Paris, hero of the clerks of the quai des Orfévres in those long-ago days before the Estates (and yet only four summers had passed!), since then a furious royalist, was overheard speaking for the Court in the Tuileries gardens. An angry mob attacked him, tore his clothes to bloody shreds as he fled to the Palais-Royal. There he found shelter behind closed doors while the bloodthirsty rabble shouted outside. The Gardes sent for the mayor, who came running, found the former judge a specter on a bloodstained mattress. Duval whispered, "I too, Pétion, have been idolized by the people. . . ." Pétion fainted.

Paris remained tranquil up to the eve of the event. I waited like the sheep who watches a fight between the dogs and the wolves.

On the ninth I attempted a promenade that I cut short when I found the Pont-Neuf and the Pont-Royal both occupied by battalions of the Gardes and shut to the public. No one knew which of the Gardes were loyal to the king, which supported the Commune.

The Assembly had voted to absolve Lafayette of all accusations of treason. That same afternoon a speaker at a gathering near the Cordeliers called them a pack of cowards. He quoted Marat, who had written that the present Assembly was as ridiculous as a troop of clowns on a tightrope, having been elected by a handful of the rich, advising that aside from the Declaration of the Rights of Man the present Constitution must be rejected.

Many shops closed early that evening. At eleven a drummer passed by shouting that all windows must be illuminated. The streets seemed quiet and I dared a stroll in the neighborhood. I saw the Gardes hurrying to join their battalions, a troop descending the rue St.-Jacques toward the Hôtel de Ville; otherwise no one about. A soft night. With a full moon and the lamps in the windows the streets were a décor for a masked ball.

In the dark early hours of the morning the tocsin pealed over the waiting city.

Of August 10th itself, I report only what I saw. After an insomniac night I am awakened by the sound of cannon fire. I go out. It is a market day but the stalls on the Place Maubert are shut. Anxious citizens ask each other for news.

A band of ragged men comes running down the rue Galande. "To arms! to arms! they are killing your sons and brothers!" A company of the Gardes marches past. I follow, as far as the quai Mazarin, across from the Louvre and the Tuileries.

Several fieldpieces are readied on the Pont-Royal, pointing toward the palace. Afraid to remain on the quai, exposed to the fire of anyone shooting from the gallery of the Louvre, I took the rue de Seine, then the rues de l'Université and Beaune, which brought me to the quai Voltaire on the far side of the Pont-Royal.

Some men are sprinting across the bridge, trying to escape from the palace. They run for their lives; not one finishes his breathless race. The air vibrates with the crackling of musket fire; the fleeing men are picked off one by one; their bodies drop to the cobblestones as they fall.

Near me a cluster of women clap their hands and shout, "Bravo! Bravo!" as if it were a scene at the theater and the slain men would get up and walk to the wings when the curtain falls.

There are other men across the river who clamber down to the water's edge to be sheltered by the parapet of the quai. There are rifles firing from the windows of the Louvre. I have no idea who anyone is, which side they are on. I hear the guns and see men fall.

The day is cloudless and still, without a breeze. A pall of smoke hangs over the palace, now the last stronghold of the monarchy, obscuring the view, so that it seems that the place itself is about to dissolve along with the institution it shelters.

A patrol comes up the rue de Beaune, orders the spectators to disperse. I wander as far as the church of St.-Germain des Prés at the Abbaye, try to learn what is happening. No one knows.

After a while I return by the rue du Bac. All is quiet, but the cannon and the bodies are still there.

I circle back again and cross the Pont-Neuf. The Café Manoury is shut. I advance along the quai. All is quiet but the acrid scent of gunpowder hangs in the still August air. A rifle fires. I drop to the ground beside the wall. A woman who tries to run down to the river is killed, not twenty paces from where I cower.

When the shooting stops I wait, then retrace my steps, seeking whatever cover is available. At the passage of St.-Germain-l'Auxerrois a butcher's boy is cut down by a bullet fired from the colonnade of the Louvre. I dash to safety in a side street, holding my breath.

All this slaughter in the places I walk every day is hard to believe, even when I remember that it was the bell of St.-Germain-l'Auxerrois that gave the signal for the massacre on St. Bartholomew's day, two centuries ago. I am surprised that I have been so foolhardly in the hours that have just passed. I might easily have been picked off, like that woman on the quai du Louvre. But while a battle is going on, the whole notion of *safety* seems to change; I felt the bullets must be meant for someone else.

Later I saw a troop of the Gardes returning to their section, scraps of the red uniforms of the Swiss Guards tied to the ends of their bayonets.

Piecing the reports together afterward, I realized that all the deaths I had seen that day were useless. The king had already fled from the Palace to the Manège, where he called upon the Assembly for protection.

Agnès picked that evening to reproach me for the way I have treated her, saying that I should have stayed at home instead of wandering about and exposing myself to being killed. She was almost hysterical; she wept and cursed her miserable life. For the first time I realized that she is no longer young. There are wrinkled pouches under her eyes, her cheeks are hollow, her complexion unhappy. I am sorry for her; she is thirty-one, the age when most women lose the bloom of youth; she has always had a difficult life and her marriage could not have been worse. I would do anything to help her but at the same time when she weeps and accuses me of neglect I only find myself repelled by the spectacle.

When she begins again in the morning I tell her there are more important things on my mind and escape to the street.

What a haven for an old sinner! what joy to be able to wander, unnoticed, in my old clothes! The world can turn upside-down—it will find me in the back alleys of the Capital of the Universe! I began life as a creature of the fields but I end it as a city rat. . . .

To the Tuileries. A melancholy spectacle. The weather has been so dry these past weeks that the leaves have turned yellow prematurely and are beginning to fall.

The bare ground near the palace is littered with the corpses of the hundreds of Swiss Guards killed in yesterday's assault. All have been stripped of their uniforms; some are heaped up in an obscene promiscuity, others scattered about where they fell. The naked white flesh is a reproach to the serene sky and the August sun.

Near the Feuillant terrace, another huge pile of human flesh, the flies buzzing about. A crush of gawkers, many women among them, not at all put off by the gruesome spectacle. Hundreds of the assailants were killed also, plus others shot from the palace windows by the royalist gentlemen inside. This extinguishes the pity that the sight of the dead Swiss might otherwise arouse.

It is reported that the palace was stripped of all valuables when it was finally taken. But there was no looting; the plate, gold, and works of art were delivered to the Assembly to help finance the war.

Curious as to the facts, I went into the palace, now open to everyone. But as I was about to go up the grand staircase I heard shouts; some men carried down a thief who had been beaten unconscious when he was discovered making off with a doorknob. I changed my mind about taking another look at the royal apartments. . . .

On the far side of the Carrousel the barracks of the Swiss Guards were still smoldering. They had been set afire during the night and a crowd had prevented the firemen from putting out the blaze. Some of the corpses of the defenders of the palace had been thrown into the flames, and the scent of burnt flesh still hung in the air, like the odor of singed chickens on a Sunday morning. My stomach turned, my curiosity evaporated, I returned home. . . .

Again, as after Varennes, the epithet "royal" has been effaced on all shingles and shop windows; this time, I would think, permanently. The predecessors of Louis XVI have been deposed along with their descendant. The statue of Louis XIII no longer rides its pedestal at the Place Royal; that of Louis XIV lies on its side in the Place Vendôme; Louis XV no longer contemplates the square that bears his name, in fact the name of the square has been changed to Place de la Révolution.

For some reason or other the doormen of the inns that welcome travelers have always been called "the Swiss." Because of the ignorance of the rabble, some of them were massacred on the 10th. Now they insist that they be called something else;

the signs at the bell that used to read, *"Parlez au Suisse"* have all been changed to *"Parlez au Portier."*

The royal family fled from the palace soon after the attack began and took refuge in the Assembly. They remained there for two days, in a tiny apartment belonging to the legislative stenographer. The Assembly couldn't decide what to do with them. This is the legislature that in its first session last October changed the title "King of France" to "King of the French," then reversed itself the next day because of the hue and cry sent up by the royalists. On the 13th the king and his family were taken to the donjon of the former monastery of the Templiers at the edge of the Marais, a place that can be guarded both against attempted escape and attempted assassination. Avoiding the issue, the deputies declared the king *"suspended,"* then called for a National Convention to decide his fate and write a new Constitution. The elections, this time, are to be open to everyone, not just men of property. Meanwhile the Commune, at the Hôtel de Ville, is the government of Paris. But where is the government of France? The armies of the Coalition are at the frontier. What will they do when the news of August 10th arrives from Paris?

The weather continues to be dry and hot.

August 14: Astonishing how quickly everything returns to normal. The shops and markets have reopened, the anglers are back on the riverbanks, children play in the Tuileries garden where the corpses of the slain Swiss were sprawled just two days ago. If a foreigner had just arrived in Paris and was not informed of the bloody events of August 10th he would have no idea that this was not a perfectly ordinary summer and that enjoying the fine weather is not the chief concern of the populace. Of course for many it *is* the chief concern.

August 15: Papers, Café M. Many of the royalist sheets have ceased publication, and those still available sound bewildered, although they would have had plenty to say if things had turned out differently. The papers of the left have lost all restraint. Many accounts of what happened on August 10th, all contradicting one another. Who was responsible for the attack on the palace? Did the Swiss fire first or the assailants? Did Louis command the slaughter or try to prevent it? Did the Assembly receive him as king or as a prisoner? How many were slain, hundreds or thousands? Here it is five days after the event and it is impossible to know what really happened. And yet our historians will tell us every detail of the death of Caesar!

The *Révolutions de Paris* scolds the people of Paris for taking revenge only on the bronze statues of the kings, demands that Louis be put to death immediately, along with Lafayette, Barnave, Lameth, and the royalist deputies. The *Orateur du Peuple* echoes the same sentiments. Marat, of course, goes further than anyone else; he would slaughter a good half of the Assembly. And this may well come to pass. Danton has been named Minister of Justice, a Revolutionary Tribunal is being created; the prisons are filling up.

August 18: Encountered Rollin of the Gardes, Place Maubert. He told me that a bullet had creased his hat the morning of August 10th on the Place du Carrousel, then added that he was surprised not to have seen me at any of the meetings of the section, now that they are open to everyone. I pleaded poor health—but decided that in the interest of my future "health" it might be wise to let myself be seen from time to time.

This evening I took myself off to the meeting, which was held in the church of St.-Etienne-du-Mont behind the Panthéon, one of the oldest and most elaborate churches of Paris with its lacelike rood screen—a strange setting for the proceedings. The name of this district has been changed to the Section du Panthéon, "Sainte-Geneviève" sounding too clerical for the present mood. I had thought my old clothes would be sufficient to mark me as one of the people, but as I was not *sans-culotte* and sported neither a red cap nor a pike I received some suspicious glances.

A more disorganized assembly would be hard to imagine. The chief item of business was the election of a deputy to the National Convention, but that was never discussed. The presiding officer was a grocer named Hué, a substantial-looking man in his late thirties, but he never managed to control the discussion. It is a lovely-sounding idea that each neighborhood of Paris should govern itself, each like a *polis* of ancient Greece, but as the people have no experience with this kind of democracy the result is that those who shout the loudest and make the most inflammatory speeches have their way. . . . Much talk of traitors, royalists in hiding, priests and monks in disguise. A young man who works for the baker on the rue Galande made a long harangue, demanding that the king be executed immediately, without a trial, and along with him all prisoners arrested during the past week. When others objected that execution on suspicion alone would be contrary to the Rights of Man there were hoots and jeers, shouts, "We want action, not lawyers' talk!" Fortunately Hué—he can shout if not keep order—was able to announce that Danton had created a Revolutionary Tribunal to deal with all these cases. At the mention of Danton there were cheers and the subject was dropped. . . . It seems strange that a Revolutionary Tribunal should be a guarantee of *legality,* but that is where we are.

As the meeting broke up some young scoundrels in rags began to tease me about my old-fashioned clothes, saying I must be an abbé. At the present time such jests are not to be taken lightly. I steeled myself with the memory of Tourangeot the Tartar, the most foul-mouthed of the workers at Fournier's shop in Auxerre. "Kiss my ass you bastards!" I shouted, "I've worked all my life, I've endured more than you can imagine, and if you fucking buggers don't let an old worker go home in peace I'll see that your rumps swing on the Place de Grève!" The threat was out-of-date but the effect what I desired; the crowd around us cheered and the young bullies took off with their tails between their legs.

August 19: Edmond and Marion to dinner; she is getting large again. Afterwards to the Champs-Elysées with Agnès. We have made up after a tearful scene in which we recalled all the infamies of the two *Monsters,* Agnès Lebègue and Augé; then ended by consoling each other for what we have both suffered. There are rumors that the Prussian army has crossed the frontier, but if anyone in Paris is worried about the invasion he was not visible this Sunday afternoon.

The fine weather continues; there was dancing on the lawns,

lovers hid in the dells, pantomimes and puppets shows entertained the crowd. One fellow had set up an improvised stage on which a trained monkey played a thousand tricks. When the master accused the bright-eyed animal of being an aristocrat it flew at his throat with every sign of rage; when he called the monkey *"un bon patriote"* the little creature cooed and caressed his trainer. I wonder how many *"bons patriotes"* in Paris are as recently trained as that little ape who ended his performance by stealing his master's cap and passing it around for coins.

We returned through the Tuileries. Here and there men mounted on chairs in the style of the Palais-Royal three years ago, orating to little circles that form about them. Their theme: the crimes of Louis-Veto-Nero; the debaucheries of Antoinette-Austrian-Messalina, the latter described in salacious detail.

August 23: Last night, leaving the Palais-Royal at about nine-thirty, I see crowds heading toward the Carrousel. I follow and discover a fearful tableau. A *guillotine* has been erected near the grille (the instrument has been baptized with the name of the good doctor who advocated its use) ; it is larger than the one I saw in April on the Grève; torches about its base throw its shadow against the palace wall, pockmarked from the bullets of two weeks ago. Whoever decided to erect the machine in that place had a decided sense of theater and, given the hour, the torchlight, the gaily chatting spectators arriving as if in the lobby of the Opéra, it was hard not to believe that the strange towering device was not a theatrical prop, the torches footlights, and the palace where so many died two weeks ago only the painted canvas of a stage set.

Fortunately I didn't remain to witness the *performance.* Today I learn that the condemned man was a royalist conspirator, Colennot d'Angremont; he had tried to bribe the Gardes from the fashionable neighborhoods into siding with the unfortunate Swiss. In his death he managed to take the executioner with him, or rather the executioner's son, who had been deputized to officiate at that evening's proceedings. (That post is the only hereditary office remaining in France.) When Sanson *fils* picked the dead man's head out of the basket and held it up for the crowd to see, the blood on the platform was so thick that he slipped, fell to the ground, and dashed out his brains on the cobblestones. . . . The Commune has decided that henceforth executions will take place by daylight.

August 24: Supper rue de Tournon, the company much reduced. Bad news about old Cazotte; his son Scévole was killed on August 10th—he was one of the *gentlemen* who had camped in the palace to defend the king. Even worse is the news that Cazotte himself and his daughter Elizabeth have been arrested at their home in Pierry, brought to Paris and imprisoned at the Abbaye. Of course Cazotte is a rabid royalist, but what harm can that white-haired old visionary do, hiding out in his country house? If people are to be arrested for their opinions, the Bastille might just as well be rebuilt. . . . A sad evening that ended early.

The more I learn about the events of August 10th, the more sickening the story becomes. The king left the palace for the Assembly before the fighting began. Why couldn't he have given an order not to shoot, if only to save the lives of his Guards? The answer can only be that he thought they would win the battle and that he would return as master. The first shots seem to have come from the Swiss and they were murderous, hundreds of Parisians armed only with pikes cut down by rifles. That explains the fury of the populace against the defenders of the palace. But that fury led to barbarism. After the palace had been taken, scores of the Swiss guards were slaughtered trying to flee. Thirty died at the base of the statue of Louis XV in the center of the *place* of that name; others were massacred in the streets. And is there a word forceful enough to describe the actions of those noblemen who fled by the gallery of the Louvre and fired from the windows at ordinary citizens, as I saw with my own eyes?

August 25: Learning that the Commune has declared that anyone refusing guard duty in his section would be considered a "bad citizen," I decided it was the better part of valor to volunteer. I spoke to Rollin, who managed to inscribe me in his battalion. He promises to excuse me from night patrols, in deference to my gray hair. Alas! my promenades are to be replaced by drilling and patrols! For the moment my old coat will serve for a uniform. I've been issued a pike, which I find extremely heavy. It leans against the wall beside the door to our rooms; every time Agnès passes by I see her shiver, as if there were a head on its point.

August 26: The news that the fortress of Longwy has fallen to the Prussians has thrown everyone into a state of panic. What is terrible is that this fortified position, capable of withstanding a long siege, was delivered from within. Who is to be trusted? Instead of fighting the enemy, Lafayette ordered his troops to march on Paris to undo the effects of August 10th. The Assembly declared that the general was to be arrested, sent several deputies to carry out its order. Lafayette put them under guard. Then, seeing that his troops would not obey his orders, he went over to the Austrians. End of the Hero of Two Worlds and his white horse.

Paris already feels like a besieged city, the roads closed, coaches and horses requisitioned for the military, troops everywhere. . . . This morning I was on patrol, Place Maubert. I heard a market woman shout, "Do you think those old geezers and children will save us from the Prussians? Their pikes are no better than their pricks!" To be sure our patrol was hardly formidable—two lads of thirteen and four men of my age or older, none of us trained.

August 27: I went to the Tuileries to attend the ceremony for those who died on August 10th. On the Place de Grève a guillotine is being readied. I ask what is happening. Three counterfeiters are to be executed—one of them is Guillot, the bookseller! When he was arrested in July I thought his friends would save him, but it seems that they were the wrong friends. If he had managed to live a few more weeks they might be the right friends again—it is reported that those arrested since August 10th expect they will all be freed when the Prussians arrive, their places to be taken by those who sent them to jail.

I've known Guillot since '81. Certainly counterfeiting is a major crime and many men have been hanged for far less serious offenses, but the thought of the blade descending on his neck makes me shiver. He published *Les Françaises, Les Parisiennes, Les Filles du Palais-Royal* and *La Semaine Nocturne.*

Will his name on the title pages of those books now be held against me?

Longwy had fallen; the Prussians were besieging Verdun, that is to say they were hard by the village of Varennes where the king's ill-fated escape had been halted, at a distance from Paris that the slow-moving berline had covered in less than two days. Look at a map—after the hills of the Argonne there is only the open valley of the Marne, leading directly to the capital. At the same time disturbing reports arrived from the west, where fanatical priests led the peasants of the Vendée in a bloody counterrevolutionary revolt. But the army Paris feared most was in Paris itself, the thousands of royalists who wished to undo August 10th, some of them already bold enough to mass about the Temple to demonstrate their support for the king-prisoner by their cheers. The most horrible rumors circulated. At my section a man cried that the royalists were planning to have the *entire* population exterminated when the Prussians arrived—everyone will be taken to the plain of St.-Denis, forced to dig his own grave, and shot. The report was believed and there were cheers at the proposal that all royalists be guillotined immediately. The frenzied rhetoric of the press, royalist and revolutionary alike, the nightmare fantasies of Marat and his imitators, *L'Ami du Peuple* and *L'Ami du Roi,* seemed ready to be translated into fact.

The Assembly, having voted to end its existence, was weak. The Commune, its power derived from the forty-eight sections, strong but disorganized. One man stood between the two and took command—if indeed anyone was in command during these terrible days—Danton, the orator of the Cordeliers, suspect in his private life and his finances, but audacious and powerful, the Mirabeau of this second bellicose phase of the Revolution. There were two dangers—despair and anarchy. Did either prevail? History will be the judge.

On the 28th Danton, as Minister of Justice, addressed the Assembly, asked it to authorize that every house in Paris be searched for concealed arms, royalists and priests in hiding. The

Assembly voted the measure immediately; the decree was sent to the Commune. The next morning on patrol we were informed of the measure. All traffic in and out of Paris had been stopped, including that on the river; we were all prisoners, all suspect. Rollin excused me from duty in the evening, but admonished me to be sure to remain at home.

At four o'clock drummers pass through the streets, advising everyone to be indoors by six. At six the shops closed and the streets were as deserted as if the capital had been abandoned by its inhabitants. A long wait. The patrols did not begin their search until midnight. Ours arrived at one in the morning; we heard them first at Frazé's downstairs. Fifteen minutes later they knocked at my door. I knew two of the men but the search was as thorough as if I knew no one. My name, age, occupation and other details were duly noted, the same for Agnès. They went through my two rooms, then ordered me to come down with them to my shop. One of them turned out to be a printer; he had worked at the Imprimerie du Louvre many years after me; at the sight of my antiquated press and boxes of old type he marveled that I was able to print anything at all. I responded that I marveled at the same thing myself, but that I couldn't go on much longer; so much of my type is broken that I am forced to use several different fonts on the same page. They glanced at the stacked pages of *Monsieur Nicolas* and *L'Année des Dames Nationales,* fortunately not discovering the subscription list for *M. Nic.* which begins "The king, the queen, the princes, etc."—not that any of those august personages ever bothered to subscribe. A last question: have I ever published a newspaper? I was glad to be able to answer that my press was a private affair (although, alas! I am at the edge of bankruptcy by this circumstance). After that they departed.

For an hour more there were men of the patrols up and down the street, calling to each other; lights at the windows flickering on and off. When one considers that the same thing was taking place on every street in Paris one has some idea of the scale of the affair.

Needless to say there were many errors and abuses that night, given the nature of the patrols. In some sections the leaders thought they ought to arrest everyone who had signed the petition protesting the events of June 20th. The Commune declared the next day that those suspects should be released. In all there were several thousand arrests; the prisons could hardly contain them all.

On the 30th everyone exchanged stories of the night of the patrols, many of them piquant. Whatever the circumstances, the Parisian will never lose his taste for gossip—or his inventiveness. In my section, two priests in disguise were discovered hiding in a basement on the rue des Rats, across from the Ecole de Médecine. They were wearing women's clothes but were found out when a lad on the patrol, feeling frisky, tried to flirt and ran his fingers across the "girl's" cheek. The "girl" had a stubborn beard. They were taken to the Abbaye.

I wish I had been at the Palais-Royal that night. Many priests and aristocrats were discovered in the chambers of the *filles,* trying to pass themselves off as lovers, libertines or pimps.... A coach was stopped on the rue St.-Honoré. Inside, what looked like a fashionable party, coming from the theater—but all the theaters were shut that night. They were, again, priests in disguise, trying to flee. Why is it that all the tales insist on this circumstance of priests disguised as women? Perhaps it has something to do with the clerical vow of celibacy, and the ways in which it is broken....

Another instance: A pious fishwife of the Place Maubert was hiding a former canon of Notre-Dame in her basement, unbeknownst to her husband. The ecclesiastic wore women's clothes, wore them so well that the patrol was deceived and went on. They were in another apartment when the husband returned, having finished his guard duty. This man was a young gallant devoted to wine and women, and had been partaking of the former as he accomplished his rounds. Seeing a creature in his wife's clothing, he had no doubt that it was his spouse, an error facilitated by his inebriated state and the flickering candlelight. This man had a habit, which his wife indulged, of deciding to exercise his marital rights at the spur of the moment. Unbuttoning his pants, he would say to his better half, "Get down, Jacqueline, and give me something!" The canon receives the order and, very confused, tries to comply. The husband goes directly to the hub of the matter and encounters a pair of black breeches. He begins to shout for the patrol, who are in the apartment upstairs. They return. The excited spouse shouts, "Messieurs, you've given my wife a black ass!" They examine the black ass and discover its composition. The fishwife, who had been in hiding, appears. The husband, delighted to rediscover his wife, and paying no attention to the presence of the patrol, flips up Jacqueline's skirts to make sure that her bottom remains as rosy as her face. The canon of the black breeches was taken to prison.

These tales would be more amusing if one didn't know what was to follow.

Dies irarum! It finally came to pass, all the horror that had been feared, foretold, predicted, preached, signaled, shouted, whispered, warned, cried, dreamed but never quite believed since the beginning of the Revolution! Was this truly Paris, center of the universe, city of light? I had thought myself an expert on the mechanism of the human heart; I find I am only a beginner.

The MONSTERS among us, the de Sades, the Augés, are more numerous than anyone would have guessed.

But these atrocious events must be described with impartiality. The writer must remain calm even while he trembles; otherwise he will become an orator instead of an observer.

On the 31st a call went out for volunteers to dig fortifications on the heights of Montmartre.

There were rumors that the Prussians had cut off the ears of the municipal officers in the towns they had captured.

The prisons of Paris, overflowing with those arrested the night of the patrols, became temples of merrymaking, the guards so many well-paid valets and footmen for their charges. Passing by the Abbaye I saw a jailor carrying in three roast ducks on a spit, dripping fat and butter; from the high windows came the sound of cheerful singing, as if the place were a banquet hall. A patrol went by; a young *sans-culotte* shouted up at the prisoners, "Shut your fucking royalist mouths!" A voice shouted back, "When the Prussians arrive, it will be our turn!"

The next day a common thief was exposed before the Hôtel de Ville, *"au carcan,"* which is to say, attached to a stake with an iron collar about his neck. The poor man took it into his head to shout, "LONG LIVE THE KING! LONG LIVE THE PRUSSIANS! AND FUCK THE NATION!" The mob tried to tear him limb from limb on the spot but Manuel, *procureur* of the Commune, managed to have him spirited into the Hôtel de Ville, promising that a people's jury would determine his fate.

He was condemned to death, but his words were taken as confirmation of the rumors of another royalist plot. When one speaks of rumors, what matters is not their veracity or even probability but how widely they are believed. I heard this one several times. When the Prussians arrived at the gates of Paris the prisoners would overcome their guards and escape, the aristocrats taking to the streets with weapons they had concealed, joined by the common criminals of the Châtelet and Bicêtre, bought with royalist gold—also the monks and priests of the monasteries of St.-Lazare, St.-Firmin, St.-Sulpice and the Carmes, all armed to the teeth. Joined by the aristocrats in hiding elsewhere they would spread terror through the city, free the king from the Temple, then attack the fortifications from behind to let the Prussians enter. . . . Posters were stuck up about the city advising the volunteers not to leave Paris before "justice" had been done to the enemies of the people in the prisons. They were signed "Marat."

Political intrigue continued its course despite the dire state of affairs. The expiring Assembly ordered the Commune to dissolve itself, pending new elections. The Commune responded by creating a "Vigilance Committee" to take command of the city. At its head three men—Danton, Marat, Robespierre. But Robespierre disclaimed any intention of a dictatorship, saying that at this moment safety lay only in "returning power to the people." *Power to the people,* an ambiguous phrase. It could mean either waiting for the election (which it surely did not mean), calling for a state of permanent insurrection, or else encouraging the most violent agitators to act on ther own.

The morning of September 2nd the tocsin pealed, drummers passed through the streets with a proclamation of the Commune calling on all citizens to go to the Champ-de-Mars to create an army of 60,000 men for the relief of Verdun. On that day Danton spoke the words, immediately celebrated: "The tocsin that is ringing is not a signal for alarm, it is a call to attack the enemies of the Nation. To defeat them, messieurs, we need audacity, again audacity, and still more audacity!" But the people in the streets immediately concluded that Verdun had fallen, betrayed from within as had happened at Longwy. Their instinct told them the truth, although the news of the surrender of the fortress had not yet reached Paris.

After a short stroll, I returned for a frugal Sunday dinner with Agnès. At six I went out again taking the Pont-de-la-Tournelle to my isle. The noble façades facing the Seine were bathed in the soft light of a late summer afternoon. I began the tour of my fading inscriptions.

At rue le Pouletier I hear a kitchenmaid call out of her casement, "Catherine, what's going on? The mistress says we shouldn't go out."

Catherine answers, "I don't know, but monsieur has locked all the doors."

Cutting short my promenade I cross the Pont-Marie to the Port-au-Blé. At the cabaret beside the stairs couples are dancing. But a tough armed with a pike comes by and shouts, "This is the wrong day for a ball! they're playing a different tune at the prisons!" The music stopped; the dancers milled about, but no one knew any more than I.

I took the quais to the Café Manoury. I entered and saw my little Swiss Fragnières, smoking his pipe and reading a paper. I took a seat near him and didn't have to wait long to be informed.

"The *sans-culottes* are killing the prisoners," he said.

I didn't want to believe him. I ordered a coffee and tried to read. But a host of cruel images rose in my imagination, less striking, it must be said, than the truth. Fragnières somehow felt my distress. "It's only in the prisons," he said. "You're perfectly safe."

Safe or not I found I was trembling. "Would you walk me home?" I asked, "I don't feel well."

"Certainly," he answers. We pay the check, leave and cross the Pont-Neuf. All seems calm. "Let's go by the Abbaye," Fragnières suggests. I hesitate, but agree. We take the rue Dauphine, usually busy on a Sunday afternoon but today deserted. At the corner of the rue St.-André I say that I would rather go straight home, but Fragnières insists. We continue by the rue de Bussy.

At the prison door, a crowd of the curious. Fragnières insists that as a writer I must observe what is taking place. He pushes me past the thugs at the door and into the guardroom.

An impromptu court is in session. At a table, in the role of judge, Stanislas Maillard, known to everyone as the first man to enter the Bastille during the siege, one of the leaders of the march to Versailles in October '89. A tall, thin man with an unhealthy face. It was immediately apparent that what was going on had been organized by someone. The personnel of the prison had been replaced by the brigands of the *faubourgs*. Other toughs filled the room, acting as the jury. The prisoners were brought out one by one. Maillard had the prison records before him. It was the nature of the accusation alone that determined the sentence, whether it was justified or not. Many of the prisoners had been picked up by the patrols four days before on the least-founded suspicions. That made no difference to the mob.

A tall man is brought out, dignified, his hair touched with gray. He is accused of being an aristocrat. "I've done nothing wrong," he declares with great sincerity. "I've been here for three days because of a malicious accusation; there is no evidence against me."

One of the self-appointed judges remarks that the man may be innocent. But he had spoken too well for his own good. A rough voice with a Provençal accent cries, "An aristocrat! Just listen to him! To the Force! to the Force!"

"So be it!" the man responds, "I will be no less guilty for changing prisons." Poor man, he didn't know that the words,

"To the Force!" were a sentence of death. He is pushed out the door that leads to the courtyard. When he sees what is taking place he stops, tries to claw his way back into the room. A bloodied thug appears, cuts him down with a saber blow in the sight of all. The spectators cheer.

I, who have never been able to stand the sight of blood, even from a minor cut—imagine what I feel as Fragnières takes my hand, leads me to the door so that we can observe the scene outside! Speechless and terrified, about to faint, I follow. I have the absurd feeling that if I lose touch with my little Swiss I will never get out of this hellish place. He had promised to take me home.

At my first glimpse of the courtyard my legs buckle under me. There is a spongy pile of corpses, seeming to sweat blood. The killers, armed with sabers, are the sort of men who work as stevedores at the ports or meat haulers at Les Halles. Indeed they look like nothing so much as butchers, stomping about, blood all over their shabby clothes and their heavy blades. They are passing about a demijohn of wine, drinking directly from its mouth.

I would have fainted had not another condemned man been shoved past me. The butchers converged. The anguished cry of the dying man as the sabers descended restored my strength. I grabbed Fragnières by his collar and told him to get me out of there. He nodded his assent, looking white as a sheet. We pushed back through the "courtroom" and out to the street. A patrol of the Gardes was going by. They went past the prison without a glance.

Fragnières led me back to rue de la Bûcherie and up to my rooms. As soon as the door had shut I became violently ill. Despite all the tender ministrations of Agnès I was trembling and sweating for over an hour. Even after that I couldn't sleep; as soon as I closed my eyes nightmare images rose up to plague me. . . .

At two in the morning a band of killers passed under my windows. They were drunk, yelping and singing to keep up their courage. I heard shouts, "To the Bernardins! to St.-Firmin! Death to all priests!" Others cried, *"Vive la Nation!"* but one

PLATE 14: The massacres in the courtyard of the Abbaye prison, September 1792. A contemporary print from *Les Révolutions de Paris.*

among them had another motto and I wish I had seen the hideous face that screamed the ultimate blasphemy, "VIVE LA MORT!" Is that what the Revolution has come to?—"LONG LIVE DEATH!" . . .

The massacres continued for *three days*. No one admitted to being responsible for the butchery; no one took the responsibility for stopping it. Afterwards—immediately afterwards—a veil was thrown over the crime by attributing it to the "justice of the people," although it was obvious that the events were the work of relatively few men, not "the people," who took part only by their passive acquiescence. But what were "the people" to do when all the authorities did nothing to stop the killing? The Assembly assembled, the Commune communed, the patrols patrolled; the shops were open; people went about their affairs, exchanging stories about "the disasters" as if they were occurring somewhere on the other side of the world. Meanwhile the killers went where they would; the prisons and monasteries without exception were open to them; the corpses piled up in the streets and eventually were carted away.

I spent the morning of the 3rd in bed, recovering from the shock of what I had seen the night before. In the afternoon I felt well enough to try to join my patrol, but Rollin excused me saying that I didn't seem up to it. He told me that almost no one had shown up at the section meeting the night before. After all, why bother?

Since I was out I made a little tour. Passing by the Conciergerie, where they had been killing that morning, I see a bloodstained man, unshaven, rings under his eyes, buying a *crêpe* from a street vendor. His accent was that of Marseilles. As he ate the snack from his bloody hand I noticed that his wrist was swollen from overwork—killing takes its toll, even of the butchers.

Outside the Châtelet the corpses were stacked like firewood. And yet the Châtelet takes only common criminals, not political suspects. The curious come up, sniff, and perhaps spit in the gutter; delicate souls pass on the other side of the street—that is the distinction. . . .

Later I heard that at the Châtelet the underworld of Paris

mixed with the crowd that acted as jury, thieves and pickpockets loyal to their pals. When one of their buddies was brought down they all shouted that he was innocent, a fine patriot, unjustly accused, etc. But if too many of these "innocents" came in a row and the killers began to be annoyed at being idle, one or two would be sacrificed to keep the show going. Of course it was this scum that shouted the loudest when anyone they didn't know was brought out. "An aristocrat! a royalist! Kill him! Kill him!"

It was that morning the Princesse de Lamballe was murdered in the rue St.-Antoine outside the prison called La Force. She had been detained there since August 10th. The princess was known and detested for being an intimate friend of Marie-Antoinette. She had been in safety in England but had returned earlier this year to be with the queen. Was her fate merited? Perhaps, but surely not the indignities visited on her body. It is hard to believe but the fact is incontestable that after her death her body was stripped, exposed to all, her head cut off and carried at the point of one pike, her genitals carved out of her corpse and stuck at the end of another, these two obscene trophies carried first to the Palais-Royal, then to the Temple, to frighten the queen in case she should glance out the window of her prison.

The night of the 2nd a woman suffered a horrible death at the Châtelet. I do not recount the death of an innocent creature. A well-known shopkeeper at the Palais-Royal, she was a royalist, which means little, but she had been imprisoned for a hideous crime—having discovered that her lover was a member of the Gardes Nationales she had mutilated him, *à la façon d'Abélard,* leaving him half-dead and half a man. She was recognized when brought down to the guardroom, her crime made known to the butchers. Instead of finishing her off in the usual way they stripped her naked, then stuffed her private parts full of straw, the way a slaughtered sow is displayed at a country market, nailed the woman to a stake, set the straw on fire. Someone killed her by a sword thrust to her guts—an act of mercy, in the circumstances—then her breasts were lopped off and her body burnt.

The killing had become an orgy, an orgy of butchery, so it is no surprise that it should take on obscene forms. The killers were indulging their perverted tastes, taking advantage of the moment, just as the pederasts of the quai de la Vallée indulge theirs in the open air on the riverbank, taking advantage of the darkness of the night. That perversity should take such a bloodthirsty turn will not surprise anyone who has read the infamous *Justine,* where all that was suffered by Mme. de Lamballe and the shopkeeper of the Palais-Royal is prefigured in every detail. What is written and printed will *always* be translated into actions sooner or later. That is why I hold the rhetoric of Marat and the fantasies of de Sade responsible for the massacres of this hideous September, even if neither of them personally has ever harmed a fly.

I go on, through the neighborhood of St.-Antoine. Little sign that anything unusual is taking place; this is not an insurrection. At the door of the Force another pile of corpses. Here the killers are at work in the street itself; they have just gorged themselves on a man with white hair, watched by a circle of idlers. A new victim appears. He has seen the fate of his predecessor; he is still alive, he has legs that still function; he charges into the crowd of spectators. One of them, returning from his patrol and still carrying his pike, not a butcher but simply an unreflecting machine like so many men, trips up the fleeing prey. The butchers come running, grab their victim, split him in two. The man with the pike looks around stupidly and mutters, "Well, I didn't know they were going to kill him. . . ." What did he think they were going to do? He didn't think at all, like most men, most of the time.

Today I am not at all sick at the sight of this butchery, just disgusted. I find my own insensibility terrifying. The Revolution has become a school of cruelty.

The Abbaye had been pretty well emptied on the 2nd and 3rd. After I left that night things were hurried up; they killed on the sidewalk as well as in the courtyard. Marion told me that one of her friends had passed a rough few hours that evening. She is a *modiste,* her husband a draper; they share a shop on the rue St.-Victor and employ a country girl of about twenty to take care of their little boy, age six. At about five in the afternoon this nursemaid took her charge out for a stroll, not returning until well after nine. By that hour the mistress, having learned what was going on, was half-dead with worry. The child was brought home, safe and sound, if sleepy; given a hasty supper and put to bed. The mistress asks where they were all this time and the nursemaid answers, very calmly, that she was at the door of the Abbaye, watching the butchery, and had lost track of the hour. The mistress berates the girl, saying, "If you yourself weren't horrified at the crimes taking place before your eyes, at least you should have thought of the effect the sight might have on my child and the danger of being in that place at that hour!"—"Oh, madame!" the girl answered, "there was no danger. The killing was all very orderly."

To tell the truth, it was.

There was only one prison in Paris that was spared and that was the Temple. The royal family was too valuable as hostages to be sacrificed to the butchers. The Commune sent three officials to assure its defense, which was accomplished by a simple but imaginative expedient—the walls were encircled by a tricolor ribbon, like the ribbon that had served as the *barrière de faveur* at the Tuileries in July. Even the *monsters* who carried the woeful remains of the Princesse de Lamballe on their pikes respected this symbol of the Revolution. Would the same device have worked elsewhere? No one tried.

At the Palais-Royal the duc d'Orléans came out on his balcony to salute the head of the friend of his sister-in-law.

The monasteries were the site of other horrors. They had sheltered many refractory priests the night of the patrols. None escaped. A witness later told me of the death of one of these clerics. He was obstinate in seeking to remain alive in this world instead of welcoming his reward in the next. It took twenty saber blows to silence him; he died insulting his assassins with cries of, *"Canaille! Canaille! Canaille!"*

At the Abbaye, as the killing went on, they put out benches in the courtyard for spectators. Men and women were seated separately, to preserve "decency." The bloodthirst of the gladiatorial combats of ancient Rome was renewed; the audience applauded when the butchers struck a neat blow.

By the 4th the prisons of Paris were emptied. During the night a band of killers made their way to La Salpêtrière. There may have been misguided patriots among the executioners during the first two nights, but what remained now were only thugs, pimps and informers, the lowest scum of the streets, joined by a few libertines *à la Sade,* taking advantage of this moment when the foundations of society were exposed, as if by an earthquake. This unholy band makes for the prison where women of easy virtue are detained. . . .

There were other scenes during those bloody days that were more terrible, but none more obscene. It began with the massacre of the nuns charged with the care of those poor girls, starting with the Mother Superior. After that the thugs took themselves to the dormitory of the detained prostitutes. The prisoners were not of the sort who would hesitate to accord their bodies to their "liberators"; what followed is easy to imagine.

But among the weary butchers there were some with more demanding appetites. They broke into the adjoining orphanage, seeking fresh meat. In that place young girls are detained, either those abandoned by their families or those put away for some juvenile offense. Their life is as hard as it can be and the *pensionnaires* who get on best are those who are most experienced, which is to say the most vicious.

All this took place at seven in the morning. I report what I've heard since from sure informants. The thugs charged through the dormitory, choosing the prettiest girls, jumping into their beds in full sight of all the others. One cannot say that anyone was raped, because not one resisted. Among these girls are peasants from the countryside, who have been sent away because their parents have no money to provide for them. . . . A young valet from the Faubourg St.-Marcel wandered about, trying to choose a partner. He sees a huge thug trying to force a girl on her cot. She is a little slow; her assailant threatens to beat her if she does not spread her legs at once. The valet jumps on the assailant and tries to pull him off. Hot with the frenzy of desire and the strange camaraderie it inspires among men in a brothel (which the dormitory was at that moment), others of the band try to pull the young valet off. "It's my sister!" he shouts, "Am I supposed to stand by and watch her be screwed before my eyes?" They let him leave with the girl. . . . Others were less fortunate. The light was dim; there were partners who recognized each other only when the act was done. . . .

The worst was what took place in the boys' dormitory at Bicêtre. The pale, pimple-faced young orphans were attacked by a band of thugs who accused them all of being pederasts. And what if the accusation was justified? At that age the fury of generation is at its peak and all is forgivable. But most of those unfortunates were slaughtered. Among the killers there were some monstrous enough to assuage their lust on the frail bodies of their victims, either before or after the moment of death. It was not easy to snuff out those young lives. One of the thugs was heard to mutter, as he left, "I'd rather kill men, these boys are hard to finish off."

Then it was over because the prisons were empty. The sections slowly returned to life but without enthusiasm. The Commune issued a new call for men to work on the fortifications, and ordered that they be paid a salary of two francs a day. Few responded. It is true that two francs is only half the usual pay of a day laborer, but many men are out of work. Besides, only two years ago a hundred thousand Parisians worked without pay to build the amphitheater at the Champ-de-Mars. That was for a celebration; now it is a question of defense. The fact is the pay doesn't matter; no one believes that anything will stop the Prussians.

The only spot in Paris that retains any liveliness is the Palais-Royal. Vice has its own resilience, no matter what the circumstances. The day the Prussians arrive the whores will realize they have always wanted to learn German, the croupiers will find that they prefer marks to francs. There may be a few more male prostitutes, if one is to believe the stories about the army of the great Frederick. For the moment it is the speculators in *assignats* who are the darlings of the spot. The Bourse having been closed to them, they conduct their own market quite brazenly in the peristyle near the Théâtre Montansier. With each rumor of a new Prussian advance the price descends; people want gold, diamonds, paintings, furniture—anything at all that is not merely paper money.

It was from an acquaintance at the Caveau that I learned what had happened to old Cazotte. He and his daughter Elizabeth were imprisoned in the Abbaye when the massacres began; they were called from their cells on September 3rd, the second day of the butchery. Elizabeth descended first. Maillard, the terrible "judge," permitted her to walk about the guardroom while waiting for her father. Taking advantage of her reprieve, her good looks and her charm, the young girl managed to gain the sympathy of the bloodthirsty assembly that pronounced the sentence. By the time her father appeared, with his halo of white hair, no one wanted to kill him. Father and daughter were freed among shouts of "Vive la nation!" A crowd of admirers accompanied them to the house of his son Scévole, killed August 10th, *defending* the Tuileries.

This act of mercy, laudable as it was, is an indictment of the frivolity of that tribunal that sent so many innocent men and women to their death. I am sure that none of Cazotte's actions could ever have amounted to anything. He told me in January, the last time I saw him, that he was inspired by the prophecies of Nostradamus. The man was a dreamer, an *illuminé;* it is hard to imagine anyone less of a threat to the nation. Nonetheless it is true that he *was* a member of a conspiracy to undo the Revolution. I forgot to mention this peculiar aspect of those terrible days—those prisoners who were freed, for whatever reason, called forth the tears of the killers; they were treated as heroes. Does that prove that a secret grain of benevolence lies buried in the heart of even the most hardened of men?

The official Tribunal, that established by Danton in August, was not so lightly swayed. Poor old Cazotte was arrested again in the middle of September. He came to trial on the 24th and admitted to all the charges against him. His lawyer pleaded that since his white hair had moved the assassins of the Abbaye to mercy, the judges of the Nation should not be indifferent to this defense. But they were not so moved. At seven in the evening the next day the author of the *Contes Orientales* died under the blade of the guillotine at the Place du Carrousel. His last words: "I die as I have lived, faithful to God and to my king." I cherish his memory.

One of the last acts of the expiring Assembly was a law long overdue, establishing the grounds, procedure and obligations of the holy institution of DIVORCE, necessary complement to the holy institution of MARRIAGE (*v.* my *Thesmographe,* 1789). Another ordered that all works of art belonging to the royal family or found in other edifices that have become the property of the Nation (i.e., churches, monasteries, convents, châteaux) are to be transported to the Louvre, which will become a great museum.

Meanwhile the elections were finally complete. The outgoing legislature, when it met for its first session less than a year ago (is it only a year?) was composed of men for the most part unknown. The incoming Convention contains all the great and most of the lesser men of the Revolution, whatever their origin, the orators of the clubs, the journalists, the writers. Robespierre, a deputy; Danton, a deputy; Desmoulins, a deputy; Marat, a deputy; Brissot, a deputy; Condorcet, a deputy; Pétion, a deputy; Mercier, a deputy; Carra, a deputy; Clootz, a deputy; etc.—even Thomas Paine, the American pamphleteer who hardly knows a word of French but has been granted an honorary citizenship. (Among the other honorary citizens are found Washington, Jefferson, Schiller, Klopstock, Bentham.)

The Convention met on September 21st. The same day, we learned later, the Prussians were defeated at Valmy, bogged down in the mud of the Argonne, decimated by dysentery from drinking too much bad champagne wine.

The first act of the Convention was to declare the monarchy abolished, that its acts would be dated, "Year I of the French Republic."

VIVE LA REPUBLIQUE! VIVE LA REVOLUTION! VIVE LA NATION! VIVE LA FRANCE!

TO KILL A KING

OCTOBER 1792–JANUARY 1793

LETTER to Grimod de la Reynière:

Monsieur:

I received this morning, October 8th, your letter dated September 28th mailed from Marseilles. Permit me to answer in the most candid manner. You complain that I have not written for over a year. You are sure that I must have lost my "illusions" about the Revolution because of the events of August and September. I have reread your earlier letter of July 7, 1791, to recall the reason why I was incapable of a response. To tell the truth I felt there was no way to respond to all the reproaches contained in that epistle; our points of view were too far apart. Your present missive confirms me in that opinion; you do not have the understanding of the events of the past two months acquired by the most ignorant workingman of Paris along with the air he breathes.

It is astonishing that in a country where the means of communication are as highly developed as they are in France today everyone persists in regarding events in the light of the gossip of his own circle. A peasant sees only peasants in the nation, an aristocrat only aristocrats. That, I am sure, is what led to the downfall of the king: his inability to see more than the reports of courtiers bent on leading him astray, his blindness to the cataclysmic events taking place outside the windows of his palace, his persistent belief that it was a question only of making the right gestures for everything to return to the situation of 1788. It is too bad that Louis never had any "illusions" about the Revolution; they would have served him better than what he took to be the truth.

As to the events of September, I offer no excuses aside from the circumstances: France betrayed by its generals, divided by refractory priests and other aristocrats, the enemy expected at the gates of Paris within two weeks. Judging by the terms you have employed in several of your letters you would hardly have been more merciful than the butchers of the Abbaye had it been your turn to strike those whom you consider traitors.

Let me tell you my sentiments. I honor Robespierre, Danton, all those who have become distinguished by their patriotism. Oh, dear la Reynière, my friend, born to be a patriot, you who were a democrat when only a few great men could claim that name, return to our ranks! Don't you remember that the only men excluded from your dinners were the Chevaliers de St.-Louis and that you welcomed the ill-clothed son of your footman? I was a patriot in the era of Voltaire, Rousseau and Diderot, and why should I change now?

From the depths of my heart I tell you that I have been very attached to you. The first few years that we knew each other were all pleasure and enjoyment. Your luncheons and dinners remain among my fondest memories. Afterwards my attachment turned to sorrow because of your exile, caused by the spite and egotism of your parents. Today, when there is no obstacle to your return to Paris, your former friends are desolated to learn that you have recanted your philosophic attitude. And for whom? for the monks your jailors! for the family who persecuted you! M. Arthaud, M. Cubat-Dorières, M. Caron-Beaumarchais, all your old friends find your present situation and opinions inexplicable!

As for me, the lower I fall the more I am proud. I admit that I was afraid of the Bastille during the days of the tyranny that has passed; now I am afraid of nothing. The older I get the less I care about my own life. I pity you my friend; there are times when I sigh at the memory of our friendship as I make the tour of my isle. But I have no pity for the king; let kings pity one another, I have nothing in common with that race. Having become a republican I have the courage that goes with that state. I carry my pike on patrol; I mount guard when my poor health permits; I go to the meetings of my section, sit alongside the workingman in his soiled clothes. I still wear my poor old blue suit, made in 1773, patched all over, it is quite suitable for the section and the review of the Gardes! I live as you would have been delighted to live, before your stay with the monks.... May they all perish, those execrable clerics!...

In short I have not written because I thought you too far gone to receive my reply. May this letter bring you to your senses. I see few friends these days, only Mercier, and him rarely. I am seen these days, when I am seen at all, only on my isle, which is my private cemetery, conversing only with those whom I have loved and who are now gone. I wish only to spend the rest of my life remembering my old friends. They have spoiled me for new acquaintances; I will never find any to equal them.

Let me remind you that the new order of things is the wish of the Nation. Society as a whole is above all kings and all laws: SALUS POPULI SUPREMA LEX ESTO; it is up to the Nation to decide how it shall be governed. Posterity, which will have the last word, will condemn all counterrevolutionaries; in the future only those who fought for Liberty will be admired as heroes.

Adieu, my old friend! My dear Loiseau would have been for the Republic. Keep well, I hope your affairs make you prosperous! But open your eyes! The enemies of the Nation are being defeated, the Republic will triumph! There is no hope for the wandering children of France if they do not join in her cause! Open your eyes and you will find yourself in the company of all your old friends, as well as the chance for honor and glory!

(Sent November 22nd. The French armies have occupied Mainz, Frankfort, Coblentz; Belgium has been liberated!)

No variety of human experience had yet been lacking in Paris except that it become a frontier town. This has now taken place. The call to arms is beaten daily, cannon are dragged about. The garden of the Tuileries is inundated with regiments of cavalry;

tents are erected; the feet of horses dig up the walks and paths; the bark of the young trees is gnawed by the steeds' teeth. We have become used to the sound of the drum, to the sight of blue coats, the brass buttons of the uniforms of hussars and dragoons, the vision of generals going by with double epaulets and sashes, a red feather ornamenting their hats. The citizens, and myself among them, mount guard, patrol the streets, are taught military exercises by officers of the line commissioned for the purpose. In public places you see nothing but colors and standards; clerks and notaries swear and smoke as if they were in the army; and some brave men who have never been further from the Place Maubert than the Bois de Boulogne use fragments of artillery shells as their shaving mugs. Instead of playing their age-old games the children march up and down with sticks on their shoulders and grenadier caps made of bits of paper. Everyone is on patrol, the halt, the lame and the deaf. The other day a sentinel shouted "Who goes there? who goes there?" The merchant, returning home, hoarse with a bad cold, responded as well as he could, "It is I, citizen, it is I!" The other was about to fire. "Don't kill me, my friend! you are standing guard to protect me!" The sentinel approached and the merchant discovered that it is his cook, carrying, instead of his spit, a bayonet at the end of a musket.

On November 3rd I was on the quai d'Anjou returning from the eastern prow of my isle. There was a group of children playing at being soldiers. I had visited my isle so rarely during these past few years that I thought I must be forgotten or unknown. But the leader of the juvenile patrol was one of the rascals who used to insult me three years before. He raised the alarm and all at once the pack of children began to shout at me and throw stones. I ran away and escaped by the rue des Deux-Ponts. They chased after me until I reached the guardhouse at the Pont-de-la-Tournelle where I was arrested July 14, 1789. The sentinel saw me but let me pass; the children remained behind.

This shameful scene was repeated two days later. This time I heard the little ogres whisper to one another that they would get men to kill me. Again I was showered with stones and owed my escape only to my swift legs as they galloped after me. Since then I visit my dear isle only rarely and very late at night; I kiss the stones that have been traced with my *dates* and I rediscover a bit of my former happiness. But these attacks were no accident.

Two weeks later I learn that an anonymous complaint has been received by the Revolutionary Tribunal, accusing me of publishing counterrevolutionary pamphlets in secret and being part of a royalist conspiracy, unnamed, with which I communicate by signs in code inscribed on the parapets of the Ile de la Fraternité, *ci-devant* Ile St.-Louis. The accusation is by "an individual of the section de l'Hôtel de Ville," but the signature is there quite clearly in the absurdity and the lack of originality of the charges—again Augé seeking my death, unregenerate MONSTER that he is!

I run to the Hôtel de Ville and inform M. Cubières, fortunately acquainted with my family situation from our years of acquaintance *chez* Mme. de Beauharnais. I run to Fragnières, who keeps his promise to make a deposition concerning the group that tried to entice me to cross the *barrière de faveur* in July. I run to Hué, now Justice of the Peace of my section and demand that my press be inspected again, even though it had been found clean as a whistle the night of the patrols. I speak to Mme. de Beauharnais and obtain the names of the secretaries of Roland (Minister of the Interior) and Garat (Minister of Justice since October 10). I submit my copies of Augé's previous false accusations in October '89, my full clearance by the police of that epoch (although the case is delicate—the police of that epoch are now suspect). I write to Garat and Roland pleading my constant attachment to the Revolution—in short, I do all I can, and I am successful! The Tribunal dismisses the accusation as unfounded.

Fortunately for me the MONSTER waited until this date to strike—in August I would have found myself in prison during the massacres! But the situation is hardly reassuring and I am afraid to return to my isle.

One sees in this the terrible effects of the atmosphere of suspicion that reigns everywhere in Paris since August 10th. One night at the section I heard the tailor across the street denounced as "suspect" because he had made a suit for a merchant of the rue des Noyers who was since arrested for speculation in *assignats*. I tried to defend my neighbor against this slander, saying that I had known him for years and that he was a poor man who had always been a true patriot. But a young scamp shouted that Guillaume should have known his client was a traitor, since he ordered a suit with breeches. If the tailors are to serve only the *sans-culottes* they will all soon be bankrupt. I found myself treated as an aristocrat for my words, despite the absurdity of the charge. Fortunately the meeting was so hectic that it moved on to other matters and the accusation against Guillaume-Page was forgotten. The meetings continue to be dominated by a few agitators, the enemies of all decency and order, cheered on by a crowd of fools.

The year closed for me on a happier note. I was at the Café Manoury December 8th reading the papers. Suddenly Mercier arrived in the company of M. Arthaud of Lyons. Arthaud said to me, "My friend, since we last met I've had a piece of good luck; I've just inherited a pension of 80,000 livres from my uncle."

I congratulated him with all my heart, but he cut me short.

"I understand you are having trouble printing *Monsieur Nicolas*. I would like to read that work as soon as possible. Please tell me if there is anything I can do to help."

That moment was one of the loveliest of my life! Never, even at the height of my passion for Zéphire or Mme. Fournier, never did I have a sense of gratitude to surpass what I felt then.

Do not think, Reader, that it was the offer of money that created this emotion in me; by now you know me too well for that! But I was really at the end of my rope with my creaking old press and all the ancient type I had bought from M. de Beaumarchais in 1788. Somehow or other I had managed to print one more volume of *L'Année des Dames Nationales*. But since July all work on *Monsieur Nicolas* had become impossible. Without money, without assistance, without a functioning press, I felt like a cripple!

Believe me, dear Reader! I have learned to live with my

weak chest, the pains in my shoulders on damp days, my weak stomach, my hemorrhoids. That I do not speak of them does not mean that they have gone away or that the days when I am bent under the weight of my infirmities are less frequent now than before. The contrary is true. But physical suffering can be borne with stoicism by a man of a philosophic disposition. I recognize in my maladies the marks that Nature has inscribed on my body, as I have inscribed my *dates* on the parapets of my isle. Moral deprivation is another matter. I exist today, as I wrote Grimod, a survivor of my own life; I live only to tell my tale, as it should be told and as only I can tell it, which is what I have done in *The Human Heart Unveiled.* Thus the interruption of that work is the worst calamity that could happen to me, and the means to continue it, fallen from Heaven, or rather from the generosity of M. Arthaud, the greatest gift that life can bring me at the present time. This explains my tears at his munificent offer.

M. Arthaud was as good as his word. My poor old press is repaired and several cases of sharp new type occupy the corners of my shop. I have resumed work on *Monsieur Nicolas,* with the help of my frail nephew and son-in-law Edmond. He is a father again; this time a boy. The delivery was easy; Marion is happy and nursing according to the principles of Jean-Jacques. But I find that these are dark times for a young couple with a family. I wrote in 1790, "We mustn't be deceived; our Revolution will cost us ten years of wars."

To have a printing plant in Paris today is a dangerous enterprise, as is shown by Augé's *monstrous* accusation. Mine is strictly personal and nonpolitical. But that is no defense in this era of suspicion. At the end of October the Gironde tried to restrain Marat, now a deputy to the Convention, by a law that would have ordered the immediate arrest of anyone who "provoked" disobedience to the established authorities or who "conspired" to promote an insurrection against the government. A deputy of the right with a conscience cried, "I demand that this edict be submitted first to the Grand Inquisitor!" But it was Danton who buried this infamous proposal with his cry, *"LA LIBERTE DE LA PRESSE OU LA MORT!"* It is indeed a life and death matter for myself, a moral life or death, whatever the consequences, and I personally repeat the words, *"LIBERTY OF THE PRESS OR DEATH!"*

The monarchy had been abolished, the Constitution of '91 swept away along with it. In September the Prussians had been fifteen days from Paris; since then the armies of the Revolution had astonished Europe by their success. Savoy and Nice were joined to France; our troops camped on the Rhine, occupied Belgium after the Austrian defeat. The Convention, sole repository of the powers of the Nation, decided to put the king on trial.

A strange trial—the Convention was prosecutor, judge and jury. But there was no alternative; no other court remained. France was a blank slate on which a single word was chalked: *CONVENTION*. There were some who argued that for this reason the trial was impossible; they preferred a dethroned king, prisoner of the nation, rather than a martyr. Two events made the trial inevitable: the maiden speech of a young deputy, Saint-Just, and the discovery of the *armoire de fer*.

The Revolution is like the theater; it has its heroes and villians, stalwarts and ingénues, character actors and bit players; it has its recognition scenes and intermissions, choruses and discoveries, its confrontations and an occasional *deus ex machina*. With the speech of Saint-Just we knew that we had not only a new star but also a new dramatist—he made it clear that the trial of the king was an obligatory scene. Handsome and young (age twenty-five), speaking with the gravity of republican Rome, Saint-Just argued that Louis was not a citizen but an enemy, that his judgment was not a question of law but of politics, an act of war, that all pity was cowardice, in short that the Convention must show its faith in the Revolution by this irrevocable act. (Irrevocable because everyone knew that if Louis were tried he would be found guilty, condemned, and executed—never was the outcome of a trial more certain in advance.) The speech (November 13) made an enormous impression, not only at the Convention but in the press.

A week later an iron safe, filled with secret documents, was

PLATE 15: Mirabeau's skeleton emerges from the *Cabinet de Fer (Bibliothèque Nationale)*.

discovered behind a panel in one of the rooms of the Tuileries palace. It had been fabricated by the king himself with the aid of a locksmith, a poor man named Gamain, who, aside from Louis, was the only person to know of its existence. The man was no doubt a royalist, having been employed at the palace in Versailles before the Revolution, but for some months he had been wasting away. Unable to digest any food, he began to imagine that he had been poisoned so that his secret should die with him. He ran to Roland, the minister, and revealed all he knew. The safe was opened, the contents delivered to the Convention. Among the papers were the king's correspondence with Lafayette, Necker, Talleyrand, Barnave and especially Mirabeau. It was the revelations of the double-dealing of the great leader of the Estates that caught everyone's imagination. An engraving, sold in all the bookshops, showed Riquet as a skeleton emerging from the iron closet, holding a sack of gold coins. The Convention ordered the bust of Mirabeau that ornamented its chamber to be veiled; the Jacobins, less moderate, cracked the cast that overlooked their tribune. Another copy of the same unfortunate work was hung on the Place de Grève and insulted by the mob.

To tell the truth the contents of the iron safe revealed little about the conduct of the king that was not already suspected. But they proved that Louis had never been sincere in his professions of fidelity to the Constitution, that at all times he had listened to the advice of counterrevolutionary priests who wanted to turn the clock back to the palmy days of the Old Regime. On December 3rd Robespierre made a speech repeating the arguments of his young disciple, Saint-Just. On the 6th the Convention voted that Louis would be tried; on the 11th the trial began.

But if the Convention considered itself the only legal authority in France, there were many Frenchmen, and not only the peasants of the Vendée, for whom the king was still king. When the royal family was first sent to the Temple there were crowds at the portals day and night. Messages were sent into the prison by the venal hands of servants and washerwomen. Gentlemen and ladies appeared at the windows of the houses making encouraging signs to the hostages. The police ordered the windows be kept shut and Gardes patrolled the streets night and day in that neighborhood that was usually so quiet.

The night of December 10th, the eve of the trial, I went out late, wrapping my heavy coat about me, ventured a tour of my isle, the dear laboratory of my heart, hoping the cold and the fog would hide me from my enemies. And to be sure the quais were deserted. But for once the memories of the past did not seize my spirit; the affairs of the present moment seemed too pressing.

As I passed under the balcony of the *ci-devant* Hôtel Lambert, that grand mansion whose elegant *rotonde* is like a lighthouse for the boats descending the Seine, I overheard two men inside the closed doors of the *porte cochère.*

"Tomorrow he goes to the Convention to be interrogated. —Yes, but will he agree to appear?—He must or he'll be taken by force, these republicans have no respect for anything; all seems lost."

With that I decided to abandon my sentimental promenade. I crossed the Pont-Marie, then took the rue des Nonnains-d'Hyères and the rue de Jouy, rue Michel-le-Comte, rue des Vertus, etc., threading my way through the ancient district of the Marais toward the Temple where the king-prisoner-accused found himself a captive. At almost every corner I was assailed by memories, the house of Beaumarchais, author of the *Marriage of Figaro,* the house of Mlle. Victoire and my first inscriptions, windows behind which I had suffered, hoped, made love, shivered, all now dark and silent, as if the cold had drawn a funerary shroud over all my past. As I approached the royal prison I found the patrols doubled and the streets even more deserted.

Afraid of being conspicuous I did not even pause at the gate that led to the Temple, but walked on and circled back toward my own neighborhood. At the corner of the rue de la Perle and the rue du Chantier there was an old woman sitting on a stone bench; with her a tall young woman and a boy. Even in the flickering light of the streetlamp and despite the plainness of their dress there was something *distinguished* about their bearing that marked them as aristocrats. The old woman seemed to be

PLATE 16: Curious Parisians gazing at the tower of the Temple where Louis and his family are imprisoned. Contemporary print from *Les Révolutions de Paris*.

sick; she held her arms crossed over her bodice, rocked from side to side, moaning.

"Hush, Mama!" the young woman whispered as I approached, "someone is coming!"

"May I help you, ladies?" I asked, walking up to them.

"Alas, yes!" the girl responded. "My mother is not well. Could you take her arm? I'll hold her on the other side."

I helped the old woman stand up. The boy spoke to me, "Citizen, we are much obliged."

"Citizen, citizen," the old woman muttered, tottering along, "Why don't you call monsieur, monsieur?"

The daughter shot me a questioning glance to see how much I understood. "Be quiet, mother," she said in a firm but gentle voice, "that is the custom these days."

We went along slowly. As we passed the Palais-Cardinal, formerly the Hôtel Soubise, the old woman asked, like someone awakening from a dream, "Monsieur, do you think the king will agree to go to be tried tomorrow?"

"Yes, madame, I do," I answered.

"But why should he, monsieur? After all he is the king."

"I hope he will for his own good," I said.

"Then you aren't one of his enemies? Please hold me, I feel weak!"

"I his enemy?" I exclaimed, taking a firmer grip on the old woman's arm. "He has enough enemies as it is at the present moment."

The daughter glanced at me again but said only, "These are hard times; we must bear it."

"He should have cut off the heads of the Estates!" the old woman chirped. "He was too kind, trying to please everyone!"

"Quiet mother!" the daughter whispered adding, across the old woman's shoulder, "Excuse her words, citizen; her mind is wandering."

"They say my mind is wandering but it isn't!" the old woman went on. "I come every evening to pray before the prison of the anointed head of the nobility and thinking of his plight makes me sick!"

"Be calm, madame," I said. "No one has more sympathy

for human weakness than I. You are a noble and I respect your sentiments. But you must also be a Christian, since you have prayed. The Gospels teach us that it is the poor who will be blessed. Unfortunately the priests have misled the king and he will pay with his crown if not his life."

"Get thee behind me, Satan!" the old woman shouted, wrenching herself free from my grasp with a sudden burst of strength and running ahead a few steps.

"Her mind is wandering, we are desperate!" the daughter shouted, running after her mother.

I followed them for a while, to be on hand in case they were attacked. They went into a house facing the Place Royale (now Place des Fédérés) and I retraced my steps, crossing the Ile St.-Louis again as midnight sounded at the Hôtel de Ville.

Perhaps I should have been more kind to the old woman, but I truly believe that it is the ignorant, deceiving, apostate clergy that is responsible for the predicament of Louis and of the Nation. If you read the New Testament from one end to the other you will find that Christianity is the religion of gentleness, humility, fraternity, unselfishness; that in the days of the first Christians a noble convert had to abjure his rank to become the equal of all, that the Gospel is the most republican and democratic book ever written! It is the successors of Peter, the popes with their hypocritical formulas, who have turned all that inside out, so that we find ourselves where we are today. . . .

In the morning I was up at six to join my patrol. We were posted on the rue des Capucines near the entrance to the Place Vendôme; there were Gardes along the entire route between the Temple and the Convention. My only emotion was resentment at being taken from my own work in order to stand guard, but I tried to console myself with the thought that the experience would be useful in the future. I waited four hours until the king's carriage passed, my shoulders aching. By good luck I found myself placed alongside a former secretary of M. de Liancourt, the ex-Constituant. As we waited he told me that his former employer had emigrated after August 10th, which was clever of him since his brother, the duc de la Rochefoucauld, was slain at his country house in September. And yet these two brothers, of one of the most ancient and wealthy families of France, had been among the most liberal and philanthropic of the nobility before the Revolution. All that counted now was their title. When our patrols were dismissed I accompanied the secretary to the Convention, where one of his friends got us admitted to the galleries.

The chamber, as might be expected, was packed, but it was completely orderly; the president did not allow even a murmur from the benches or the public. The list of accusations was read, then Louis was brought to the bar, seated (I was told later) at the same place and in the same chair as on the day when he accepted the Constitution. He looked like a simple bourgeois, a man you might expect to encounter taking the air in the Tuileries on a Sunday afternoon accompanied by his wife and children. He answered the questions with more *sang-froid* than I would have expected; perhaps he was already resigned to his fate.

Everyone has read the questions and answers of that interrogation, which added little to what was already known. The drama was in the occasion itself, rather than any of the points discussed—a great monarch, once feared by all, his power respected abroad, now appearing as an accused criminal before the representatives of his own people. But I must admit that if others shared my astonishment, they kept it a secret. Afterwards I decided that perhaps it was I who was wrong. "He is only a man before other men," I thought, "a weak man at that, in the power of those who are strong. His presence is embarrassing and there is little doubt what they will do with him."

With this thought I will admit my head nodded and in my drowsy state I had a vision. It seemed to me that two centuries had passed. I saw the men of 1992 reading the history of our times; I tried to hear what they said and when I did the severity of their judgment terrified me. It seemed to me that there were some who reproached us for our lack of humanity while others, as extreme as anyone today, took us as a model. I saw all of Europe united under a new sort of government, but I read on the pages of history the terrible upheavals this precious continent had experienced before it found peace. I seemed to hear the conversation of those men. "How lucky we are not to have lived in times when human life counted for so little!" A philosopher answered, "We are those same men of two hundred years ago, composed of the same organic molecules. If we are in peace today it is because those molecules are tired after so many long years of war."

Is it true that if the fate of Louis the Last (as he is called in the press) were to be decided by a popular plebiscite he would be pardoned? That was the opinion of Robespierre in his address of December 3rd, rejecting an appeal to the people (proposal of the Gironde). "What other means would you propose if you wished to reestablish the monarchy?" Later, when the question was put before the Convention again, Robespierre rejected the appeal to the vote of the people saying, "Virtue has always been *in the minority* on this earth." True, no doubt, but if the virtue of the *minority* is to rule, what has become of democracy? In the end it was another statement, or rather question, of Robespierre's that summed up the case for the judgment. Addressing himself to those who said the trial was illegal, he asked, "Do you want a Revolution without a Revolution?"

On Christmas Day there was an astonishing spectacle at the church of St.-Etienne-du-Mont, scene of the meeting of my section but for this one day a church once again. The crowd of worshipers was so numerous that a thousand men and women were forced to remain outside, facing the bleak rear wall of the Panthéon, shivering in the cold. It is true that St.-Etienne has always been popular at this season; it contains the shrine of Ste. Geneviève, patron saint of Paris. One sees cripples, the blind, children devoured by smallpox, hunchbacks coming to kneel on the cold stones in the hope of a miracle. Their faith remains as ignorant, as ardent as during the Middle Ages. On this day I saw a peasant woman kneel on the church steps with a baby's coffin balanced on her head, praying for a resurrection as contrary to Christianity as it is to natural science. But the number of people present was a sign that the people felt this an extraordinary Christmas, and there was nothing to explain it but the trial of the king. It is not only the aristocrats who retain an attachment to the Old Regime and it is not only the peasants of the Vendée who are credulous. Louis had been destroyed on

August 10th. The trial now, even before its outcome, gave him substance again.

The new Commune has decreed that the Fête des Rois (Twelfth Night) is to become Fête des Sans-Culottes.

Everyone knew that the execution of the king would force England to join the Coalition and declare war on France. It became a point of honor for every member of the Convention to declare that this had no influence on its debates, that the fate of Louis would be decided without any regard for the opinions of other nations. Why? If Louis is only a man like any other, why should his life or death weigh more heavily in the balance than the life or death of the thousands of soldiers who will surely be killed if Great Britain joins the declared enemies of the Revolution? Honor, republican or otherwise, is a peculiar affair.

There were four votes that occupied the Convention for a week, January 14th to 20th. (1) Is Louis guilty? (2) Should his sentence be determined by the people? (3) The sentence. (4) Should there be a reprieve?

One would think that these sessions, many of which lasted all through the night, would have been a scene of meditation, silence, and perhaps a religious awe. Not at all. On the 17th I managed to get admitted to the galleries to observe the vote on the sentence, a vote that began at eight in the evening of the 16th and ended only the following night at the same hour.

To kill a king, even one deposed, is no trivial act. Nonetheless you would have thought you were in a theater or perhaps a carnival pageant. The front ranks of the public galleries were filled with charming ladies in ravishing negligées who ate ices, nibbled oranges, sipped liqueurs, receiving meanwhile the bows and compliments of a swarm of well-dressed young gallants. The guards in that section of the hall acted the part of ushers at the Opéra, constantly opening the doors of the side galleries to escort to their seats the mistresses of the duc d'Orléans—brother, be it remembered, of the man whose fate was in question—all of these fine ladies decked out in gay tricolored ribbons to prove, improbable as it might seem, their serious attachment to the patriotic cause. In the upper ranks, where I found a place among the ordinary people, wine and brandy were passed from hand to hand as if it were a country tavern during a spring fair. Bookmakers accepted wagers at all the neighboring cafés, and with each vote messengers scurried in and out to change the odds.

Any demonstration from the galleries was supposedly forbidden; nonetheless with each vote for death one heard loud exclamations of "Ah! ah!", especially from the ladies. Young girls in elegant robes sat with cards in their laps, keeping count of the vote by pricking marks with pins beside the names of the deputies, as if keeping score at a tennis match.

It was only the deputies who did not seem amused. I should like to believe that their gravity was the result of their full appreciation of the solemnity of their responsibility, but in some cases it was only boredom. Some had to be awakened when it was their turn to vote, and went to the tribune yawning and sniffling to cough out the words, "LA MORT!" all the while rubbing the sand from their eyes. There was one, at home sick in bed when his name was called, who arrived in his dressing gown and nightcap. The appearance of this phantom caused a good deal of merriment in the assembly.

This was the vote that tested the conscience of each deputy. (Louis had been found guilty of treason the day before. The vote was unanimous.) My dear friend Mercier committed, as he put it, "a political imprudence" by casting his ballot for life imprisonment.

Some other votes:

Robespierre: Death.
Danton: Death.
Camille Desmoulins: Death.
Marat: Death within twenty-four hours.
David (the painter): Death.
Robespierre the younger (brother of Maximilien): Death.
Philippe d'Egalité: Death.

D'Egalité was no other than our old friend the duc d'Orléans, brother of the king. Elected a deputy in September, the *ci-devant* duke requested and received permission to change his name to what had previously been a sobriquet. At the Convention, to everyone's surprise, he took his seat on the high benches to the left alongside Robespierre and Marat. Strange proximity—the wealthiest private individual in Europe, brother of the king, rubbing shoulders with the incorruptible lawyer from Arras and the penniless, ulcerated, fanatic journalist adored by the Faubourg St.-Antoine! He was nicknamed now—another paradox—"Prince Egalité"!

To the first question, "Is Louis guilty?" d'Egalité answered, "Yes." To the second, "Shall the sentence be decided by plebiscite?"—"I care only for my duty; I vote *No.*" On the third his words were, "Convinced that all those who have threatened or will threaten the sovereignty of the people merit death, I vote for death." An incredulous murmur swept through the assembly, the benches of the left as well as the right. The same murmurs were repeated on the 19th, on the question of a reprieve, when Egalité again voted *"No,"* i.e., for immediate death. Robespierre himself was heard to remark that the *ci-devant* duke was the one deputy who could have been excused if he had voted for mercy.

The final vote was completed at three in the morning on the 20th. At two in the afternoon, Garat, the Minister of Justice, carried the sentence of the Convention to the Temple, informing Louis that he was to be executed the next day.

It was a Sunday, chill and gray. I had worked in the morning but after dinner I went out to see what effect the news would have on the people. Nothing was apparent, unless the deserted look of the street could be attributed to fear, but the weather was a sufficient explanation. I took my usual route, across the Pont-Neuf where the empty pedestal that had supported the statue of Henri IV was a reminder of the fall of the Bourbons. The Protestant of Navarre had said, "Paris is worth a Mass," delivering his descendants to the disastrous influence of the Church. Now another kind of *sabbat* was about to close an epoch. I followed the rue St.-Honoré to the Palais-Egalité (its name had been changed along with that of its fratricide proprietor). By five it was completely dark. All windows were illuminated, by order of the Hôtel de Ville, a preventive measure against any disorder, but the effect was sinister, with the streets empty.

A sad, cutting wind whistled through the arcades. Even the whores had deserted their posts; I didn't see those four colossal blondes, reputed to be the indefatigible consolation of the royalists and the Gironde. This district, cradle of the Revolution, was now exclusively the sanctuary of its enemies, speculators, gamblers, libertines, all living the fevered life of those who have no future. There were many proprietors of shuttered houses of the Faubourg St.-Germain or the Chaussée d'Antin, reputed to have fled to Coblentz, who would instead be found dissipating their ancestral fortunes at the gambling tables and falling into a drugged sleep in the chill attic chambers of girls of easy virtue.

I had turned up the collar of my old coat and was about to enter the Café Corazza when I noticed an unarmed man fleeing the arcades by the passage Montpensier. Having seen so many singular events in that Babylonian garden I was not surprised at the appearance of the fugitive. My only thought was, "There goes someone in trouble."

As it happened I was feeling sympathy for a murderer! Some men in dark capes came running, searching in all directions. Would the assassin have been caught if I had told them where he had gone? Knowing nothing I remained silent. He had passed so swiftly that I couldn't have said even how he was dressed.

A crowd assembled, pouring out of the restaurants and cabarets. Mixing with the throng I learned what had happened. Other details were reported afterwards by the press.

The deputy Lepelletier de St.-Fargeau had dined at Févier's restaurant, alone. He went to the cashier to pay his check. A well-dressed young man approached him. "Are you St.-Fargeau? —Yes, monsieur, I am.—You seem an honest man; I'm sure you didn't vote for death. . . . —I did so vote, monsieur, according to the dictate of my conscience.—Then here is your reward!" With that the young fanatic pulls out a dagger, stabs Lepelletier, and flees.

Can such things really happen in France, a nation of law and reason? I still ask the question although we have learned that *anything* can happen in France.

I wandered about the Palace, visiting the Café de Foi and

the Café de Chartres. Everyone talked about the assassination; there was scarcely a mention of the king.

The murderer was one of those young royalists who have made the temple of vice their nest, a young man named Paris, formerly employed by the Comte d'Artois, now living with a girl who sells perfume in one of the boutiques of the rue St.-Honoré. It was reported that he belonged to a band that hoped to save the king by kidnaping him en route to his execution. The elaborate precautions ordered by the Convention, the streets filled with troops, thwarted all such attempts.

Sometime later I left the arcades, wandering through back streets toward the Temple. All was quiet, more quiet than usual, patrols at every corner. I passed by the gate to the royal prison but again did not dare stop for fear of being observed. Returning home I saw an old woman kneeling on the steps of Notre-Dame de Nazareth, facing toward the tower where Louis was passing his last night. A patrol with torches passed by, but paid no attention to the gray-haired penitent.

I returned to the Place Vendôme (or rather Place des Piques, as it is now called). Lepelletier had been carried into one of the houses fronting on that elegant square. A crowd was waiting for news. "I hope he lives!" a young girl said to her mother. A man in the crowd muttered, "With a wound like that he is already dead!"

A messenger arrived from the Jacobins to announce that the Mother Society had gone into an all-night session. Robespierre had asked that all patriots remain calm, pleaded that no disturbance mar the solemnity of the great event of the morrow. A short while later a physician appeared and told the crowd that Lepelletier was dead. There were shouts, "No! no! no!" One hothead shouted, "Death to the Gironde!" But the crowd dispersed peacefully.

I went home through the illuminated streets, all heavily patrolled. It was too late to think of sleeping. I had to report to my company at five in the morning—we were to join the line of troops along the king's route from the Temple to the scaffold. For this occasion the guillotine had been moved from the Place du Carrousel to the *ci-devant* Place Louis XV, now Place de la Révolution.

At five-thirty, a very cold five-thirty, I was at the Grève where the Gardes assembled. At six our captain appeared. Inspecting our ranks he noticed that I was trembling. "You look sick," he said, "go home and rest." I left the ranks, keeping my pike with me. . . . A warm drink in a tavern revived my spirits. At seven I was at the door of the Temple. The sky was still dark, the street-lamps still burning. At eight Louis appeared, but I was too far away to see or hear anything except the slow rattle of the coach as it began its long ride to the scaffold via the boulevards. All shops were closed, the roads in and out of the city guarded by troops, orders had been given to keep the lamps and houses illuminated all day. The troops along the route had received the command to shoot immediately at any window that was opened.

The carriage arrived at 10:10. At 10:22 the remorseless blade sliced down. The papers are full of anecdotes of the king's last moments. If they were all true he would have been at the scaffold twelve hours instead of twelve minutes.

I was at home when I heard the cannon announcing that the king was no more. It reminded me of the loud report of the rockets over the Place St.-Etienne in Auxerre, September 1754, celebrating the birth of the duc de Berri, future Louis XVI. I was then twenty, an apprentice, in love with Mme. Fournier, chasing after girls, with no idea that I would become a writer and certainly no suspicion that thirty-eight years later I would hear another report announce the *execution* of that babe, grown to be king of France.

Of all the Bourbons since Henri IV, this man was the most devoted to the good of France. The weakness and intrigues of Louis XIII led to the horrible civil wars of the Fronde; the vanity and bigotry of Louis XIV bled France white behind the false façade of the palace of Versailles; the indifference and sensuality of Louis XV made Paris a harem and Versailles a whorehouse while the state sank into bankruptcy and the English stole our colonies abroad. The first years of the reign of the fifth Bourbon were auspicious; his desire for reforms was real even if he was frightened by what was proposed and backed away; his worst enemies could discover no greater vice in his personal life than overindulgence in the pleasures of the table. His sins against the nation were real and he never escaped from the insidious influence of the clergy, but he died more for the misdeeds of his ancestors than his own. His most serious crime was involuntary; in the words of Camille: *"IT IS A CRIME TO BE A KING."*

By noon the shops were open, the street vendors again filled the air with their cries. On my promenade that afternoon I passed the site of the execution. A cabaret had been set up near the river, couples were dancing on the bridge. "Why not?" Messieurs the Reasoners will ask, "the man guillotined this morning was but a man, no more than millions of others." Yes, but that man had a direct relation to every last person in France, was a sort of intimate acquaintance to each, was heir to a tradition that had lasted a thousand years and that made him, as KING, the symbol of the communion of twenty-five million human beings. If a GOVERNMENT may kill a KING then anything at all is possible. Unless nothing is possible.

Saint-Just: *THE REVOLUTION* BEGINS *WITH THE DEATH OF THE TYRANT.*

The body of Louis XVI was thrown into a pauper's grave behind the Madeleine and covered with lime. The deputy Lepelletier, assassinated on the 20th, received the national funeral denied to the king. The martyred deputy had begun his career as a delegate of the Nobility at the Estates General. Oddly enough he was the only aristocrat who persisted in his refusal to join with the Third Estate, even when ordered to do so by the king. But afterwards he became a republican, sitting on the Mountain at the Convention. The ceremony had an excessive character, grandiose and horrifying. The body was exposed in Roman style at the Place Vendôme, naked, bloody, livid, and displaying to all eyes the large wound, work of the assassin. This fearful object reposed on the base that had formerly supported the statue of Louis XIV. A funeral oration was pronounced for the crowd gathered in the bitter cold. The body then was put on a sort of litter and taken to the Panthéon by the rue St.-Honoré and the rue St.-Jacques. I saw it pass at the rue

Galande. The entire Convention marched together, after them the Jacobins.

Three days later, under the pretext of looking for the assassin of Lepelletier, there was a raid on the Palais-Egalité. It was about nine in the evening. I was strolling the arcades when I saw the troops of the Gardes Nationales arrive and block all the exits. Anyone who wanted could come in, but no one was allowed to leave. Despite the announced excuse for the raid, I believe its real purpose was to surprise the habitués of the gambling tables and hidden royalists *in flagrante delicto.* Having nothing to hide I had nothing to fear.

The Gardes discovered some reputed *emigrés* at the gaming tables, risking their fortunes as well as their lives. The other capitals of Europe must be dreadfully dull, considering what men will risk to return to Paris. There were a number of amusing scenes; strange characters scurried about like insects smoked out of their nests. I saw a priest—Constitutional, of course—discovered in bed with a girl of fourteen. "Hey, Monsieur l'Abbé," a soldier on patrol shouted, "you can get married these days, you know!"—"Too many complications, my friend. Besides, I'm not used to the idea!" . . . A girl is marching chastely through the garden of the temple of Vice, watched by her parents, well-established merchants of the rue St.-Denis who are blind enough to think this a good place to take the air of an evening. Her secret lover arrives, military and dashing in his uniform (which may have been what seduced the young lady in the first place). The young man uses his authority to make a disturbance; in the confusion the girl is lost . . . and perhaps loses something also. . . .

To tell the truth I was in no hurry to go home; I knew that my papers were in order. Here a fat watchmaker is smoked out, accompanied by his little mistress; in the garden they encounter the watchmaker's wife, on the arm of a young gallant. The wife, deciding to take the offensive, begins to berate her husband.

"Who is your companion, monsieur? The girl looks like a prostitute!"

The watchmaker: "Quiet, madame, quiet! Each of us can

see whom the other is with and if we don't want a scandal we should stay calm."

The wife: "Who *I'm* with! who *I'm* with! I've asked one of our servants to escort me through this terrible place since I have to come here to look for you! Now please let go of that whore and come home with me!"

The girl: "Whore! Whore yourself, madame! What is to become of me? Your husband took me away from my dear mother, set me up with a louis a week, now twenty-five francs in *assignats.* If I went home now my father would ship me off to reform school!"

The wife: "Whore!"

The girl: "I'm no whore, I'm a *kept woman!*"

The wife answered with a slap. The girl began to shriek.

An officer approached; he may have been an acquaintance of the squabbling pair. "Shame, shame, my friends! what a scandal!"

The foursome, about to come to blows, separated.

"You, monsieur," ordered the emissary of the Republic, "Take this girl back to her room and be sure you don't leave before she is happy. Have no fear, we're not after the likes of you."

He turned to the wife. "You, madame, who I saw just a short while ago laughing so heartily at Févier's, let this young man escort you back to your table. A newly opened bottle of champagne is waiting for the two of you, if the proprietor is honest."

The foursome went their ways, to the amusement of all. Half an hour later the search was complete and I was free to leave. This rather silly raid was ordered by a new committee of the Convention, invested with enormous powers: THE COMMITTEE OF PUBLIC SAFETY. One can only hope that in the future they will initiate more serious actions than this search that yielded nothing but a few laughs.

January 29: In the *Annales,* a letter from Sanson, the executioner, solemnly denying the rumor heard everywhere that he has been selling scraps of the hair of the dead king to the curious and the devoted as if they were the relics of a martyred saint. He insists that he has always done his duty and wishes to be absolved of all suspicion of irregularity. A curious man this Sanson; he comes of a family that has performed the same function for generations; he received his present post from the man whose life he terminated a week ago; and yet for some reason his patriotism is unquestioned; he continues to perform his duties and draw his salary, having adapted perfectly to using the guillotine instead of the sword or the noose.

The guillotine has been moved back to the Place du Carrousel.

SETBACKS

FEBRUARY–AUGUST 1793

I am strolling in the district of the Palais-Egalité near the Théâtre des Variétés; I encounter a young girl with a good figure and a provocative stride. All at once I feel the tempest of desire light its fire in me, after so many weeks without a woman or the desire for one. I want to resist and don't want to resist. The girl, with all the knowledge of a true professional, has noticed my glance. Without further ado she takes hold of my hands, but when she sees my face she is taken aback. "Aha! it's you!"

I ask her who she is and how she knows me. "Later," she says, "now come up with me; I'm dying to make it with you!" Curiosity as much as anything else makes me consent.

Her room is the usual sordid den, on the *entresol* of a building filled with whores, one of those buildings where the walls sweat the grease of hasty dinners, the stairways are rancid with tired perfume and the furniture sags from too many amorous contentions—in short a site sufficient to make an anchorite out of the most determined libertine.

Another girl was stretched out on the bed as we entered, her legs bent at the knees and hanging over the side in the most inviting pose, nor did my arrival spur her to assume a more modest posture. My Circe displayed me to her companion as if I were Ulysses himself taken captive despite the plugs in his ears, holding the single candle in the room before my face and saying, "You see! he's a prize!"

The other girl nodded, pulled herself up and slouched away. I began to think that the ceremony of recognition was nothing more than a game; perhaps a code between the two poor girls, forced to share a room. Without preliminaries I found myself the object of the most direct and stimulating caresses, skillfully performed. Not a mention of money, which astonished me; usually these girls are scrupulous about establishing the price for their services before the transaction of the flesh takes place. Shall I say I was indifferent? I haven't lied before and see no reason to begin on that doubtful course. But the other doubtful course incited by the touch of the girl's hands was one that grew less hesitant and more firm the longer it continued.

"Pretty child," I said, for she was little more than that, "what do you want of me?"

I expected some gross expression but instead she put her answer innocently, although the action of her fingers at that moment was as far from innocent as possible. "I want only to make you happy! But I want that very much!"

"But why, my child?"

"My whim!" Suddenly she became a fury, although still an enticing one. "Do what I say or I'll stab myself here and now!"

I would have thought that a vain threat if she hadn't pushed me away, drawn a knife from some hiding place, and stood before me like a tragic heroine with the dagger pointed at her palpitating breast.

"Don't . . ." I muttered. But at that word she pricked her skin with the blade, not very deeply but enough to send a trickle of blood flowing down the white bulging flesh.

At the sight of her blood I concluded that the girl was crazy. But I became crazy also.

What a scene! I wouldn't have thought that I was capable of such feats at my age! It is true that the girl had the most delicious sort of *cunnis,* one that shivers at each thrust of your *mentula.* And she was delirious with a very unprofessional surrender. That confirmed me in the idea that she was mad. But it was a madness I shared.

"I'm very happy," she said afterward. "You've fucked me and I'm your niece!"

At that moment I realized who she was—the daughter of my younger sister Catherine. Her name was Suzanne; I had last seen her in 1786 at the time when Agnès had finally separated from

Augé. Agnès, when she took refuge with me, introduced me to two of her friends, the demoiselles Raguidot. The older of these caught my fancy and was not averse to my advances. One afternoon, thinking I was alone, I was enjoying the caresses of this girl. Young Suzanne wandered in and observed us; I had forgotten to lock the door. I learned later that, excited by what she had seen, the child gave her virginity to one of the stevedores of the Port-au-Blé. So I felt indirectly responsible for the state in which I rediscovered her.

Observing, no doubt, the expression of dismay on my face, Suzanne exclaims, "One word of scolding and I kill myself!" The knife was again in her hand. I was hardly in a position to scold her. I made her promise only to agree to see me again, without saying for what. She agreed at least to that. . . .

A week later we met again. To be honest, my motives were mixed. I wanted to save her from her horrible condition; at the same time, since she was already what she was, and young, and pretty, and responsive to me, I was tempted to enjoy her body one more time. I reconciled these two purposes by imagining that if I won a place in her affections I would be able to guide her to live a different life. But it didn't work out that way; I was frustrated on both counts.

As soon as I began to hint that I thought her condition unworthy and destructive, she pushed me away from her and shouted a frenzied tirade that really cannot be repeated in French: *"Me futuas; hoc solum a te peto, moeche! Lupa sum, et lupa permanere volo! . . . Incestus tantum me promovet. Ha! si me mentula patris perforatam teneret! cunnis hinniret! voluptate repercutiendo emorerer! Si cunnis hic adesset matris, illum trecenties super cubiculo vitiari cogerem!"*

Interrupting this mad flow of obscenities, I fell weeping at her feet to plead with her at least to find circumstances for her profession that were less degrading. I told her of the Leblanc sisters who have long been established at the Palais-Egalité and try to treat the girls who work for them in a decent manner. After a long discussion, during which I avoided any suggestion that she ought to live in any other way, she agreed to come with me to the place I had mentioned. It was not very far.

The younger Leblanc, an old acquaintance of mine, agreed to accept my niece as one of the houris in her third-floor paradise, and to see that she was well-treated. It was Suzanne's good looks that were the chief argument in her favor, as well as my personal assurance that she was not lacking in the skills of her craft. She moved in at once, the sisters Leblanc preferring that she leave behind her pitiable wardrobe, for fear of vermin.

Was this action of mine a good deed? Only relatively. I have long maintained that in a society such as ours the elimination of prostitution is an impossible ideal. All our present regulations serve only to aggravate the evil by making it more furtive, more criminal and less humane. This is one area in which the abuses, if anything, have grown worse since the Revolution.

In *Le Pornographe* (1769) I detailed my ideas on this subject. In that work I said that this necessary social evil should be managed by the state, both in the interest of the girls who find the oldest profession their lot in life and of the good health of their clients. The book was refused by several booksellers, rewritten, and finally approved by the censor Marchand. I printed it myself in a partnership with one Michel, who supplied the funds. Michel was one of the employees of Quillau, the printer, and a scheming chap. Originally from Germany, he had lived a while in England, where he had accumulated a small capital. He put up the money for the expenses; we agreed to share the profits. I composed the type myself with the help of an apprentice.

When the work was printed, Quillau had the nastiness to denounce it because of its subject. The censor tried to retract his approbation. Fortunately the matter came before an enlightened judge, M. de Sartine, who found it decent enough to be sold. It sold very well, probably because of the title, which I will admit was deceptive.

Haunting the bookstores in my workingman's clothes I was often in a position to overhear the comments of the customers. Some observed that I must be mad; others thought I should go to jail; some did me the honor of regarding me as a zealous propagator of libertinage. Never was a sensible project worse received; perhaps there were two or three reasonable men in

Paris who did it justice. I made very little from the sale despite the book's popularity; counterfeiting thieves made off with most of the profits. The net effect of the publication was that I acquired a reputation as a scandalous writer. Did that serve me well or ill? I leave it for the reader to decide.

This encounter was not the only one of its kind, although it was the most dramatic. At the time that I was writing *Le Pornographe,* my senses were too *accessible* for me not to have fallen a number of times to the subjects of my study. I have always been tender, even with whores. As tenderness is the cause of generation the most used-up and worn-out became fertile. The result of this is that over the years I made mothers of sixty or so of these unfortunate creatures, thus removing them, by my love and the effects of nature, from a life of degrading debauchery. If all men resembled me prostitutes would not be lost women, nor would they be considered vile, since they would never be asked to sin against Nature; even their miserable state would have its decency.

So it is not remorse I am expressing but only regrets as to the fate of these natural children. Some of their mothers had a soul and warm feelings that dictated true maternal care. There was little Duplessis, who nursed her child because she saw her own portrait in its tiny face. This girl, who was a ravishing blonde whom I encountered in 1772 at the Nouvelle-Halle, later had an attack of smallpox, which left her ugly. After that she was an even better mother, becoming a scrubwoman and bringing up her daughter by hard work. The girl today is one of the leading actresses of a theater . . . that is well known. But others turned their infants over to foundling homes and some, worse yet, raised them only as a source of income, profiting from the earnings of the first stages of a life of prostitution, often commenced before puberty, then letting them go when they were too old to be controlled. These I regret bitterly, but there was nothing I could do to prevent it, having no money and usually not even knowing who these children were!

My conscience, however, was never at ease on this score, and that is one of the reasons for my frequent visits to the Palais-Royal, now Palais-Egalité. In the arcades, the garden, the surrounding streets, I look for my lost children by following the thermometer of my heart; that is the only means I have of recognizing them. By this I mean an innate instinct whose workings appear magical, but which has never failed.

When, therefore, a young beauty does not arouse my disgust by her flat-heeled shoes, when in fact I find her childishly agreeable, I examine her features with care and am not long in discovering the trait that serves as a talisman. It is usually the eyes, the brows, the aquiline form of the nose, or some other detail. Aside from the abominable flat-heeled shoes, the style of the past few years has been delicious, especially when worn by adolescents. A fur stole curling about a finely shaped wasp waist, a long skirt that hides the misfortune of flat slippers or else reveals only the agreeable tip, a "capricious" coiffure, which is to say free-flowing and uncontrolled—this is what I have always desired in women and what enchanted me twenty years ago in the few young beauties who had the genius to rebel against the stiff modes of that epoch. I cannot desecribe how much, because of this costume, some of these young beauties have touched my heart. I examine every detail of their persons; I compare impressions; I reflect. And often those whom I decide to approach, if I manage to talk to them, turn out to be my daughters!

The story of these encounters is to be found in *Monsieur Nicolas,* notably in the section, *"Mon Calendrier."*

If I were a man of fortune I should have rescued them all from their condition, but this was beyond my means. There were some I was able to persuade to lead a different life. But others were convinced that they had no possible alternative to their despised profession. Instead of castigating them for this choice I gave them some guidelines for their conduct, based upon my thirty years of experience with women who follow that *métier.* But first of all, Reader, a question. Do you believe that all women who sell their bodies are vicious? Yes, you believe it, I can see that; while writing this I can look into your soul and see that you hold that opinion, which was mine also before I knew better. Well then, you are making a mistake; both of us have made the same error. There are prostitutes whom I find honorable; what I honor is the virtue they have preserved in a vicious condition imposed by society. Men are not made for monogamy and many women are unable to satisfy their husbands or their lovers. Nature abhors a vacuum; this need will be fulfilled, either by libertinage or by prostitution. As long as we live in an imperfect society, the condemnation of all the poor creatures who exercise one of its necessary functions is sheer hypocrisy.

What I said was this: "My dear child, if your actions were absolutely to be condemned, like those of the thief or murderer, or absolutely useless, like that of monks and nuns, I would say to you: Your life is a mistake; it would be better that you die than continue to live as you do. But that is not the case. You are not depraved so long as you don't agree to masturbation, to anusation, to oralization, to mamillation." (I know very well that these words do not exist in French, but I take them from Latin: *masturbari, paedicare, fellare, mamillare.*) "Remember that you owe a debt to Nature and, without destroying your health, be guided by the honor of your sex. Learn to get men attached to you and, far from avoiding pregnancy, use it to tie men to you, like the courtesans of ancient Greece. If a man falls for you, stick to him; permit him every error. But if this doesn't work, don't despair. By the pleasure that you give, by the arts you have acquired in your profession, you keep your clients from becoming depraved with others less moral than yourself, or you keep them from destroying their health with others who are not so careful. Don't be too demanding; remember that women like you are the means by which a good man can rediscover his true self. So long as you remain healthy, sweet, charming and attractive you will be accomplishing a necessary function. So long as you have agreed neither to masturbation, to anusation, to oralization, nor to mammification you will not be degraded. You will always have the possibility of finding a man who will lead you back to the paths of honor and honesty, my daughter!"

Those who had a soul—and I believe that all my daughters have a soul—took advantage of my lessons. Thus my advice led them gently to the paths of Nature and eventually to marriage. I hold the world, such as it is, responsible for their misfortunes.

The king had been executed in a city that was absolutely calm. That same afternoon children played peacefully on the public squares. An uninformed visitor arriving at the capital the next day would have had no inkling that anything unusual had taken place. But a month later there were assemblies, riots, looting; a glimpse into the abyss of anarchy. The cause: the high price of soap. Sober lesson for the legislator and the philosopher, his head too often in the clouds.

On Sunday, February 23, two deputations of laundresses went to the Convention to complain that they could no longer make ends meet. But the Convention was too occupied with reports of the war to pay more than ritual attention. Monday was quiet, perhaps because the grocers were closed as usual on that day. The trouble began Tuesday morning, apparently in the Gravillers section, home of the "red priest" Jacques Roux, later blamed for having instigated the trouble—although Marat, outrageous as usual, had called on the people to hang the grocers on their own doorsteps.

As usual I was at home working all morning and knew nothing of what was going on, but when I went out in the afternoon I found an angry crowd at the door of the grocery in the rue des Grands-Degrés, for the most part women, shouting angrily that the price of sugar, soap, coffee, candles, etc., were all too high and that they refused to be robbed any longer. The grocer and his assistant, both familiar to me from the meetings of the section, tried to argue with them, but the door was forced. To my surprise the shop was not simply looted; the women all stopped at the cashier to pay for what they grabbed from the shelves, but they paid only half the posted price. (This forced bargain was later called *"taxation populaire"*—a phrase that means the opposite of what it says.)

I went on and found the grocery facing the Pont-de-la-Tournelle completely devastated, the windows smashed, the shelves empty. "And where?" I wondered, "will those women go for their supplies tomorrow?" As yet I did not know the same thing was taking place all over Paris; I thought it must be only a neighborhood disturbance, especially as the Gardes had not been called out.

I crossed to my isle, now renamed Ile de la Fraternité but for me forever *Ile des Souvenirs.* As yet all was quiet there, but behind the Port-au-Blé, in the rue de la Mortellerie, a shop was pillaged. The same thing again at the corner of the rue des Barres. On that day women proved the stronger sex. A strapping mason, covered with stone dust, was carrying off six sacks of sugar. A band of harpies surrounded him, shouting that they had to feed their children, and left him empty-handed.

I returned to my own neighborhood. A shop on the rue de la Huchette was being looted. A passerby asked what was going on. "The Nation is taking its coffee," answered a wit. "I see," remarked another. "I notice that it takes it with sugar."

The patrols were few and did little to stop the thefts. Was this by order from the Hôtel de Ville or merely the Gardes' sympathy with the people? Some of the Gardes were observed joining in the pillage. Also some respectable bourgeois when they noticed that no one was being arrested. I heard of one housewife on the rue St.-Jacques, too fastidious to join the looting herself, who sent her cook and scullery maid to stock up her larder.

Afterwards the disturbances were blamed on the agents of Pitt—we had been at war with England since February first. I find it hard to imagine the financiers of the City of London plotting against the grocers of Paris. But those same financiers have flooded France with counterfeit *assignats,* printed in England, so perhaps anything is possible.

Our armies were successful until the end of February, Belgium and the Rhineland joined to France, the invasion of Holland well under way. Our setbacks began in March, and the reverses were so rapid that they terrified everyone. But be consoled, O France! Your misfortunes are due neither to weakness nor a lack of courage. They are the work of traitors, who will pay with their heads!

The Austrians began their offensive March 1st. Aix-la-Chapelle fell at once, then Liège. Danton arrived from Belgium on the 8th, announced the news to Paris and the Convention, called for volunteers, thirty thousand men to be rushed to the front at once. The Commune met, alerted the sections; the black flag of THE NATION IN PERIL flew from the towers of Notre-Dame.

That same flag, in July, had united the nation, united the parties. Now it divided them. Why? There was no longer a king to be united *against*.

There were no longer any royalists. But many who had been royalists, secret or avowed, now joined the Gironde. For example, the municipality of Lyons, where the clubs were suppressed and the envoys of the Convention insulted. The Gironde seemed to fear Paris more than the Austrians, keeping a troop of *fédérés* camped outside the barriers to protect its deputies against an insurrection, rather than sending them to the front. The Gironde had started the war, just a year ago, overriding the objections of Robespierre and the Jacobins, objections that had proved all too justified since. Now they and their generals conducted it badly, hesitantly, while the Mountain, which is to say Robespierre and the Jacobins, called for radical measures to meet the situation.

Les Révolutions de Paris published two letters from officers with the army in Belgium accusing Dumouriez and other generals of treason. No one wanted to believe it then.

On Saturday March 9, ascending the rue de la Harpe, I find the rue Serpente closed off by twenty men in uniform. No one will say what is going on. I circle about, descend rue Hautefeuille, find a similar guard at the other end of the street. Then suddenly they disperse. I inquire and learn that forty men have invaded the printing plant of the journal *La Chronique,* put the presses out of commission, broken the cases, torn up all sheets that were printed (including works that had nothing to do with the newspaper) then rushed away. At the same time, the same scene was repeated at rue Tiquetonne, at the press of Gorsas, who was there at the time. A pistol in each hand, the journalist managed to escape the fury of the mob, jumping over garden walls. There were other devastations that same day, all at journals supporting the Gironde.

In October Danton had cried, "LIBERTY OF THE PRESS OR DEATH!" What now? The case of Gorsas was particularly grave; he was a deputy as well as a publisher.

At the Café Manoury my little Swiss, Fragnières, tells me that he had heard rumors of these events the day before from an individual in his section, rue des Mathurins. The plan, therefore, was not a secret, but again the Gardes were not called out (as with the looting of the grocers).

The Convention, informed of these events, reacted strangely. It decreed that the same man could not be both a journalist and a deputy. A back-handed slap at Marat (who of course was both), but hardly a response to these attacks on the press.

In October the Convention had seemed the embodiment of the Revolution. In December it had assumed the dignity of a High Court, for the trial of the king. Now, torn by party strife, unable to act except when forced by events, its prestige had evaporated. The Commune and the Jacobins were more decisive. Perhaps that was inevitable. This body of seven hundred men was asked to govern an immense nation at war with all of Europe —England, Austria, Prussia, Spain—while *at the same time* continuing the Revolution, writing a new Constitution.

Would March be a second September, the enemy at the gates and Paris torn by anarchy? It seemed possible. The Convention created a stronger Revolutionary Tribunal to deal with traitors and delegated enormous power to the Committee of Public Safety.

Our setbacks did not stop with Liège. Louvain, Malines, Brussels, Bruges, even Antwerp and Ostend fell to the enemy. The Vendée was in flames, and Brittany. There were reports of fanatic peasants, led by priests and noblemen, slaughtering hundreds of patriots in the cities they had seized.

On April 2nd we learned of the treason of Dumouriez.

Who was he?—a general of the Old Régime, Foreign Minister in '92, commander in chief of our armies in the north. He had convinced everyone of his patriotism and probity, including Danton and Robespierre, both of whom defended him before the Convention—everyone but Marat, who was always suspicious of everyone. It was Dumouriez who demanded the invasion of Holland, an invasion that led to the disastrous defeat at Neerwinden, March 18th. Danton had gone to Belgium again and returned to declare his confidence in the general. Then a letter from the commander arrived, asking that the "anarchy" in Paris cease if he were to continue to serve the Republic. What anarchy? A few shops looted. The Convention chose three deputies to treat with its general. They were arrested. Dumouriez tried to convince his armies that they should march on Paris. The armies, even in defeat, preferred to fight the Austrians. Dumouriez deserted to the enemy camp.

It was the story of Lafayette all over again, but much worse the second time.

As soon as the news reached the capital, all Paris was in the streets. I saw one group debating at the Pont-St.-Michel. Another at the Pont-Neuf. Every open space in the city became a furious debating society, like those at the Palais-Royal in '89. Given the circumstances the phenomenon should not be surprising. Had anything like it ever been seen before? The Palais-Egalité was packed with agitators, also the Tuileries.

These assemblies frightened me, but at the same time a slow and deep change of my sentiments was taking place, which must have been true of many more volatile than I. To be sure, I heard men shouting all kinds of stupidities, and bringing up issues that had nothing to do with the treason of the general. Workers shouted that wages must be raised; women decried the prices they had to pay for the necessities of life. It is an old story; as soon as the foundations of society begin to shake, a crowd of the ignorant and discontented rush into the breach with their revindications. But on this occasion, I will admit, I was more confused than ever before.

The reader knows what I had thought of Marat when I first met him, when he first appeared at my shop in the summer of '89 saying he wished to start a newspaper, how I have always had faith in the men of reason, the men of moderation, those who took the middle of the road. But now I recognize that it is the men of reason who have been proved again and again to be wrong; it is the fanatics, the radicals, the maniacs, who are justified by the events. It may send me to the guillotine, but I will admit that I had faith in Lafayette, in Bailly; I thought Mirabeau a great man; I trusted Roland and all the ministers of last year. I had faith even in the king. But Lafayette deserted to the Prussians, Dumouriez deserted to the Austrians, Barnave was in the pay of the queen, Mirabeau was in the pay of the queen, Louis was a dissembling hypocrite and if we say he was guided by the priests it is a merciful judgment since it puts the blame on someone else. The men of good sense and moderation whom I trusted because they were men of good sense and moderation have been proved wrong again and again.

But who has been proved right? Marat! Marat the madman, Marat the bloodthirsty, Marat the maniac, Marat the eternally suspicious! And now, because for so long the people of France have put their faith in men of good sense and moderation, we find ourselves betrayed within and without, the armies of the Coalition again camped on our frontiers, whole *départements* overrun by bands of fanatic peasants, the Church calling for a Holy War against the Revolution, and the commander in chief of our armies going over to the foe!

Dumouriez had hinted that he wished to restore the monarchy with d'Orléans as king. On April 1st the Convention had abolished the inviolability of its members. On April 3rd Philippe Egalité was sent to prison as an accomplice of Dumouriez. He was the first deputy ever arrested. The second followed nine days later; it was . . . Marat. . . .

Robespierre accused the Girondins of being responsible for the treason of Dumouriez. A petition from the Commune demanded the expulsion of twenty-two leading delegates of the Gironde. The arrest of Marat was the counteroffensive of the right against the Mountain, but its form seemed strange. The "Friend of the People," who had written so many outrageous articles, was indicted for a document that he had signed as presiding officer at the Jacobins, a petition asking the recall of all deputies who hadn't voted for the death of the king. Marat, always impudent, ducked out the back door when he was arrested and went into hiding, pretending that this was a generous act—he wanted to prevent his enemies from committing a crime!

The Revolutionary Tribunal began its operations. In April nine persons were guillotined for political crimes, eight acquitted. The number was not great, but the trivial nature of some of the accusations was frightening. For example, the story of Catherine Cler, as reported to me by a printer of the Observatoire section, who was close to the case:

One night in March a Citizen Bugneau, architect and member of the Conseil Général de la Commune, is returning home at about eleven by the rue Mouffetard, that long narrow street of markets that begins behind the Panthéon and descends to the open countryside beyond the Faubourg St.-Marcel. Before reaching his house, Citizen Bugneau encounters a woman of a "certain age," alone, stumbling and drunk, very drunk, so drunk that she bumps into him and then falls into the gutter, mumbling to herself. The good citizen bends over and is surprised to hear the words, "I won't let them cut the boy's head like the father's!"

"Whose head?" he asks.

"I'm talking of the little boy prisoner at the Temple. . . ."

Bugneau decides that this is no ordinary tippling woman. But he goes slowly, interrogates her, learns she is a cook employed by François de W______, a man of letters, living in the rue des Poules not far away. Our citizen, a true democrat, paying no attention to the difference in their ranks, offers to accompany the servant home. They arrive, knock on the door; no one answers. Bugneau then offers his personal hospitality, but leads her instead to the guardroom at St.-Firmin, in the section des-Sans-Culottes (formerly Jardin des Plantes). There he puts her in custody of the officer of the post, who turns out, as is appropriate for the Jardin des Plantes, to be a naturalist, Jean-Baptiste Lamarck, known for his strange theories of the evolution of animals and plants.

Having recovered her spirits, our Catherine marches in happily, singing bits of songs and shouting, *"Vive le roi!"* The sight of the pikes and rifles of the Gardes only revives her still more.

"I'm not afraid of weapons, my boys!" she shouts, "My father was a soldier of the king for thirty-seven years and would be a soldier of the Nation if he was alive today! And I'll sing you some soldiers' songs!"

Which she did, not omitting the unexpurgated verses.

Then she began to talk about politics, saying that the army wasn't what it had been in her father's day, "that all the scum who fill the ranks these days could be sent flying by thirty thousand real troops," adding that, "the only good thing is that Paris is being purged of all that garbage!"

Some of the men tried to make her be quiet, but a baker named Garnier intervened, and said the woman should say whatever she had to say.

She went on, "As for the Convention, since they say they are the leaders of France they ought to march in front of the troops and be the first ones to meet the enemy!"

She added, in a whisper, "All the deputies and all the Jacobins are going to be assassinated on March 25th."

She concluded, proudly, that she was married to the driver of the coach to Lyons and had two sons, both in the army.

After two hours of this ranting she falls asleep. In the morning she is surprised to find herself surrounded by soldiers. They remind her of what she has said; she denies it. She is sent to prison.

The preliminary interrogation is conducted by a judge Dufriche. Bugneau, whose zeal had ferreted out this enemy of the Republic, tells the judge that "he'd learned that she had been drinking in a café on the rue de la Contrescarpe earlier in the evening and that the barman had to kick her out because of her aristocratic remarks."

The barman was called, a dark-jowled tough named Trouard. He testified that he had kicked the accused out of his café because she was drunk, adding that it was no surprise, she was often drunk. He admitted that her "unpatriotic remarks" had shocked one of his customers who had gone so far as to say that, "If she wasn't a woman and dead drunk on top of it, I'd give her a kick in the ass!"

Simart, another barman in the neighborhood, testified that he had often seen the accused and that she was always tipsy, "making a lot of noise and singing soldiers' songs." He added that she made her unpatriotic remarks only under the influence of alcohol.

The naturalist Lamarck repeated what had taken place at the guardhouse.

Citizen W______ was summoned to the bar. He testified that he had hired the woman on the recommendation of some neighbors when his wife died five months before, that he knew she was often drunk, that he had scolded her for that failing and threatened to fire her but that his daughter had asked him to be kind. Also that when she was drunk she said all sorts of things, but that he had never heard her mention politics.

Catherine herself denied the remarks attributed to her, explaining humbly that she was "only a poor servant who knows nothing about such subjects" and had never heard them discussed in the houses where she was employed.

The judge decided that she must be kept in jail. A second interrogation repeated all the same facts, but revealed that she was fifty-six. Should her age have been considered a mitigating circumstance?

The case was heard again by the new Revolutionary Tribunal on April 18th. The Tribunal sentenced her to be guillotined the next day on the Place de la Réunion (formerly Place du Carrousel). The news spread about Paris that a servant was about to be executed for words spoken while she was drunk and there were many who grumbled. The Convention itself was notified and certain deputies became alarmed. But I quote *Les Révolutions de Paris,* the source of my information:

"The people of Paris were not at all happy with the condemnation of an unfortunate cook, convicted of unpatriotic remarks, a sentence carried out Friday, April 19th, at noon. The citizen who employed her had no complaints about her fidelity to her work. No doubt her head was turned by wine and we believe that her persistence in royalist remarks should have been attributed to that circumstance. . . . Who will not tremble at the following tale? At the moment when that unfortunate woman was on the way to the guillotine, Mazuyer (deputy of Saône-et-Loire) was at the podium of the Convention, asking for a reprieve of twenty-four hours to reexamine the case. Isnard (a deputy of the Gironde) vehemently supported this proposition and that was the downfall of the poor woman. What happened was that the time the Convention lost listening to the prolix oratory of her defender settled her fate. The Convention was about to vote for the reprieve when a messenger arrived with the news that the sentence of the Revolutionary Tribunal had been carried out. The representatives of the people returned to their agenda! ! ! !"

On the subject of the guillotine the same journal had this to say: "The new instrument has been perfected; it would be hard to imagine a means of execution that better reconciles the demands of humanity and that of the law, at least until capital punishment is abolished. But the ceremony of the execution should also be brought up to date and all the vestiges of the customs of the Old Regime eliminated. That *charette* that brings the convict, and which Capet himself was spared; the hands tied behind the back which oblige the patient to assume a graceless and servile posture; the black robe that the confessor still wears despite the decree forbidding ecclesiastical costumes—all this is unworthy of a nation that is enlightened, humane and free.

"Another drawback to this procedure: if it spares the condemned all physical pain, it hardly spares the spectators the sight of blood that is seen pouring out when the blade falls, soaking the planks and the pavement under the scaffold. This revolting spectacle could be shielded from the eyes of the public without great difficulty; a measure that is more important than it might appear since a familiarity with the idea of murder, even that committed in the name of the law, can lead to a *sang-froid* about death and a reflex ferocity.

"Haven't we already heard people complain that this punishment is too kind for the scoundrels being executed, many of whom, to tell the truth, seemed indifferent to their death? The people are becoming degraded by this demand for vengeance instead of being satisfied with the simple administration of justice."

Marat came out of hiding and was tried after spending one night in prison. That morning, April 24th, I saw the streets full of toughs of the *faubourgs* and market women trooping to the Palais de Justice to be sure that no harm would befall the "Friend of the People." But it was not a trial; it was a triumph. The accused arrived, surrounded by guards; he was immediately covered with flowers. The market women led him into the courtroom. He came and went as he wished, sat down where he wished, interrogated the judges instead of they him. The evidence consisted of a recitation by the accused of his life since the start of the Revolution. Everything he did was done well; everything he said was well said; all his writings exhaled a profound wisdom and if, perhaps, he had sometimes exaggerated, the course of events had justified even his exaggerations. The jury retired for an instant, returned with the surprising news that the accused was innocent. At that moment his guards served only to prevent his being crushed by his own followers. His head was covered with laurels. Someone brought an armchair, seated the skeleton in it; four strong men carried this strange object down the grand staircase. The crowd carried him across the Pont-Neuf, down the rue St.-Honoré to the Assembly. The progression moved slowly because the crush of admirers was so great; the girls of the Halles deserted their work, all traffic in the center of Paris was at a standstill. The legislators continued their debates while awaiting the inevitable interruption. Mercier told me that Robespierre looked particularly green that morning, no doubt with envy. Finally the mob appears. A strong man, who resembled one of the butchers of September, asks if the people shall be permitted entrance to the hall. The deputies quickly agree; the chamber is invaded by the mob; Marat carried to the Tribune. Danton remarks that "It is a fine thing to see that the people of Paris have such respect for the Convention that they make a holiday when one of its deputies returns to its bosom!"

Marat turned on his accusers, the deputies of the Gironde. "The people will cheer you also," he said, "but at the guillotine!"

The Austrians advance in the north; the Prussians are at

Citoyens
La Patrie
est en
Danger

PLATE 17: The execution of nine *émigrés* on the Place de Grève. From *Les Révolutions de Paris.*

Mainz; the English besieging Dunkirque, Valenciennes and Toulon; the rebels in the Vendée take town after town and slaughter the patriots with all the barbarism of which fanaticism is capable.

Mme. de Beauharnais is in Lyons. Marion is pregnant again. Her sons will be soldiers.

May 8th, on patrol with my pike, Place Maubert, we see a knot of people near the rue St.-Victor. An old workingman in shabby clothes, a bottle in his hand, drunk or foolish or both, is leaning against a wall and shouting:

—VIVE LA REPUBLIQUE and meat at twenty sols!

—VIVE LA REPUBLIQUE and candles at thirty sols!

—VIVE LA REPUBLIQUE and shoes for fifteen livres!

Our captain orders the crowd to disperse. We take the man to the guardhouse where an officer of the section interrogates him. Asked his profession, the man answers, "Worker." Asked why he is shouting in a public place he answers, "Liberty!"

Everyone is embarrassed. No one wants to send this man to the Tribunal. The captain asks why he was shouting *"Vive la République!"* while adding facts that could only make it hated. The man winks, grins, and responds that he had said only what everyone knew already.

One of the youngsters on our patrol spoke up, asked the man why he was making a disturbance. The answer, "You can put me in prison; all the same what I said is true!"

The officer observed that there might be people who had other things in mind. The man nodded but maintained that nothing should be hidden from the people.

The captain asked his motives. The man was confused by the question. When it was rephrased he responded that he saw no harm in his remarks and that whatever the law permitted was not forbidden.

The officer asked if he would do the same thing again.

"Not if I'm told not to."

To everyone's relief the man was dismissed with the advice that he be more circumspect in the future.

The Convention has voted a *maximum* on the price of grain. But what of the price of everything else?

The Convention moved from the Manège where successive Assemblies had sat since October '89. A new chamber was constructed in the Tuileries, palace of so many sad memories. Many members complained that the room was too small, overcrowded, badly lit. The public was unhappy also; it had only two small balconies at either end of the long, rectangular room. This may have been by design; many delegates had complained that the reactions of the galleries had an undue influence on the debates of the Assembly. To be sure the Manège had been only an expedient from the first, a former riding school in a block of undistinguished buildings difficult to protect. But was it wise to move into the palace of the Bourbons, where so many had perished on August 10th?

The delegates found it unseemly that they should see the guillotine from the windows of the chamber where they deliberated. The scaffold was transported from the Carrousel to the Place de la Révolution, *ci-devant* Place Louis XV. It stands midway between the gates of the Tuileries gardens and the pedestal of the statue of the old king, now surmounted by a statue of Liberty, that is to say, at the same place where the blade met the neck of the descendant of Henri IV.

A clever man has obtained permission to open a refreshment stand alongside the guardhouse near the new bridge, formerly Pont-Louis XVI. He does a good business on days when there is an execution. The people refer to this establishment as the *"cabaret de la guillotine."*

What can I add to all that has been written about May 31st, June 1st, 2nd, 3rd, 4th, 5th? To tell the truth I remain confused myself, despite having read all the papers available at the Café Manoury (their number has diminished of late). No doubt the historians of 1993 will all agree on the meaning of this moment in our Revolution. But perhaps they also will be mistaken.

Let others write of the intrigues and maneuvers on the floor of the Convention and in the corridors. I report only what I heard at the Place Maubert, the Palais-Egalité, in all the streets that formed the usual route of my daily promenades, at the meetings of my section, the remarks exchanged while I was on patrol.

The Gironde had become what the king was a year ago; the cause of all setbacks, the origin of all treason, the creator of scarcity, the party of speculation, the agents of Pitt and Coburg, the scapegoat for high prices, low wages, unemployment and bad weather. In addition, by the end of May, it had become the party of the *départements* against Paris.

Since October 1789 Paris had been the cockpit of the Revolution. Not only was it the scene of the great events, it made them. Nowhere else was there a comparable mass of people so well informed, so alert, so attuned to the moment. Avignon, Lyons, Nantes, Nancy had lived days that had altered the course of events, but none so important as the insurrection of August 10th or the massacres of September. The rest of France had followed the direction set by the capital but not without a certain resentment. Now that resentment became a conflict of two institutions.

The Commune, dominated by the Mountain (the new name for the far left), had become the enemy of the Convention. Its leaders seemed obsessed by the idea that it was time for another insurrection, like that of August 10th, with the Gironde suffering the same fate as the former royal occupants of the Tuileries Palace. In the Convention the Gironde could usually command a majority. They did all they could to limit the powers of the Hôtel de Ville (the Commune). But because they were physically stuck in Paris they feared for their lives.

Was there really such a great difference between the spirit of the people of Paris and that of the rest of France? I doubt it. But the leaders of the Gironde thought their lives were in danger. On May 25th one of their spokesmen, Isnard, then President of the Convention, warned that if any harm were done to the delegates, Paris would be destroyed. "Men will journey to the banks of the Seine and search for the spot where Paris once stood."

That was one of those thoughts that should never be spoken aloud. The word spread through the streets that "The Convention has called for the destruction of Paris!" The people needed nothing more to imagine armies of *fédérés* advancing on the capital like the armies of the king in July '89.

Nonetheless Paris remained calm. The theaters were full, the streets busy. The storm, when it did break, was the work of relatively few men.

On the evening of the 30th I noticed doubled patrols in the streets as I returned from the Café Manoury, but no signs of agitation. At three in the morning of the 31st the tocsin pealed as it had on August 10th a year before. I had no idea what it meant. At four someone knocked on my door. I heard a voice shout, "Don't disturb people at this hour!" I got dressed and went out to join my patrol. No one knew what was going on. As for myself I guessed that it must relate to the quarrel of the Convention and the Commune, but I was far from divining what was going to happen.

We remained under orders all day, without news. The next morning, June 1st, we were called again and forced to remain at ready all morning. The men complained and wondered about the reason for this unusual activity (which was, in our case, forced inactivity). Some thought we were ready to protect the Convention from an attack by the *faubourgs,* others that we were ready to defend Paris from an attack by *fédérés.* Everyone was confused except for an *enragé à la Marat* who thought the solution to everything would be to set fire to the Tuileries while the Convention was in session, taking care only to warn a few chosen delegates to stay home, such as Robespierre, Danton, Desmoulins, etc. (Surprisingly enough this proposal came from the tailor Desmarquets, proprietor of the shop across the street, a very orderly bourgeois. But then the proud cry, "We are the *sans-culottes* and the rabble!" came from Robespierre, with his silk suits and powdered wigs.)

We were dismissed in the afternoon. I went to the Café Manoury to learn the news. The National Guard had a new commander, Hanriot, a friend of Robespierre's. An insurrectionary committee was meeting at the Archevêché, near Notre-

Dame, site of the insurrectionary committees of '89 and '92—by now we have a *tradition* of insurrections. I took a stroll and noticed many troops camped in the vicinity of the "Palais-National," also at the Place Vendôme, the Champs-Elysées, the Tuileries gardens, etc. Some of them were members of the Gardes, others new recruits who had not yet departed for the Vendée, a few students from the Ecole Militaire. There were fieldpieces on the Place du Carrousel. Was all this military display intended to protect the Convention or to intimidate it? The only thing certain is that there had been no violence as yet.

That night the tocsin sounded again; the *générale* called us to our posts. We passed a sleepless night and in the morning were ordered to march toward the palace. My patrol got no further than the quai de la Vallée; I managed to slip into Duchesne's for some refreshment. When the sun went down we were dismissed.

The next day I learned that twenty-nine Girondin deputies had been put under house arrest. I will admit I was as astonished as many other Parisians. Whatever the differences of policy between the Gironde and the Mountain, the men proscribed were all patriots, or so they had seemed to me.

What passed in the Convention on June 2nd, the crucial day, was related to me afterwards by Mercier. For some time now it has become our custom to have dinner once a week, often accompanied by Citizen Arthaud, through whose generosity I have a new press and have been able to continue my work. Mercier is more and more discouraged these days; he feels that since the trial of the king things have gone steadily downhill, that the party called the *Mountain,* far from being the staunch republicans they claim to be, are actually leading France toward a dictatorship that will prove a worse despotism than the Old Regime. The suppression of the Girondin press is only a start. Besides, the author of the *Tableaux de Paris* finds the style of this new breed of solons offensive. On the one hand there are Marat and those like him, who do not hesitate to use the language of the streets at the tribune of the Convention, calling their opponents "imbeciles who belong in a madhouse" or sometimes even "pigs." And then there is a new republican pomposity, such as is seen in the grandiose statues by David that have now replaced the bronze kings of yesteryear. Or the custom of taking new names like Cato, Brutus, or Aristides. One day, he admitted, he grew so furious at some of this nonsense that he interrupted a speaker by shouting, *"No! You are not Romans!"* In short, he is afraid our new leaders are demagogues rather than statesmen, that they are drunk on their own rhetoric. On hearing Robespierre propose that any general who ordered a retreat be accused of treason, he asked, "Do you have a treaty with Victory?"—"No," came the answer, "we have a pact with Death!"

Mercier is bitter about Camille. He feels his malicious *Histoire des Brissotins* or *Secret History of the Revolution* is as much responsible for the course events have taken as anything else, making people believe that the Gironde are paid agents of England and Prussia. They no longer even nod. (And yet only two and a half years ago Mercier was a witness at Camille's wedding—along with Robespierre.)

On June 2nd at the dinner hour, the deputies found themselves prisoners in their own chamber. The place was surrounded by troops; guards at the doors would let no one leave. One deputy with a pressing natural function was escorted out by four men with bayonets. There was much oratory and then the Assembly decided to try to break through the troops by sallying forth all at once. Leaving behind only thirty or so delegates of the Mountain, the Convention descended to the garden, made a circle about the Palace. No one was harmed, but everywhere they found themselves hemmed in by a row of bayonets. When the presiding officer approached Hanriot, general of the Gardes, demanding that the Convention be allowed to pass, the answer was a command, "Cannoneers, to your guns!" The delegates returned to their chamber and voted the arrest of twenty-nine delegates. The names were dictated to the clerk by Marat.

Mercier says the Gironde could have called for help from outside Paris. But this would have meant a civil war, the triumph of the Coalition, the destruction of the Revolution. They preferred to sacrifice themselves. Along with seventy-two other delegates, Mercier has signed a petition protesting the events of June 2nd as an insult to the Convention. He is afraid that, along with his vote against the death of the king, it may be his biggest political mistake.

The deputy-prisoners were not well-guarded. Several escaped to their *départements* where they raised local revolts against Paris. The news from the Vendée continued to be disastrous. But I leave such facts to others, preferring to report that on June 8th there was a concert in the Tuileries gardens by a chorus of young girls who sang the *Marseillaise* and other patriotic airs. The audience sat on benches brought out for the occasion and the paths had been sprayed at midday because the dry weather had caused an excessive amount of dust. The Champs-Elysées have been turned into a pasture with sheep grazing everywhere, as in an English park. Nonetheless the price of meat remains atrociously high.

At the Palais-Egalité I encountered a soldier of the Garde Nationale who looked more like a pirate, his hair falling in ringlets, a black mustache, his face pale, his eyes sparkling, a scimitar at his side and two pistols at his belt; with all that somewhat drunk. Noticing that he had caught my attention, he drew me aside and asked in a whisper if I knew that ten thousand Bordelais were marching on Paris to set their deputies free. I said I had heard some such rumor. "All the same, they'll get it in the neck!" he shouted. "I'm from Bordeaux myself, and the Bordelais themselves will send them to the national razor!" (By that he meant the guillotine.) He went on to complain that there hadn't been a repetition of the September massacres—the first time round had been too short.

The purged Convention wrote a new Constitution in less than a month, proving how much easier a task is the second time. Everyone was surprised that the new document spoke of a "Supreme Being." But then Robespierre was educated by the priests.

On July 13th I dropped in at Mérigot's bookstore to inquire after the sale of the *Semaine Nocturne* which he is handling along with the first fourteen parts of the *Nuits* since the execution of Guillot a year ago. I've been thinking of writing a Part XVI, utilizing much of the material of this present work (which it is dangerous even to *write* at this moment). But the uncertainties of politics make me hesitate.

Let me make my attitude clear. My great works, the ones that give meaning to my entire existence, are *Monsieur Nicolas* and *Le Drame de la Vie*. To them I have sacrificed everything, my health, my reputation, my family, my fortune, and even then they would not yet be nearing completion if it were not for the unexpected gift from M. Arthaud. As for the Revolution, I feel like a survivor of a past generation, someone from before the flood. Whatever my sentiments I cannot influence its course and therefore I prefer to stand on the bank as an observer and not try to breast the flood. But even this attitude is suspect at present. Therefore I kept silent, waiting for the crest to pass. Great rivers have a tendency to divide in their lower reaches, expending themselves in all directions, but eventually they all reach the sea.

It was eight in the evening but as yet neither of us knew anything of the sinister event of that day. Mérigot wasn't there, but I stayed to chat with the adorable Adèle, who has blossomed into a lovely young lady. After a while I left to go to the Café M. At the Pont-Neuf I overheard a man locking up a stall talking to a shopgirl.

"She was about to leave. They arrested her at the doorstep. He is dead."

Thinking it some private affair I went on. The chess players and other customers were as ignorant as I until Fragnières arrived. He announced the news to everyone: Marat assassinated, in his own house, in his bath, by a young woman who had got past the housekeeper under false pretenses!

My first thought was that the deputies under arrest would pay for this unfortunate event. Each new arrival brought us a new version of the occurrence. One reported that the assassin had been torn to pieces in the rue des Cordeliers by an angry mob. Another that she had managed to escape. Each table had its own theory before learning any more facts—the girl was an agent of the English, of the Austrians, of the Gironde, a peasant from the Vendée, the daughter of an *emigré*. The "Friend of the People" had so many enemies that all these hypotheses were plausible. Later we learned that the police had managed to get the killer to the Abbaye, fortunately close by, while some deputies restrained the crowd.

July 14th, fourth anniversary of the fall of the Bastille, was devoted to mourning. It was agreed by everyone that the national holiday be postponed to August 10th, anniversary of the fall of the monarchy.

Tuesday the 16th witnessed the funeral of Marat. His body was deposited in the garden of the *ci-devant* church of the Cordeliers, awaiting, it is said, the honors of the Panthéon. When he was alive Marat said that he would hate to be buried in the Panthéon, since the place had been spoiled by Mirabeau. But his funeral recalled that of the great orator of the Estates, lasting well into the night. These national funerals have come to be the great ceremonies of the Revolution. The entire Convention paraded past to drop flowers on the bier. Two theatrical objects made a great impression, the bathtub in which he had been killed and his shirt, soiled with his blood.

But even more people turned out the next day for the execution of Charlotte Corday. The space devoted to the assassin in the press is extraordinary in these days when the papers have all become so circumspect. All published in full the record of her interrogation by the Revolutionary Tribunal. All reported her beauty, her dignity, her firmness, her conviction that her act was justified. All related that she went to her death with modesty, radiating an assurance that can come only from an inner faith. She mounted the steps of the scaffold as gracefully as was possible with her hands tied behind her back. No one accompanied her; she had refused the services of a priest, Constitutional or not. In short, although an assassin, she had all the attributes of a republican heroine, a feminine Brutus. She was accused of royalism, but she claimed only to be attached to the proscribed deputies, several of whom had fled to her native Calvados.

This assassination seems to have justified the events of May 31–June 2nd, after the fact.

When her head had fallen into the basket, one of the executioners picked it up by the hair and slapped it. The crowd gasped with horror at this gesture; several witnesses claimed they saw the severed head blush. The reprobation was so general that the man was arrested several days later for his presumption.

The prisons are filling up again. In my section a former judge of the Parlement of Paris was discovered living with a whore on the rue de la Huchette. Was he supporting her or she him? We never knew.

The forces of the Republic suffer one defeat after another. Mainz is abandoned to the Prussians. Valenciennes surrenders to the Duke of York after an heroic siege. Lyons is in full revolt against the government of Paris, the patriot Chalier guillotined by the Girondins of that city. The peasant revolt in the Vendée spreads like an inkblot; there are more reports of republicans being massacred by the priests. Even the "good" news has a strange sound. I read, for example, "Victory by our troops in Calvados . . . Avignon taken by the army of Marseilles. . . ." The undeclared civil war and the fight against the Coalition seem to merge into a grand disaster. Is France to become again what it was a few centuries ago, an infinity of little fiefs, as many governments and powers as there are towns and cities?

In September I trembled with horror at the massacres in the prisons, but now, looking backwards, they seem to have been necessary. Am I losing my sense of humanity? At the present moment a sense of humanity seems *suspect.*

Paris remains calm. Paris remains Paris.

Volume VII of *L'Année des Dames Nationales* is now printed, as well as the first three epochs of *Monsieur Nicolas.* I am writing nothing except for Part XVI of the *Nuits* and the final acts of *La Drame de la Vie.* When I say "nothing" I mean that what I have accomplished during the past year would have been completed in six months in normal times. But these are not normal times and a GENIUS is compelled to spend hours and hours marching about with a pike on his shoulder. I have withdrawn *La Semaine Nocturne;* the judgments of the events of 1789 in that volume would now be considered counterrevolutionary.

Agnès has applied for a divorce from Augé, under the wise new law that is one of the glories of the Republic. Despite all the crimes of the MONSTER she is pleading only incompatibility of

PLATE 18: Charlotte Corday taken to her execution. The guillotine is set up on the Place de la Révolution, *ci-devant* Place Louis XV, today Place de la Concorde. From *Les Révolutions de Paris*.

character and the fact that she has been separated from him and supported by me for seven years. To my astonishment, L'Echiné has made no objections to this action and asked for no special conditions. It has required only a few trips to a notary and the bureau at the Hôtel de Ville, where Cubières has been helpful (he is still secretary to the Commune). The bureau is of course overworked, having to deal with the pent-up demand of all the years past. (There are an increased number of marriages celebrated these days also; recruits making honest women of their sweethearts before leaving for the Vendée or the frontiers. Does the possibility of divorce have anything to do with this?)

Will it seem unnatural if I admit that this flat dénouement to the tragic history of my daughter's marriage, while infinitely preferable for Agnès herself to any further scandal, left me somewhat disappointed *as a novelist?* Also embarrassed for my *Drame de la Vie,* written contemporaneously with the events it contains. A polite, civilized divorce is not the stuff of which drama is made, even if it is the stuff of life.

This literary dilemma appeared insoluble, until I was saved —by a dream! There can be a truth in dreams that is more valuable than the truth of real life. At least that is so in this case. . . .

I was surrounded by my daughters, my *natural* children, a swarm of the lovely girls I have discovered by the thermometer of my heart at the Palais-Egalité and elsewhere. Or rather *I* was not present at all and yet I saw them, heard them, could even read their thoughts—and their thoughts were of me! Ah! the delicious sentiment of paternity, the delicious sight of all those young beauties, for they were all beautiful! They were assembled in a large, airy room, sunlight streaming in the windows; a buffet was spread with dainty tidbits fit for their delicate fingers and mouths; their feet were all shod in the fine pumps of the sixties instead of the despicable slippers of this degenerate decade—tiny pointed pumps with a fine arch and pointed heel—all those delicate, pointed feet half-hidden by the soft flounces of ruffled skirts and petticoats, sometimes a glimpse of an appetizing ankle, a well-turned leg surmounting the arched foot, divine shaft rising through the gauze and lace to the very temple of love. They spoke of me, all those lovely daughters, sweet fruit of past joys, incarnations of the tenderness I have felt for every woman whose body I have enjoyed, even the lowest whores of the rue St.-Denis—they spoke of me, they consoled my old age, each more eager than the next to offer her swelling white bosom as a pillow for my graying locks and wrinkled face. . . .

Charming creatures! charming vision conjured up by the desires of my lonely bed! But all was not to remain sweetness even in this dream—and dreams are but the handmaidens of our wishes. . . . There was a sudden uproar in the street below, the voice of a woman shouting for help, screaming with pain, the sound of her fists beating on the door. My young lovelies were filled with pity for their unknown sister, ran to the hall, undid the bolt.

Enter Agnès, followed by the ECHINE, the MONSTER Augé. He is beating his wife, shouting, "Today you shall be spared nothing!"

His face is livid, even more hideous than in real life; his teeth the fangs of a hyena; his furious expression mirrors all the bestiality of his heart.

The swarm of nymphs, of sylphides, surrounds Agnès, protects her by forming a screen that confuses the MONSTER as they flit this way and that.

For a moment I fear that he will slay them all; he is as ravenous for blood as a vampire; the sight of so much young flesh excites him to a frenzy; he lashes out savagely with teeth and claws. But the nymphs are untouchable; they fight him off without being harmed. Consumed by his own fury the MONSTER flees.

The unfortunate Agnès, pale and bleeding, covered with bruises, her clothes in shreds, is carried to a divan. "I merit all I have received!" she weeps, "I married this man without my father's consent!" . . .

The scene changes. *Augé,* a mad dog, is howling through the streets. He encounters, oh horror! my wife, *Agnès Lebègue,* mother of his spouse. Deprived of the daughter he falls on the mother, leaps on her from behind and clutches her in an obscene embrace, tugs at her gray hair, bites her neck until the blood flows, tears her dress open, grabs her ancient sagging breasts with his green hands and wrenches them from her body. She screams, is drenched in blood, turns pale as death, and expires.

A crowd has gathered. They call for the Gardes. Voices shout, "To the guillotine! Assassin! To the guillotine!"

I am sitting on a hitching post. Agnès and Marion kneel at my feet, weeping at the death of their mother. The MONSTER sees us. He attacks, a knife in his hand. I have my pike, the heavy weapon I carry on patrols. I turn it toward him. It is also a musket. I pull the trigger. Even after the bullet has penetrated his heart the MONSTER does not fall. He immolates himself on the bayonet.

The musket drops from my hands. The MONSTER falls with it. My daughters embrace me, weeping.

"He killed our mother and you have killed him! She mistreated us but yet we weep for her; we came from her womb! Oh, dear Papa, we shall never leave you!"

. . . I am on my dear isle, l'Ile St.-Louis, at the eastern prow, opposite the Hôtel Lambert. On the parapet I inscribe these words: "HODIE 30a JULLII 1793, MORS AUGE DICTI L'ECHINE-MORESQUIN, SCELERATI HOMINIS, ET AGNETIS LEBEGUE, SCELERATAE MULIERIS, ILLA A AUGAEO OCCISA, ILLE A RESTIF OCCISUS CUM JAM ERAT RESTIFAM . . . LAUDANANDA NATURA QUAE ABSTULIT MALOS." . . .

Agnès and Marion are with me, and the swarm of nymphs all about. I translate the *inscription* for them: *"Today, July 30, 1793, the death of Augé, known as l'Echiné-Moresquin, an evil man, death of Agnès Lebègue, guilty spouse, she killed by Augé, he by Restif at the moment when he tried to stab him . . . Praise God, who removes evil creatures from the earth."* . . .

Then I show them my other *dates* on the stones of my dear isle, and they weep with me at each memory. . . .

(This is the source of the final act of the ninth regular play of *Le Drame de la Vie,* "Felicité." All that now remains to be written is a number of detached "shadow scenes," detailing the events of the Revolution.)

August 10th was celebrated as the Fête de le République. The Commune ordered all the whores off the streets and the order was *obeyed;* nothing like it had ever happened before. The envoys from the *départements* were all searched on their arrival at Paris to make sure they were not smuggling in any Girondist pamphlets. Two new museums were opened to the public: the Louvre and a Museum of French monuments, containing statues, tombs, carvings, taken from deconsecrated churches and monasteries all over France. The same day three colossal statues by David were unveiled, marking three stops of the long procession that was the ceremony of the day. First, on the ruins of the Bastille, an immense and hideous representation of Nature, a huge plaster woman with one hundred breasts, water spurting from each mammilla. The second, at the Place de la Révolution, where the guillotine remained posed on its scaffold before the gates of the Tuileries gardens, a huge Statue of Liberty, unveiled at the same time that three thousand doves were released. Last, at the Invalides, a statue of the People represented as Hercules, subduing the dragon of the Gironde and Federalism.

The entire Convention marched in an interminable procession that ended only at the Champ-de-Mars, where a new altar was erected on the Mountain of the Fatherland constructed in '90 and now rather dilapidated, but whose name has since acquired a new political significance. They were surrounded by a tricolor ribbon that reminded many people of the *barrière de faveur* of a year ago and which Mercier said seemed designed to show the captivity of what is formally the supreme power of France.

The statues have been left in place. Constructed of nothing more permanent than plaster of Paris, they are rapidly becoming antique monuments.

It was the wrong season for a fête, the military situation was too disastrous. On the 23rd the Convention decreed a "general conscription" to create an army of TWO MILLION men. Everyone not at the front was to be considered part of the army, forging weapons, digging saltpeter for gunpowder out of the cellars, making tents, working in hospitals, sewing uniforms. If commerce suffered, if the harvest suffered and bread was again scarce), so much the worse!

For as long as anyone could remember, war had been the pastime of the aristocracy. Now no one was exempt. TOTAL WAR.

On the 27th, Custine, general of the Army of the Rhine, was guillotined. The event made a great impression in Paris. The tears that fell on the mustache of the old soldier, the pious kiss he gave his confessor, his last words, "I am not a traitor!" —so many signs of the desperate state of the nation. Custine was an aristocrat. His crime: he had been defeated.

Toulon was delivered to the English the same day; again it was treason. The news arrived in Paris September 2nd. There were still some royalists in Paris bold enough to celebrate the event by promenading with white cockades.

On the 5th the Convention declared: "THE ORDER OF THE DAY IS—THE TERROR." . . .

DIARY OF THE TERROR

SEPTEMBER 1793–MARCH 1794

SEPTEMBER 4: A "march against hunger" today, the rough and ragged workers of the *faubourgs* filling the Place de Grève and shouting, "Bread! Bread! And right away!" It could be June '89 except for the pikes and red bonnets.

September 5: According to the *Gazette de France* there are more than 1500 political "suspects" in the prisons of Paris. A year ago the massacres were just ending, the Revolutionary Tribunal had just begun its work.

September 6: A meeting of my section last night, the first under the new regulations. St.-Etienne-du-Mont was as crowded as on an Easter Sunday although the congregation was hardly pious. The Commune has decided to pay all *sans-culottes* forty sous each time they attend. If the Church had ever thought of this system instead of passing the plate France would still be a Catholic country.

The Justice of the Peace Hué made a proposal that was passed immediately and unanimously: only citizens who have been constant in their principles *throughout* the Revolution should be issued civic certificates. (These *cartes civiles* must be signed by two members of the Committee of the section. Without one in your pocket it isn't safe to walk the streets; any patrol can clap you in prison with no further questions.) I shouted, "Yes!" along with everyone else to prove that I had nothing to hide. But I thought that if anyone is curious enough to read *La Semaine Nocturne* with its praise of Lafayette, Bailly, etc., it will be all over with me. These are times when it pays to be a neglected author. Could Robespierre himself pass this test if anyone thought of applying it to him?

(This is one device the Church did anticipate. It was called the Inquisition.)

September 8: Out all morning on patrol making house calls. The section has ordered a census of all young men. Everyone age eighteen to twenty-five, married or not, is to be conscripted into the army. Gone are the days of volunteers. . . .

After dinner, a short promenade. In the Tuileries men standing on chairs, reading aloud from the latest numbers of *Le Père Duchesne,* long tirades denouncing aristocrats in the Navy as criminals responsible for the fall of Toulon. Hébert's journal has replaced *L'Ami du Peuple* as the bible of the *sans-culottes.* Its style makes Marat seem a man of letters in retrospect. Not a sentence without a "fuckit" or "bugger" and the rest using all the latest slang with the facility of a stevedore at the Port-au-Blé, all the argot of the streets that has never before been seen in print. But Hébert is also a member of the Commune, leader of the faction that would like to send most of the Convention to the "national razor." I wonder if these readings are truly spontaneous.

September 10: To the Palais-Egalité but found the gates shut. A raid on the speculators in *assignats* who conduct their illegal traffic in the peristyle near the Théâtre Montansier.

September 13: The section decided last night that identity cards are needed to get into meetings.

September 20: The papers all publish the text of a new law defining those who are to be considered as "suspect."

1. Everyone who by word or writings has shown himself an enemy of liberty.

2. Anyone who can't explain the source of his livelihood.

3. Anyone who has been refused a civic certificate or been expelled from a patriot club.

4. Any public official who has lost his job.

5. All *ci-devant* nobles and their families.

6. Anyone who left France since the start of the Revolution, even if he or she has since returned.

In short everyone except an illiterate deaf-mute from a poor family.

September 21: Anniversary of the proclamation of the Republic.

This morning at the market, Place Maubert, a shouting, clawing, scratching catfight. Some of the girls at the stalls began it by snatching off the cockades of some housewives who complained of high prices. They shouted that they weren't to blame, that the Republic meant only high prices and shortages and that they were fed up. These rough strong-armed women are the only people in Paris who don't seem intimidated by the threat of prison. But then they have never been intimidated by anything.

Our patrol suffered several minor injuries trying to restore order. The Convention ought to add an Amazon battalion to the Revolutionary Army; the market women of Paris would be more than a match for the peasants of the Vendée.

September 22: To the Hôtel de Ville to pick up the final papers certifying the divorce of Agnès and the MONSTER. To my astonishment as soon as the papers were in her hands Agnès announced that she was moving out to some rooms she had already taken on the rue d l'Egout in the Marais. She said that Marion already knew of her plans; they had arranged that I could take all my meals around the corner with Marion and Edmond. At this new blow of fate all I could do was bow my head. Does Agnès have a lover? That is the only explanation.

Thus in my fifty-ninth year I find myself alone and abandoned, in poverty, just as when I first arrived in Paris forty years ago—but without my youth. My own misfortunes are compounded by those of my country. I am very much in style, *sans-culottes, sans famille* and *sans* everything else.

September 24: To the rue de l'Egout to see Agnès. Her two rooms are nicely if simply furnished. She certainly did not receive the money from me. Her *carte civile* is in order, duly signed by her new section. She says she has made arrangements with a *modiste* of the rue St.-Honoré to do piecework. A strange time to start in a new profession; Agnès displays some of the headstrong character of her mother.

Returned by the former Place Royale. It is covered with

blacksmiths turning out pikes at open-air forges. A strange sight before the red brick façades of that noble square, now almost two hundred years old.

September 29: The Law of the *Maximum* has been extended to cover flour, soap, wine, meat and a few other articles that are considered necessities. Great satisfaction among the *sans-culottes* at my section. I would have thought that anything as technical as price control would be too abstruse to arouse any popular enthusiasm. I wonder if they have noticed that, at least on paper, the law should apply to wages also.

September 30: A new slogan, on all public buildings: *"Liberté, Egalité, Fraternité* OU LA MORT!" Strange Liberty that proclaims, "Be my brother and equal OR I'LL KILL YOU!" Fraternity in the style of Cain and Abel.

October 3: Dinner with my benefactor, M. Arthaud, at a restaurant near the Palais-Royal. A lovely fall day, the yellow leaves of the trees in the Tuileries occasionally dropping into the paths and fountains. Mercier was one of the company. It almost seemed like old times until a friend of Arthaud's arrived, breathless, with the terrible news that Amar of the Committee of Public Safety was presenting his report on the seventy-three deputies who had signed the petition protesting the events of June 2nd.

"Aha! I am lost!" shouted Mercier, jumping up from the table. "Something told me not to go to the Convention today!"

Arthaud asked if there was anything he could do to help but Mercier just laughed.

"My friends, I fear there is no escaping this new tyranny; it is much more efficient than the old sort. I must leave at once or you will be compromised by my presence."

Arthaud insisted that we finish our bottle of champagne together. Mercier accepted. He was trembling, despite his courage. I was touched beyond words that he thought first of the safety of his friends rather than his own fate.

"I've acted according to my conscience," Mercier said. "I voted against the death of the king because I thought it was the wrong course for France. I signed the petition because I thought the dignity of the elected representatives of the people had been insulted. What is happening today proves that I was right.

"My only regret is that I won't see what happens from here on. So many of our best men are in prison. So many who have taken their place are completely incompetent."

We embraced him, weeping. Only Mercier's eyes remained dry. He wished us all well, telling me that he still hoped to read *Monsieur Nicolas* when it was complete.

"The only scenes missing from my *Tableaux de Paris* were those in prison," he added as he left. "Now, perhaps, I'll have a chance to fill the gap."

He didn't mention the guillotine, out of delicacy. Arthaud accompanied him home.

October 4: In the *Moniteur,* a report of yesterday's session at the Convention. What is surprising is that only forty-four delegates are declared *accused,* that is, indicted to be tried by the Revolutionary Tribunal. This includes the twenty-two arrested last June, plus assorted others. The seventy-three who signed the petition are merely "under arrest," *i.e.,* in prison. Who is responsible for this relative clemency?—Robespierre. The bulk of the Convention would have sent all of them to the guillotine to prove their Revolutionary ardor had not Robespierre intervened.

"The Convention should not inflate the numbers of those who are guilty; it is sufficient that the leaders will be tried. If there are others guilty of treason, the Committee of Public Safety will inform you in good time. Among those who signed the petition there were some who were simply mistaken, others who were duped, others who did not realize what they were doing."

His words changed everything. The Convention followed his wishes. Mercier's life now hangs on a slender thread—the clemency of Robespierre.

At the same session it was decreed that Marie-Antoinette and the duc d'Orléans are to be brought before the Tribunal.

October 7: The Convention has adopted a new calendar, to take effect immediately and even retroactively, its starting date to be considered September 21st, 1792 (Old Style), the Proclamation of the Republic. Therefore we are in year II. It will take me a while to adjust.

October 12 (*21 Vendémiaire*) : News that the rebels in Lyons have surrendered. What is astonishing is that the victorious army, led by Robespierre's right-hand man Couthon, let two thousand of the rebels escape. Robespierre again stands accused of what has become, in the eyes of many, the most horrible of sentiments : humanity.

No matter, the Convention has ordered a terrible repression. The name of the city will be changed to *Ville-Affranchie.* The Convention decrees: "Lyons made war on Liberty, Lyons no longer exists."

October 16 (*25 Vendémiaire*) : Marie-Antoinette guillotined at noon, Place de la Revolution.

She was tried by the Revolutionary Tribunal on the 14th and 15th. Her answers to most questions were a short "Yes" or "No." Sometimes, "That is not the way it happened."

On one occasion she wrote out her answer and asked that the paper be given to the judge. He responded that the procedure was not allowed. This relative to an accusation that she had incited her son and daughter to indulge in sexual explorations unsuited to their tender ages—and with each other. She was even accused of having joined in these shameful practices with her son.

Her answer, spoken aloud: "The thing is impossible, I call on all mothers to answer for me!"

There was also talk of a liaison with a young gendarme while she was in the Conciergerie. But none of that was proved and I think that such accusations bring more discredit on the Tribunal than on the queen.

What matters is that she constantly worked against the Revolution, inspired an "Austrian party" in Paris, convinced the king to flee in '91. When that scheme was thwarted by his arrest at Varennes she continued to conspire, bribing members of the Assembly to revise the Constitution in favor of the monarchy, communicating with the *emigrés* and the Austrians even after war was declared.

Her trial, like that of the king, revealed little that was

new. The men of 1993 will regret our haste; many unanswered questions remain. But these are not really trials; they are political actions.

The expected verdict was brought in at four-thirty in the morning. The former queen was returned to her cell at the Conciergerie, that medieval prison that adjoins the Palais de Justice, the last residence of everyone destined for the guillotine. She slept about two hours, then drank some hot chocolate. She spent two hours with a priest. When she emerged into the courtyard her hair had been cut off; she was dressed in a plain white robe with a small black ribbon to hold her bonnet in place. She did not ask to see her children.

Her last request was that she be taken to the scaffold in a carriage, a privilege that was granted her husband. But even that was denied her. She mounted the *charette* accompanied by her confessor, an old man with white hair. The *charette* took the usual route, along the rue St.-Honoré. I saw it pass at the corner of the rue des Pouiles. She sat very straight, looking at no one, silent. Her blotchy skin had the pale cast of all prisoners, except for the rouge on her cheeks. She seemed a quiet resigned old woman.

Just nine months ago the whole city had been under tight guard for the execution of the king. His widow was hardly noticed as she went by. The shops remained open, including all those that had once been proud to advertise that they enjoyed the patronage of "Her Majesty, the Queen." But what could that plain old woman care about wigs or robes, hats or pumps, now that she was going to her death?

It was reported that the blade fell at twelve-fifteen. No cannon or other interruption in the life of the city. A former gendarme was arrested for having dipped his handkerchief into the queen's blood, presumably to keep as a relic. Exaltation, forgetfulness. . . .

October 19 (*28 Vendémiaire*): News of another victory over the Austrians. News that the rebels in the Vendée are in retreat. Bordeaux also has rejected the enemies of the republic.

October 24 (*3 Brumaire*): The trial of the Girondin deputies opens. As ten of the original twenty-two have either died or managed to escape, ten others have been added to make up the magic number of those arrested June 2nd. Among them, Carra. . . .

No mention of Mercier, which is a good sign. His only hope is to be forgotten.

October 27 (*6 Brumaire*) : Drummers in the street this morning to warn all shopkeepers to remain open despite the fact that it is Sunday, old style. Anyone who puts up his shutters is to be considered suspect. . . .

Still long lines at the bakeries.

October 28 (*7 Brumaire*) : Working directly at the case, the final pages of Part XVI of the *Nuits*. I declare that I have related what I have seen, that I mention obscenities when they are part of my subject but only then, that I have left my opinions as they were at the time of the events since they are a reflection of public sentiment as it was and thus part of history. (To tell the truth I have cut out certain passages that now would be considered counterrevolutionary.) But will my attitude be understood in these days when the Commune led by Hébert finds the Convention as onerous as the Court, when the loudmouths at my section denounce Robespierre for being too *moderate,* too *merciful?* I think that I shall not distribute this work until the times change.

October 29 (*8 Brumaire*) : Fanny's daughter has been arrested as a royalist. No news of her mother. When I last heard from her she was in Lyons, but that was almost a year ago.

October 30 (*9 Brumaire*) : Death of the twenty-two Girondin deputies. Although expected, the news is unbelievable. If just a year ago it had been foretold that Brissot, Vergniaud, Carra and so many other ardent patriots and revolutionaries had been executed just two weeks after the queen was guillotined it would have seemed obvious that a counterrevolution had occurred in the interval. But both the queen and the twenty-two were condemned by the same court!

The trial took less than a week. Two days for Marie-Antoinette, six for twenty-two elected deputies! And all twenty-two tried *en masse,* as if they were one person! The defendants had no lawyers and several were not even permitted to speak on their own behalf. But those who did speak were too eloquent, too convincing. Whatever mistakes those men might have made, it was easy for them to poke holes in the indictment which accused them of responsibility for every misfortune of the past two years—including the September massacres! Their opponents grew impatient, afraid that public opinion would be swayed if the trial went on too long. At the urging of the Jacobins the Convention passed a decree authorizing the jury to declare that it had heard enough evidence to make up its mind once a trial had gone on for three days. No sooner said than done. The proceedings were cut short. The jury retired for two hours and brought back the inevitable verdict. It was ten-thirty, the night of the 29th.

All were condemned to death the next day.

Inevitable or not, the moment was terrible. Valazé, one of the accused, put a dagger through his heart.

Camille was in the courtroom. His heart got the better of his prudence. "Poor men!" he shouted, "my book has killed them!"

I learned the news in the morning. The execution was set for noon. A gray day with a soft rain falling from a dirty gray sky. Paris went about its affairs. For the market women and street vendors the Girondins were old stuff, out-of-date politicians who were already dead.

I went to the rue St.-Honoré and saw the five *charettes* go by. The corpse of Valazé was propped up on a bench between two of the other condemned deputies; to carry out the sentence he too was guillotined. The sparse crowd was silent. I caught a glimpse of Carra; he looked dazed and astonished. Much has been written of the stoicism of the victims of the guillotine; I think it must be numbness rather than philosophy; the short interval between the sentence and the execution contributes to this effect. Some of the others were singing the *Marseillaise*. I noticed that they sang:

> Contre nous de la tyrannie
> Le *couteau* sanglant est levé

substituting *blade* for *banner*.

Afterwards I went to the Café Manoury, but found it hard to concentrate on the papers; the print kept swimming before my eyes. At two, Frangières arrived. He had seen the execution. The condemned men went on singing the *Marseillaise* in a diminishing chorus as the blade fell. Finally there was only one voice left, then silence.

October 31 (*10 Brumaire*): In *Le Père Duchesne,* Hébert's description of yesterday's execution:

"Some of them pretended to be cheerful and a few tickled themselves for laughs, but, fuckit, it was only a show and stick a pike up my ass if the devil was bothered. As each head rolled into the basket all hats were raised and the square echoed with shouts of *Vive la république!* That's the end of the Brissotins, and that will be the fate of all traitors."

This from the most popular journalist of France.

November 3 (*13 Brumaire*): Three thousand suspects in the prisons of Paris.

November 6 (*16 Brumaire*): Philippe Egalité, *ci-devant* duc d'Orléans, executed.

November 8 (*18 Brumaire*): Mme. Roland executed.

November 10 (*20 Brumaire*): Fête de la Raison, at Notre-Dame, ordered by the Commune, i.e., by Chaumette and Hébert.

I was required to attend, along with the rest of my patrol. We left our pikes at home—no arms were permitted inside the cathedral which is no longer a cathedral, the bishop of Paris having resigned three days ago. It must be said that the ceremony was even more boring than a Mass.

A plaster "mountain" had been erected in the choir of the church, surmounted by a circular temple in the classical style, the Temple of Reason. Its entablature was inscribed with the words: "A LA PHILOSOPHIE." At the base of the columns, busts of Voltaire, Rousseau, etc.; at the base of the "mountain" a flame, the "Light of Truth." Music by a military band assisted by a chorus of young girls in white robes, their hair crowned with wreathes of oak leaves. The band played the *Marseillaise;* then Liberty herself emerged from the Temple in the person of a young actress in yet another white robe, a red stocking cap on her head and a stage-prop wooden pike in her hand. "Liberty" was seated on an armchair draped with a green cloth; the chorus of young girls sang a "Hymn to Liberty" especially composed for the occasion. Liberty then returned to her temple and the church echoed with the half-hearted cheers of the audience. The ceremony had only one virtue—brevity.

The Convention had been invited to attend but it pretended to be too occupied with its debates. Its suspicion of the Commune was the cause of this refusal; in fact the session that morning was occupied with the question of who could declare a delegate *suspect*. The Convention voted to reserve this right for itself. But even the leaders of the Commune were becoming wary of the Terror. Chaumette declared that a false accusation was as great a crime as treason and should carry the same penalty. As a conciliatory gesture the chorus of young girls and Liberty herself were sent to the Tuileries. To return the compliment the Convention marched to Notre-Dame early in the evening; the morning's ceremony was repeated for their benefit. Fortunately the Gardes were not required to attend a second time.

(The Terror has taken on a life of its own, terrorizing even its creators.)

November 11 (*21 Brumaire*): Bailly guillotined at the Champ-de-Mars, scene of the massacre of July 17, 1791, while he was mayor of Paris. He was accused of having ordered that crime.

November 13 (*23 Brumaire*): Working at my press at ten in the morning I hear a loud rapping on the door and the sharp "Psst!" which is the "Open up!" of our Revolutionary patrols. I open and find myself face to face with Hué, presiding officer of the meetings of my section. Behind him a patrol, none of whom I recognize.

"We wish a word with you, citizen!" says the justice. His tone is ominous. I step out and am seized by two men while the rest of the band rushes inside and begins a thorough search of all I possess.

"My time has come!" I think, wondering who can have accused me of what. Was it the words I spoke the few times I joined the debates at my section? or my friendship for Mercier? or the sentiments in *La Semaine Nocturne?* My impetuous imagination raced ahead, placed me in the box at the Revolutionary Tribunal, heard the accusation read by the envoy of the Committee, pictured the hard faces of the bloodthirsty jury and banks of hate-filled spectators. I saw myself held by gendarmes with unsheathed bayonets, heard the thundering voice of the judge, "You no longer have the floor!"—then the sentence to eternal silence, my work left unfinished, the long night in a crowded cell, my hair being sheared off in the early dawn, the cords about my wrists holding my hands behind my back. I was riding down the rue St.-Honoré in the fatal *charette,* casting a last glance at the Palais-Royal; I heard the jeering crowd on the Place de la Révolution; I mounted the fatal staircase, knelt at the plank . . . the blade hissed down . . . the blood gushed out. . . .

"We've come to put seals on your property!" Hué intoned, interrupting my reverie.

"Seals? . . ." I was already dead.

"Where is your wife? We are here at her request."

"My wife . . . she left this house nine years ago."

By then I was breathing again. Indignation took the place of terror, a clear improvement. So, my wife was at last asking for a divorce! But unlike Agnès she couldn't do it in a decent manner; she had to send the patrol to impound my property, thinking no doubt that they would discover a hidden fortune that she could claim as hers, a last robbery before dissolving our miserable union.

Ha! the patrol searched and found nothing, neither coin nor *assignats,* not even this manuscript, which I always keep well hidden. They put their seals on my creaking old press and my wardrobe of shabby old clothes—all to protect the pretended rights of a spouse who had never kept house, never cared for her children, who had stolen whatever I owed her a thousand times over! Within an hour they were gone. We parted on good terms, my obvious poverty having convinced them I was a bona-fide *sans-culotte.*

But I was still trembling and furious. If something compromising had been found it would have meant my death. And what might not be compromising these days? an engraving of the king, the wrong books, even Grimod's letters if anyone had taken the trouble to read them. But my wife would never think of my welfare, driven as she is by malice and greed!

Unable to work, I went to Marion's to complain about this new blow. She immediately sent Edmond to get Agnès. Ah, my daughters are lovely! Not only did they sympathize with me fully, but they gave me good advice. I was about to leave for the Hôtel de Ville to protest but Agnès said it would be better to try to get my wife to change her mind. She and Marion are both writing to their mother to tell her she has nothing to gain from this cruel action. I hope their letters will have the desired effect.

November 17 (27 *Brumaire*): To the Palais-Egalité, now a sad shell of its former self. The Commune's campaign for republican virtue has had an effect. If any gambling dens still exist they are in hiding; no barkers stand in the arcades inviting you to try your luck. Half the cafés have closed and the others are almost deserted. No orators—politics has become too dangerous a subject for cafés. The strollers still present all look dull, the men wearing drab colors, women without jewelry; there are uniforms everywhere but they too have become sober, all braid and other flashy marks of rank having been abolished.

Only the whores remain as numerous as before but they look famished; the rouge on their cheeks is like daubs of blood. The Republic has not managed to abolish vice but it has made it terribly sad, without even the illusion of gaiety. The speculators in *assignats* have been driven away from the galleries near the Théâtre Montansier, but their place has been taken by children of both sexes, some of them prostitutes, others simply waifs. What I saw at the rue de Beaujolais in the summer of '91 was bad enough, but this spectacle is worse.

Wandering alone through the city, these children have grown old before their time. Dressed in threadbare clothes, paying no attention to the chill November wind, they flirt with one another while at the same time offering to sell their bodies to any adults that pass by. Their language is as crude as possible. With a true innocence that at the same time is a perverted parody of innocence, they are not ashamed to embrace one another in public and in ways that indicate a familiarity with the worst practices of the most blasé debauchery.

My eyes filled with tears at the sight of these children. I should like to have gathered them all together and taken them to Sacy to grow up in the fields and orchards of my native village. It is not that country children are as pure as porcelain shepherds and shepherdesses; far from it. My friend Le Corticou told me fairy tales that were masterpieces of obscenity. A peasant girl of twelve, assigned to take care of me when I was six, caused my first erection by playing with my member, then showered kisses on the phenomenon she had created. A few years later I was present at a *monture,* a circle of adolescent lads who gathered in a field hidden from the village to masturbate in unison, vying with one another to see who had the biggest prick and who could ejaculate first. But all this is only country fun compared to the children of the Palais-Egalité.

November 21 (*1 Frimaire*): My daughter's letters, as accurate as they were terrible, had the desired effect; my wife has desisted and the seals have been removed from my press. I hope she continues with her divorce action, even if there is no money to be gained from it. Whatever she pleads I shall not object. Now I can get back to *Monsieur Nicolas.*

November 25 (*5 Frimaire*): The ashes of Mirabeau are removed from the Panthéon. News that the ex-minister Roland, in hiding at Rouen, killed himself on learning that his wife had been guillotined. The weather is suddenly atrocious, terribly cold and wet, just like the beginning of the awful winter of '88–'89 five years ago. A bad omen for this poor city where bread remains scarce, women line up at the shops in the early hours of the morning and firewood is terribly dear. Poor, hardworking women of Paris! After four years of Revolution you still cry, "Bread! Bread!"

November 29 (*9 Frimaire*): In *Les Révolutions de Paris* a list of those guillotined at the Place de la Révolution between 2 Brumaire and 2 Frimaire (October 23 to November 22, old style). I examined it closely. Fifty-nine victims in thirty days. The twenty-two Girondins. The duc d'Orléans-Egalité. Bailly. Manuel, *procureur* of the Commune at the time of the September massacres—he had resigned from the Convention to protest the execution of the king. Two ex-deputies. Two generals. Eleven ex-municipal officers. Five aristocrats. Two workingmen, two soldiers, two servants, a speculator, a roofer, a policeman, a watchmaker, a *rentier,* a "woman of letters," an invalid. Nine of these convicted for "statements" tending to discredit the Republic. In the same thirty days the Tribunal acquitted six men accused of anticivic "statements" and ordered the arrest of seven false witnesses for calumny.

Fifty-nine victims may seem few for a city as large as Paris, but it means the "national razor" descended almost every day with twenty-two perishing in the hecatomb of October 30th. Add to this the fame of thirty of those executed and you see why, after the shortage of bread and the weather, the guillotine is the first subject of all conversations.

There are four thousand suspects in the prisons of Paris.

December 1 (*11 Frimaire*): I find it hard to get used to this new calendar. In *Les Nuits de Paris* I had proposed a similar reform. According to my scheme the new year would have begun at the winter solstice, December 21st or 22nd. But the Convention chose September 22nd, the fall equinox, by a happy coincidence the date of the proclamation of the Republic. That was in '92—the new calendar having been decreed this October we find ourselves in year II, having lived through year I as ignorant of that fact as M. Jourdain that he was speaking prose. We have twelve months of thirty days each, all with pretty names, such as the three already past: *Vendémiaire* (month of harvest), *Brumaire* (month of fog), *Frimaire* (month of frost). Each month is divided into *decades* of ten days; each *Décadi* (tenth day) is the day of rest, which gives us nine work days in a row. Five extra days, six in leap years, are added at the end of the year; they are called *Sans-Cullotides.* It is all perfectly logical and I suppose it will become second nature in time.

But what of sentiment, what of my anniversaries, my *dates* on the Ile St.-Louis, now Ile de la Fraternité? They are now all "old style"; they have whirled off into the mists of the past, they are one with the annals of Babylon. Half the streets I have walked for thirty-five years now have new names. We have a rue Jean-Jacques Rousseau, a rue d'Egalité, a rue de Marat, a rue de la Loi, etc. I begin to feel very "old style" myself, almost a stranger in this city where I have always been most at home.

December 5 (*15 Frimaire*) : A pamphlet by Camille, the first of what he promises will be a series, *Le Vieux Cordelier.* Now that all the press is either dull and pompous, or else filled with street language in the style of Hébert, it is astonishing to read someone who writes with style and above all from the heart. Not modesty, that was never one of his virtues—"I reenter the arena with all the frankness and courage I am known for."

"Oh Pitt," he begins, "I pay homage to your genius!" As all evils today are blamed on the Prime Minister of England, Desmoulins claims that he must be responsible also for the insidious climate of suspicion that reigns everywhere, even in the Jacobins where Danton is attacked and has to be defended by Robespierre. Most startling is his plea for liberty of the press; he states frankly that journalism today is more restricted in France than in Great Britain. "See how boldly the *Morning Chronicle* attacks Pitt and his conduct of the war! What journalist in France would dare reveal the mistakes of our Committees, our generals, the Jacobins, the ministers, the Commune, as the opposition reveals those of the prime minister? And I, a Frenchman, I, Camille Desmoulins, cannot be as free as an English journalist! Don't tell me that we are in a Revolution and the liberty of the press must be suspended! Are not England and all of Europe also in a Revolution? Are the principles of liberty of the press less sacred in Paris than in London where Pitt ought to be so afraid of truth?"

A breath of fresh air on a foggy day.

December 8 (*18 Frimaire*) : Mme. du Barry guillotined. The old whore, now a dilapidated fifty, was dragged out of her well-deserved obscurity, brought before the Tribunal, interrogated, condemned, carted off to the "little window." It may be true that she took part in royalist conspiracies, but her real crime was having been the mistress of the old king twenty-five years ago. The judges meant to strike at both vice and the monarchy but I wonder if they have succeeded. People flocked to the execution as if it were an entertainment and were not disappointed. Most victims have gone to their deaths with dignity; some have died heroically like Mme. Roland who turned to the colossal statue that now sits in the center of the square and exclaimed, "Oh Liberty! what crimes are committed in your name!" (This remark was reported as a sign of the "hypocrisy" of the condemned—weren't the journalists being somewhat hypocritical themselves?) But du Barry made no attempt to hide her fear of her last lover, Death. She shouted, trembled, wept, struggled and then almost fainted as she was dragged up to the fatal blade, crying for life until her hoarse voice was silenced forever. It was a good show.

December 10 (*20 Frimaire*): Walking down the rue St.-André-des-Arts I hear an astonishing noise coming out of the church near the Place St.-Michel—a church whose doors are firmly shut—the chanting of the Mass. Some old women passing by cross themselves out of habit. I was not the only one astonished; a patrol going by murmured that the church is the property of the state and wondered what was going on. I asked myself what priest could be foolhardy enough to make such a public display. Later I learned that it was not at all foolhardy. The Convention has passed a decree revoking the anti-Catholic regulations of the Commune, reaffirming the principle of religious liberty. The sponsor of this indulgence—Robespierre.

December 11 (*21 Frimaire*): Number 2 of the *Vieux Cordelier,* out yesterday. Disappointing. Camille attacks Hébert and Chaumette, but reserves his poisoned arrows for poor old Clootz, the "Orator of the Human Race"—he accuses him of making the Revolution ridiculous by his atheism. He seems to feel the Revolution has gone far enough and that its limit should be marked by his old enemy, Marat. "Beyond Marat there is only folly and extravagance . . . beyond his ideas we must write, like the geographers of antiquity on the edges of their maps: no more towns, no more villages, only deserts and savages, glaciers or volcanoes." So I suppose my *Andrographe* of 1782 is now "suspect" since it proposes the abolition of property.

December 14 (*24 Frimaire*): The news from Lyons makes

the Terror in Paris seem like child's play. The Convention sent Collot d'Herbois as its proconsul to put that rebellious city to rights; he has executed four hundred men in one week. The guillotine proved too deliberate a machine for this carnage; most of the victims were shot in batches by firing squads. I fear for Mme. de Beauharnais, even for Fontanes, my wife's ex-lover. He betrayed me and I despise him but I don't consider *that* treason a capital crime. The publication of his misdeeds in *La Femme Infidèle* is punishment enough.

I met this exterminator, Collot d'Herbois, seven years ago at a dinner given by Mercier, a joyous occasion in the month of June. Mercier had rented a charming garden at Montrouge. We dined outdoors with a view of rolling fields bright with wildflowers. At that time Collot was director of a traveling theater; he was in Paris infrequently; later he became the director of the Théâtre de Genève. A good-looking man, well-spoken; he had the voice of an actor (a voice that has served him well since then at the Jacobins); rather shallow, something of a buffoon. In short there was nothing about him that prefigured the future member of the Committee of Public Safety and the terrorist of *la Ville Affranchie*. I would like to say that at the time I sensed something in his character that makes his present deeds no surprise, but that would be a lie. In this Revolution almost everything is a surprise.

December 20 (*30 Frimaire*): Numbers three and four of the *Vieux Cordelier* have appeared during the past week and they are passed from hand to hand, sold at ever higher prices, whispered about everywhere. I'm afraid that the enemies of the Revolution take a secret pleasure in these latest works of one of its heroes, but no matter; should the Revolution be governed by its enemies? Camille has made many mistakes, as he has acknowledged; he has been impetuous, harsh, emotional, at times cruel, but the last two numbers make up for everything.

The third appeared December 15th. Pretending to denounce only the tyranny of kings and emperors, Camille offers a free translation of Tacitus whose application is only too obvious:

"Accused of counterrevolution, Libon Drusus for having

asked a fortuneteller if he would ever be rich. Accused of counterrevolution, Cremutius Cordus, for having called Brutus and Cassius the last true Romans. Accused of counterrevolution, one of the descendants of Cassius for possessing a portrait of his great-grandfather. Accused of counterrevolution, Mamercus Scaurus, for having written a tragedy with some ambiguous verses . . .

"You had to pretend to be happy at the death of a friend or a relative if you didn't want to perish yourself . . .

"Was a citizen popular? he might start a civil war. Suspect.

"Did he try to retire instead? Suspect.

"Were you rich? Suspect.

"Were you poor? you must be hiding something! Suspect.

"Were you melancholy? the state of the nation must upset you. Suspect.

"Were you a philosopher, an orator or a poet? Suspect.

"If you had acquired a reputation in the army, you were all the more dangerous because of your ability. Suspect.

"Every day a new accuser made his triumphal entry into the palace of death and became heir of a rich estate. . . . Accusation was the only way to get ahead. . . . The marquis Serunus denounced his old father as a counterrevolutionary, after which he took the name of Brutus. . . .

"Thus the informer, thus the courts. Instead of protecting life and property the judges became butchers who labeled as confiscation and sentence what was only theft and assassination."

In number four of this precious *Vieux Cordelier* Camille drops the veil of ancient history and speaks directly:

"No, my dear compatriots. Liberty is not an actress from the Opéra, Liberty is not a red bonnet, a dirty shirt or rags. Liberty is happiness, reason, equality, justice; Liberty is the Rights of Man and our sublime Constitution. Do you want me to fall at her feet, shed my blood for her? Open the prisons, liberate those two hundred thousand citizens that you call *suspect,* because in the declaration of rights there is no prison for suspects, only for criminals. . . . There could never be a more Revolutionary action."

He ends by calling for a COMMITTEE OF CLEMENCY. Who is

to create this new Revolutionary institution? "Oh my dear college classmate, you whose eloquent speeches will be cherished by a grateful posterity"—Robespierre.

December 21 (*1 Nivôse*): In the *Moniteur* report of a meeting at the Jacobins a week ago. Camille was attacked for the sympathy he showed the Girondins at their trial. His explanation: "Of the sixty people who attended my wedding" (just three years ago), "only two are still my friends—Robespierre and Danton. The rest have either fled or been guillotined. Seven of the twenty-two were among my wedding guests." Robespierre defended Camille as he had defended Danton.

December 22 (*2 Nivôse*): A stormy meeting of my section last night. The Secretary, Garnier, announced that Hué had been accused of taking bribes and arrested by order of the Committee. Great applause from the rabble who make up most of the members, those who attend only for the 40 sous they receive when the meeting adjourns. This is not because Hué was disliked—he had been reelected chairman several times—but because the announcement of *any* arrest is automatically greeted with applause. Garnier and Hué have long been rivals for leadership of the section; I would guess that was the real reason for the accusation. On the way out I heard a man say that Garnier was not a true *sans-culotte* since he had a state pension.

December 23 (*3 Nivôse*): At the Café Manoury I learn that our Jacobin, Fabre, has been arrested for "counterrevolutionary" statements. And we always considered him so *"enragé"!*

Nonetheless Camille's attack on the Terror has loosened tongues a bit. There was a long discussion of false accusations that sent innocent men to prison, stories of blackmail and denunciations for personal vengeance, corrupt officials, informers who live by accusations.

One of the chess players, from the Section des Piques (formerly Place Vendôme) reported that the Presiding Officer of that section had recently been arrested on orders from the Commune. He was a man who had been secretary of the section since September '92 and had become popular by improving conditions in the charity hospitals that serve the poor. Now he was accused of being a *moderate,* defending suspects and relatives of *emigrés;*

PLATE 19: A Revolutionary Committee at the time of the Terror. This engraving, which borders on caricature, was done ten years later. From *Tableaux Historiques de la Révolution Francaise* (Granger Collection).

worse yet, he was an aristocrat himself, despite the fact that before the Revolution he had spent years in the Bastille. Who is this philanthropic nobleman? the Marquis de Sade, author of the infamous *Justine!*

December 24 (*4 Nivôse*): News that Toulon has been recaptured. Before evacuating the city the English set the port on fire, as well as those ships they couldn't take with them. I hate to think of the form the reprisals in that city will take—the treason of its leading citizens last August is well-proved.

December 25 (*5 Nivôse*): Ration cards for bread issued today. Several bakers have been arrested for using their flour to make cake instead of the regular four-pound loaves that they have to sell at the legal maximum. I hope the new system works; Marion is exhausted from waiting on line at the bakery.

December 27 (*7 Nivôse*): At the Café Manoury a stout man sat down at one of the tables, called for the papers, then roared in a blustery voice that he didn't believe that Toulon had really been taken from the English. "I'll bet my horse that it's a lie!"

No one took his bet. Who can he be? a police spy, a provocateur, or simply someone who wandered in after having too much wine with his dinner?

People react to the Terror in different ways. Some are mute, others foolhardy. After one execution Fragnières reported that he heard a man remark, "That didn't look too hard. What would I have to do to be guillotined, insult one of the deputies?"

On my way home I passed the Palais de Justice. There was the usual group of anxious friends and relatives in the courtyard near the entrance to the Conciergerie, bringing food and drink for the prisoners, pleading favors of the guards, or simply weeping. Also a good sprinkling of whores who now seem to find this a more profitable spot than the rue St.-Martin.

December 31 (*11 Nivôse*): According to the new calendar it is the first day of the second decade of Nivôse (month of snow), year II of the Republic. But "old style" it is the last day of 1793 and I can't help feeling that it is the end of another year. I am not alone; in the streets many people wish one another a "Happy New Year!" The shops on the rue St.-Honoré display items "suitable for gifts," without saying what the occasion for a gift might be.

In the past thirty-five days, eighty-two persons "sneezed in the basket," to use a term from *Le Père Duchesne*. (Hébert has a slangy word for everything. The sack in which the severed heads are carried away is "*sans-farine*—no flour." The executioner is "Charlot.") One woman received a reprieve because she was pregnant.

Was that many or few? The condemned men came from all over France. The real butchery is in Lyons and Nantes, where there were large-scale revolts against the Republic. (Reports of hundreds being sent out on rafts and drowned in the Loire.)

There are four thousand *suspects* in the prisons of Paris. At the present rate it would take five years to execute all of them, if all are found guilty.

But why this obsession with treason? At the time of the September massacres the Prussians were thought to be at the gates of Paris. Now we have had one victory after another.

When I speak of an "obsession" I mean the committees, the leaders of the sections, the clubs, the Convention—one person out of a hundred. The other ninety-nine are obsessed by the shortage of bread and firewood, the high price of meat and soap, the terribly cold winter.

There are beggars on all the streets of Paris. And yet there is a shortage of labor and wages are rising. The streets are more filthy than ever. Paris has never been clean but now it is abominable. Mud and garbage.

Instead of the arrogant aristocrats of the past we have a new breed of bullies—*sans-culottes* wearing dirty clothes and vests à la carmagnole who think it is the mark of democracy to be rude. They stick a red bonnet on their heads, swagger into cafés and restaurants, demand service without paying and think they have the right to insult everyone.

Aside from Camille's *Vieux Cordelier* there are no political pamphlets, expressing an opinion has become too dangerous. But *La Nouvelle Sappho* is on sale everywhere—not only at the Palais-Egalité—an obscene Lesbian tale without even the literary grace that masks the horrors of *Justine*.

The police are so busy arresting political suspects that they neglect ordinary crimes. A peaceful citizen was attacked and murdered by four thugs who wanted his wallet—this in the Luxembourg Gardens at three in the afternoon. Bands of children dart through the streets, snatching purses, shoplifting; they meet in the parks to fight bloody battles and woe to the ordinary citizen who gets in their way.

The Palais-Egalité has been raided again and again, the brothels all forced to shut their doors. The result: there are whores all over the city, miserable shivering creatures more likely to inspire pity than desire.

Above all the cold is bitter and unremitting. The streets are deserted except in the early hours of the morning when there are lines at all the shops, pale faces wrapped in rags, waiting for bread.

Paris is half-dead.

January 5, 1794 (*16 Nivôse*): At the Café Manoury everyone reading number five of the *Vieux Cordelier*. After his near expulsion from the Jacobins, Camille is no longer on the high ground of Roman history; he has been forced down into the cockpit, with razors tied to his talons. The whole number is nothing more than an attack on those who say he is "a hair's breadth" from the guillotine, especially Hébert. The author of *Le Père Duchesne* is accused of being a late-comer to the Revolution, of having fancy dinners with the German banker Kock, of making an illegal fortune from the distribution of his paper to the army. (600,000 copies—has ever a journal been read by so many?)

One of the chess players observed, "The Attorney General of the Lamppost has a pack of enemies. And yet he makes a lot of sense."

It is astonishing that the leaders of the Revolution should be clawing at one another this way. Just two years ago *all* of them were part of a small group on the extreme left—Robespierre, Danton, Hébert, Collot, etc. Now with the royalists gone, the *Feuillants* gone, Lafayette gone, d'Orléans gone, the Gironde dead or in prison, one would think that the task of carrying the Revolution forward in the face of a coalition of all of Europe would be sufficient cause to hold the Mountain together. Not at all. Never have there been so many accusations of treason, so many plots and counterplots, with the guillotine waiting in the wings to assure the final disappearance of whoever is forced to exit from the stage. Camille remains the most human of the whole bunch; he asks for no one's head (and that may be his undoing); he pleads that everyone has made some mistakes in the last four years. Robespierre retains his ascendancy, in part because of his moral character, but even he has enemies. There are complaints that he is a true *sans-culotte,* that he defends the priests and the bourgeoisie.

Only the dead are exempt from hatred, and even they may succumb whether or not they can suffer—Mirabeau's ashes were tossed out of the Panthéon. At the Jacobins' someone proposed that between the busts of Lepelletier and Marat behind their tribune the society place a bust of Robespierre. "Agreed!" shouted an anonymous voice, "On condition that he too be stabbed!"

January 8 (*19 Nivôse*): Nothing on sale at the butcher's but roast pork, to avoid the maximum on raw meat.

I heard a market girl at the Place Maubert tell a customer, "You think they're only arresting traitors? Nonsense! If this goes on it will take the Opéra to hold the prisoners!"

January 9 (*20 Nivôse*): Another raid at the Palais-Egalité yesterday. Everyone had to line up in the garden to have his papers examined. By the time I was able to leave I was shaking from the cold.

At the Café Manoury the stout gentleman said that the leaders of the Commune would do better to get the streets clean instead of fighting among themselves. Perhaps he is not a police informer after all, only someone outspoken. Much talk of Camille and Hébert, speculation as to who will be the first to be "shortened by the national razor." Our politics have become a combat of gladiators and the crowd always cries for death.

January 11 (*22 Nivôse*): Thaw, many streets impassable because of melting ice. Some things do not change—the Auvergnats are out with their planks at street corners charging a fee for passage across the icy slush, just as I have seen them every winter for thirty-five years.

January 14 (*25 Nivôse*): Report of another stormy session of the Jacobins. Camille attacked for his *Vieux Cordelier* on the grounds that the latest numbers were read with great delight by all counterrevolutionaries and aristocrats. Robespierre defends him, but in a condescending way. "Camille is a spoiled child; his errors must be excused because of his good faith, but numbers three and four of the *Vieux Cordelier* should be burned." Camille, always impetuous, interrupts: "Well said, Robespierre, but burning is not an answer!" Danton takes up the quarrel for Camille in the name of the liberty of the press.

The liberty of the press remains the constant theme of the numbers of the *Vieux Cordelier* that have appeared since. "What is the chief difference between a republic and a monarchy? freedom to speak and write. Order liberty of the press in Moscow and tomorrow Moscow will be a republic." But the tone of these last numbers, with their citations from classical authors, their examples from the history of Greece, Rome and England, is hardly that of the moment. Camille constantly refers to his actions in '89, but '89 now seems a long time ago. At one point, responding to his critics, he says he feels like Galileo, muttering, "And yet the earth does move!" But Galileo said that only under his breath, and so was spared being burnt at the stake. Camille shouts his truths from the housetops.

January 16 (*27 Nivôse*): To the Hôtel de Ville to pick up the final papers of my divorce. In my sixtieth year I find myself once again a free man. Two great benefits of the Revolution—my daughter Agnès has recovered her liberty and I have recovered mine! Going through with this divorce is the only favor A. Lebègue has done me in the thirty years that we have known each other.

Despite the cold, despite the misery of this terrible winter, I feel twenty years younger; a great weight has been lifted from my shoulders. In the prologue to *Le Drame de la Vie,* written eight years ago, I am talking to Jeanette Rousseau, my first love. She now must be sixty-three but I imagine her as beautiful as ever. Our chairs are drawn close to a roaring fire; I tell her that I have been in love with her all my life, ever since that first glimpse of her in the church at Courgis in 1748, that it is she who has inspired all my passions ever since. And that remains the truth; I really believe that we fall in love only once, that all love springs from the same source within us. How short life seems, looking backwards, even when one has lived as long as I!

But now that prologue must be rewritten. The drama will end with the scene, inspired by my dream of last summer, in which A. Lebègue is murdered by Augé. That may not be accurate in "real life"—but my *real life* is in my works. If I am to be completely honest I must admit that there are certain episodes in *Monsieur Nicolas* that are based on the plots of my novels, rather than on factual events. Now that I am divorced I shall set the prologue to *Le Drame de la Vie* on my wedding night . . . the night of my marriage to JEANETTE ROUSSEAU, my first, my real, my only true love!

More than that, I will make that prologue a reality! I've written today to Sacy, to my two sisters Margot and Marianne, still living at la Bretonne, asking them to inquire in Courgis as to the whereabouts of Jeanette. When I last heard news of her she was a governess with a rich family in the Auvergne, never married, but that was four years ago. I've told them that the mission is urgent, since I am resolved to marry Jeanette, now that I am free!

The letter delivered to the post I find myself as nervous as an adolescent waiting for the answer. What a beautiful final chapter to my life this marriage will make when it comes to pass! Instead of closing with the sad tale of Sara, my last passion, *Monsieur Nicolas* will end with a happy old age, the well-merited fruit of a lifetime of devotion.

January 19 (*30 Nivôse*): Hué has been released after a month in prison. The Committee found there was nothing to the charges against him. Next it will be Garnier's turn. Each section in Paris plays out, in miniature, the struggle that occupies the Convention and the Commune.

Edmond is in bed with a fever; this horrible winter has been too much for him. Without his help I can do very little work.

January 21 (*2 Pluviôse*): A fête for the first anniversary of the execution of the king, or rather "Louis Capet, Last Tyrant of the French." My patrol was among those chosen to represent the section du Panthéon, so I was forced to attend. The Place de la Révolution was filled by an immense crowd, but how many were there by constraint? The Jacobins marched *en masse;* the entire Convention had its reserved place. The crowd shouted all the slogans of the day: LIBERTY OR DEATH!—WAR ON ALL TYRANTS!—VIVE LA REPUBLIQUE!" The high point of the occasion, and a barbarous high point it was, came when four "traitors" were executed on the same spot where Louis met his fate. The guillotine, that "humane" machine, was thus the altar of the principal ceremony and Sanson ("Charlot") its high priest. Several delegates of the Convention did not wish to be present at this republican *auto-da-fé* but the crowd wouldn't let them leave. Each time the blade fell I turned my eyes away, but I couldn't help trembling at the ferocious shouts of the mob.

When it was over the *cabaret de la guillotine* did a roaring business. In the evening all the theaters gave free performances.

January 23rd (*4 Pluviôse*): The men sweeping the sidewalks in front of the shops on the rue St.-Honoré shout, "To the Holy Guillotine! slanderer to the Holy Guillotine!" People in the street nod happily at this cry.

The story: a young man accused a schoolteacher of instructing his pupils in the principles of the Old Regime. At his trial the teacher produced an unusual witness—a four-year-old boy who recited the Declaration of the Rights of Man from memory. His accuser was guillotined in his place the next day.

January 25 (*6 Pluviôse*): At our section meeting last night, instructions on how to extract saltpeter from ashes, from cellar walls and floors. There is a shortage of gunpowder for our armies; on the advice of the great chemist Lavoisier this unusual source of an essential ingredient is being mined by householders all over France. But once the instructions were given the meeting disintegrated into a chorus of shouts and accusations as the

followers of Hué and Garnier denounced each other for graft, nepotism, despotism, pride, federalism, tyranny, etc.

January 26 (7 *Pluviôse*): A terrific wind blowing all day. I saw several strong men knocked down by sudden gusts. On three occasions I would have fallen myself if it had not been for the remains of the nimbleness of foot that made me such a great dancer in my youth. Chimneys were falling down all over.

But the turmoil wasn't all due to the weather. I went to the Ile St.-Louis and paused in the shelter of the *porte cochère* of the Hôtel de Lambert to watch what was happening on the Ile Louvois. A brawling rabble of tough men scrambled for the small shipment of firewood that had just been unloaded, using the logs as clubs to knock one another down.

In this neighborhood the Saltpeter Administration has turned the church of St.-Séverin into a gunpowder factory. Today the elaborately carved choir stalls were knocked down and chopped up for firewood to feed the caldrons. I heard people say they should have been sold as works of art instead and the money used to purchase fuel. Others were afraid the whole place would blow up, destroying the whole neighborhood.

At eight in the evening there was a mysterious fire in the former Augustin church on the quai de la Vallée, just off the Pont-Neuf. The fire spread to Didot's bookshop and consumed most of his stock. I was afraid that it would spread to Duchesne's or Mérigot's, both nearby. That would have been the end of what remains unsold of the edition of *Les Nuits de Paris*—which is, unfortunately, most of the copies in print.

January 27 (8 *Pluviôse*): This morning at the Place Maubert a housewife complained that there was nothing to buy. A pockmarked woman at one of the stalls shouted at her, "What are you doing here anyway, it's Sunday!"

The housewife shouted back that remarks like that one led to the guillotine.

"Screw them all!" came the answer. "They can do what they want but I'll never forget Sunday!"

At the Palais-Royal the whores are all in hiding. Their usual spots in the arcades are now occupied by pederasts who stare insolently at everyone who goes by.

January 29 (*10 Pluviôse*): In bed all day with dysentery caused by bad bread. Poor Marion is frantic taking care of Edmond, myself and her three babies.

February 2 (*14 Pluviôse*): Somewhat better. My landlord reports that everyone is talking about a woman in the neighborhood who stabbed her husband when he complained that his dinner wasn't ready.

February 4 (*16 Pluviôse*): Well enough to hazard a short tour of my isle. I found it all but deserted under a leaden sky. The thaw continues; I hope we have seen the last of freezing temperatures.

As I returned by the Pont-de-la-Tournelle I observed a scene that would have filled me with indignation five years ago. All I felt today was a distant amusement and a vague sense of shame.

A small boat loaded with barrels of wine docked at the port of the Halle des Vins. Waiting on the shore, a motley group of toughs, accompanied by a band of Amazons, those vociferous women, "furies of the guillotine," who are seen everywhere. As the craft tied up the women began to shout. Before the sailors had begun to unload their cargo the boat was boarded. I realized then that it was a gang of brigands.

The still winter air carried their shouts. "This wine belongs to us! Down with the merchants! Down with the rich! *Vivent les sans-culottes!*"

Not content simply to loot, one of the band unplugged one of the barrels. Two strong men held it aloft while the others rushed to gargle the dark red flow. The *pinard* splashed about; there was laughter, cheering. Those who had hesitated on the shore joined the bacchanal. Loungers on the quai streamed down, attracted by the noise, the sudden festivity. The bank was covered by a milling throng. The boat grew more and more crowded until, like a wounded soldier giving up the ghost—it sank. The icy gray water of the patient Seine churned up and mixed with the wine. There were shouts, cries, a frantic clambering of sodden bodies regaining the shore. The wine, patiently harvested and pressed by the peasants in some country town upstream, perhaps embarked at Courgis or Auxerre . . . the good plain wine stained the foam a lovely pink, then drifted away.

February 5 (*17 Pluviôse*): The Convention has abolished Negro slavery in the colonies, declaring that all residents of French territory are to be considered citizens of the Republic with all civic rights. An earlier decree abolished the National Lottery, as unworthy of a free people. Another ordered that all clothing, household goods and other necessities in the pawnshops be returned to their owners without payment.

February 10 (*22 Pluviôse*): The situation at the bakeries is somewhat better since the start of rationing, but the shortage of meat is terrible. Women start queueing up at the butcher shops at three in the morning.

February 15 (*27 Pluviôse*): On my way to visit Agnès I stop in a cabaret to get warm. Three hearty red-faced women are sitting at a table drinking beer out of mugs, all of them well on their way to getting good and drunk. They shout at one another in loud voices, complaining about the scarcity of meat, the high price of everything. The proprietor observes that they don't sound as if they're happy with the Republic. The loudest and most drunk of the trio shouts back, "We can complain all we want but screw it all, we're good republicans. The aristos and the English can wait for a revolt but as long as the Seine flows and we have a crust of bread and some beer we'll stay republicans no matter how much we're screwed by thieves like you!"

February 16 (*28 Pluviôse*): To the Palais-Egalité. At the Café de Foy only a sprinkling of silent patrons. Someone reads aloud from the newspapers; there are no comments. After that only whispered conversations about clandestine gaming dens and where to buy good wine. There are more drunkards in Paris these days than ever before. The child prostitutes still wait in the galerie Montansier, the pederasts are at their posts in the arcades.

February 18 (*30 Pluviôse*): An evasive letter from my sisters in Sacy. They say nothing about Jeanette Rousseau, advising me only that I shouldn't think of getting married. I had forgotten that as devout Catholics they wouldn't consider my divorce valid.

February 20 (*2 Ventôse*): At the Place Maubert this morning a woman shouted, "If I weren't afraid, I'd tell the new regime to go fuck itself!" Strange logic.

Edmond is still sick. I help Marion as much as I can by going to market. A work of genius is waiting to be completed and I am out with my basket buying turnips!

I've heard that the women of the Faubourg St.-Antoine have been stopping wagons from the country on the road from Vincennes, making off with eggs, chickens, produce, etc.—whatever is destined for the markets in Paris. Sometimes they pay for what they take; sometimes they don't. We went on a house-to-house search for hoarders. A housewife who had three dozen eggs in her larder (for a family of seven) had her supply requisitioned.

People complain that the suspects in the prisons eat better than anyone else. Perhaps they do; never knowing what day will be their last they will pay anything for a good meal. Rumors of orgies in the prisons, inspired by hope as well as despair—any woman who is certified to be pregnant the day she is sentenced is spared until her delivery.

February 21 (*3 Ventôse*): A riot at the Place Maubert. A mob of angry women seized a shipment of butter before it was carried into the dairy.

February 25 (*7 Ventôse*): The only lively spot in Paris is the courtyard of the Palais de Justice at the entrance to the Conciergerie. Relatives and friends of the accused on trial stand vigil, praying and weeping; a crowd of idlers waits to see the condemned men brought to the *charettes;* the whores pick up whatever trade comes their way.

Fragnières witnessed a grotesque execution today. A ninety-year-old senile man had to be *carried* up the ladder and placed on the plank. The crowd hooted at the executioner.

My little Swiss is but one of the many curious Parisians who find the daily beheadings their chief distraction. About a third of them, and the noisiest third, are women. They form the hard core of the crowd on the Place de la Révolution, which otherwise fluctuates with the weather and the fame of the victims.

February 28 (*10 Ventôse*): The reports from Lyons make the Terror in Paris seem like child's play—twenty, thirty "counterrevolutionaries" guillotined every day. Meanwhile Carrier has been recalled from Nantes, preceded by his reputation of exterminating angel. How many thousands have perished there, shot down by firing squads in mass executions or drowned in the Loire?

Enough to frighten even the Committee of Public Safety. Here in Paris, Carrier has been speaking at the Cordeliers, now entirely run by Hébert and his friends. That club has expelled Camille (one of its founders), forbidden him to use the title *Le Vieux Cordelier*. Camille responds that he is an "old Cordelier" because he has lived in the neighborhood for years.

March 3 (*13 Ventôse*): Robespierre has been sick for two weeks, or else merely lying low, as his enemies hint. Meanwhile his young disciple Saint-Just has served as his spokesman at the Convention, if spokesman indeed he is. Saint-Just's style at least is very much his own, lucid and yet obscure, hinting at more than he says, impersonal and lapidary. "The Terror is a two-edged sword. . . . What constitutes a Republic is the total destruction of everything opposed to it. . . . Monarchy is not a king, it is vice; the Republic is not a senate, it is virtue. . . . The poor are the great of this world; they have the right to speak as masters to governments that neglect them. . . . Those who take a Revolution only halfway are digging their own graves. The Revolution leads us to recognize the principle that whoever has shown himself to be the enemy of the Nation cannot be an owner of property. . . ."

And from that *principle* he deduces a decree that goes far into the "*terra incognita* beyond Marat"—the property of all suspects arrested for political reasons is to be confiscated and turned over to needy patriots. Immediately adopted. The Terror has become an instrument for the redistribution of wealth.

March 5 (*15 Ventôse*): The weather suddenly better, almost a spring day. I heard one wag remark, "It feels like we're already in Germinal!" A long promenade to stretch my legs. On the boulevards and the streets near the Palais-Egalité, once the exclusive preserve of the rich and elegant, many poor families taking the air; satisfied expressions that seem to say, "Now all this belongs to us!"

The Cordeliers have hung a black veil over their *tableau* of the Rights of Man, called for a new insurrection. But Paris hardly seems ready to respond. Rumors that there will be new massacres in the prisons.

March 7 (*17 Ventôse*) : The Cordeliers have beaten a retreat, said they only meant a "conditional" insurrection (whatever that may be), unveiled the Rights of Man. A new triumph for the Jacobins, which is to say Robespierre.

March 8 (*18 Ventôse*) : Awakened in the early morning by a pounding at my door. "Citizen, your help is needed!"

I open and see the men of my patrol. Is there an insurrection after all? No, only a riot.

I dress hurriedly and go out, taking my pike. On the rue Galande two hundred women are besieging a butcher shop. It was five in the morning, the shop was closed. If ever there had been a queue it had dissolved into an angry mob.

We were posted in front of the shop and told to let no one pass. Frankly I was terrified that we would be torn limb from limb. The butcher himself, a Citizen Payen, tried to speak to the Amazons. He shouted that he was a loyal patriot and would sell to everyone at the maximum price, but his delivery had not yet appeared and his shop was bare. He even offered to let a delegation inside to see that he was telling the truth, but Rollin decided, probably wisely, that the shop would be wrecked if this were permitted.

By seven the delivery had still not arrived and the women began to drift away. I heard one woman say that she would rather pay 30 sous for a pound of meat than have nothing at the maximum of fourteen.

March 14 (*24 Ventôse*) : General astonishment in Paris. Hébert arrested along with other leaders of the Cordeliers and the Commune. The accusation: plotting against the Committee of Public Safety, planning an insurrection, royalism. *Royalism?—le Père Duchesne!* The "conspiracy" is also held responsible for the shortage of food, ties with foreign powers, etc. In short they are enemies of Robespierre.

March 17 (*27 Ventôse*) : Fragnières says the Terror is accelerating. Every night men are arrested who have no idea why they are being sent to jail. The Tribunal has accusations written out in advance with the name of the "suspect" left blank.

March 20 (*30 Ventôse*) : Even the children seem to know

about the trial of Hébert. I saw two boys playing on the terrace overlooking the river at the Tuileries. One of them pointed at the guillotine on the Place de la Révolution.

"Even *le Père Duchesne* will put his head through that window!" he cried in a high, childish voice.

"And sneeze in the basket!" the other answered. "He must be having a bloody fit to find himself in jail!"

After which they enacted "The Frightful Anger of Le Père Duchesne," with all the *Damns! Buggers!* and *Fuckits!* in the right places, a perfect parody of Hébert's style, concluding with a mock execution.

Children's games. . . .

March 23 (*3 Germinal*) : A letter from my sisters in Sacy telling me that Jeanette Rousseau died two or three years ago in Clermont! What I've written about her in *Monsieur Nicolas* will remain her eternal monument.

I've learned that Minette de St.-Leger has obtained a divorce. We had an affair in '83, after which she married. But probably I'm too poor for her now.

March 24 (*4 Germinal*) : Hébert and nineteen others executed today at the Place de la Révolution. Among them poor old mad Anacharsis Clootz, "Orator of the Human Race," in prison since December, accused of being a secret agent for his compatriots, the Prussians. An unlikely charge against that bizarre man who dated his letters, "Paris, Capital of the Universe."

A grand festival of death, the crowd larger than at the execution of the king. The audience of Hébert's journal, the most widely circulated in history, was anxious to procure a last sensation from the sensational Père Duchesne. And the attendance was swelled by all the hidden royalists and defrocked priests, delighted to see the end of their most ferocious enemies—the blasphemer Hébert, the atheist Clootz, the men who had closed the churches, claimed the right of permanent insurrection.

Some clever entrepreneurs had erected stands on the corners of the square; seats were sold at scandalous prices. A file of elegant carriages at the Champs-Elysées served the same purpose, men standing on their roofs to watch the blade descend.

The cemetery of the Madeleine is full. A new ditch for the

bodies of the victims has been dug at the Parc Monceau, not far from the Etoile.

At the Place Maubert I heard a woman ask, "What will become of us poor people since we are betrayed by everyone who had our confidence?"

Paris is calm.

BAL A LA VICTIME

APRIL–DECEMBER 1794

THE armies of the Republic triumph on all fronts. Out of a nation of twenty-five million men, women and children there are a million men under arms, the largest army in Europe, the largest army the world has ever seen. No longer are they the motley "volunteers of '92." The Republic demands discipline. The Convention sends out its proconsuls with the command, "Be victorious!" Most of the officers of the Old Regime have either deserted to the enemy or been called to their last parade on the Place de la Révolution, their places taken by fresh men, trained in action. New generals rise from the ranks: Hoche, Jourdan, Massena, Buonaparte. Belgium is reconquered, the Prussians repulsed, Spain invaded, the Austrians in retreat, Italy ripe for "liberation." The Committee of Public Safety acts as general staff for this immense army, or rather twelve armies, grappling with the combined forces of all the crowned heads of Europe. It also governs France, sending its decrees to the terrified Convention for automatic approval.

Paris has become an immense factory for the war machine. There are forges at the Invalides, the Luxembourg Gardens, the former Place Royale turning out the steel that can no longer be imported from Sweden because of the English blockade. Cellars and fireplaces yield the saltpeter that supplies the immense gunpowder plant at Grenelle. Churches and convents are so many quartermaster depots; women sew tents and uniforms, children roll bandages. And not only Paris—the same scenes are repeated all over France, a nation surrounded by enemies, determined to prove that a republic of free men can defend itself against an overwhelming coalition of the slaves of kings.

The Terror continues, politics in a new form. There are eight thousand suspects in the prisons of Paris alone.

The night of March 30th (10 Germinal) Danton and Camille are arrested, sent to the Luxembourg, now a prison. The order is signed by Robespierre, Saint-Just and the rest of the Committee. No one would have thought it possible.

The Revolution has become the Titan Saturn, devouring its own children. Everyone makes this observation, but in whispers. Danton, who rallied all of France with his cry, "Audacity! audacity! and still more audacity!" Camille who gave the signal for the siege of the Bastille, whom Robespierre himself called "a good heart, an ardent republican," just three months earlier, the Attorney General of the Lamppost!

The accusations are the usual ones: conspiracy, corruption, ties with foreigners, etc.

The real accusation: Camille's having written "Clemency is also a Revolutionary measure," Danton's having defended him.

Let the historians of 1994 examine the dossier if the records of our tortured era are still available at that time. I wept at the news. Camille, the perfect young man of '89, that bright spring when the Palais-Royal represented the hopes of mankind instead of its despair. The occasional excesses of his pen came from his fervent and hasty heart. But also his *"Vieux Cordelier,"* its humanity, its sense of history, its wit, its call for justice and mercy. All that is "old style" in this era of republican severity. But I trust the human heart.

Brought before the Revolutionary Tribunal, Camille declared: "I am thirty-three, the age of the *sans-culotte* Jesus, a bad age for revolutionaries." Danton: "My name is Danton, age thirty-five. My residence tomorrow will be nothingness but I shall live forever in the Panthéon of History!"

According to the law the trial had to run at least three days if there was sufficient evidence. And what evidence! the whole history of the Revolution. The second day was taken up by the interrogation of Danton. The great leader of '92 made full use of that voice that had thundered so often at the Cordeliers, the Commune, the Convention. He was heard in the street outside the Palais de Justice. Word spread through Paris that the accused had turned prosecutor, charging the court with falsifying the evidence against him, warning against the tyranny of the Committee of Public Safety, demanding that sixteen delegates of the Convention be called as witnesses in his behalf. Under the eyes of the terrible judges the crowd in the courtroom applauded.

The next morning Saint-Just appeared before the Convention. Only two hundred deputies were present, the rest preferring to remain out of sight. Saint-Just announced that a new "plot" had been revealed to the Committee, a conspiracy to free Danton and Desmoulins, release all suspects from the prisons, assassinate the members of the Committee. He asked (or rather commanded) the delegates, "to prove the distance between you and those who are guilty." The Convention immediately passed a decree ordering that, "any defendant who resists or insults the Court will be silenced." There was no debate. The vote was unanimous.

The decree was rushed to the Palais de Justice. The judges announced that the trial was over. Camille had prepared a refutation of all the charges against him. In a gesture of childish rage he squashed his notes into a paper ball, hurled it at the bench.

The jury went out and returned. The sentence had never been in doubt. The *charettes* were waiting in the courtyard of the Conciergerie; Sanson was waiting at the guillotine.

Camille grabbed his seat, refusing to leave. It took three men to carry him out of the courtroom. He shouted insults the whole time.

Months later Mercier told me Danton's last words, as transmitted by the prison grapevine:

"I created the first Revolutionary Tribunal to prevent another September Massacre, not to be an inhuman plague.... Everything is in a terrible mess, Robespierre doesn't know how to boil an egg, I wish I could leave him my balls.... The fucking crowd in the streets will be stupid enough to shout, 'Vive la République!' "

It was also reported that Robespierre had never been more friendly toward his old classmate Camille than on the eve of his arrest.

I saw the *charettes* as they passed the Palais-Egalité. Danton seemed resigned. But Camille shouted, "People of Paris! your best friends are being killed! Who gave you the cockade? Who told you to attack the Bastille? *I am Camille Desmoulins!*"

The sparse crowd paid no attention. The spring of '89 was too long ago, an epoch, a century. Paris was too occupied with other affairs. The Terror no longer terrified. The Revolution had become a machine. Only the regulars were found at the Place de la Révolution, nothing like the huge turnout for Hébert.

Danton told Sanson, "Show my head to the people! It is good to look at!" Camille struggled so fiercely against the ropes that bound him that he was bare to the waist when he mounted the scaffold.

His lovely wife, Lucille, took the same road a week later, accused of that "plot" to free her husband.

She went in the same *charette* as another widow, the wife of Hébert—Hébert who had attacked Camille, whom Camille had attacked in the *Vieux Cordelier*. Also the ex-bishop of Paris. Also Chaumette of the Commune, the man who had closed the churches, organized the Fête de la Raison at Notre-Dame. A mixed salad. All were accused of plotting against the Convention. In prison.

The Terror had become an hallucination. It had no more enemies and therefore it accelerated, of its own momentum. But the executions became boring. When the *charettes* went by, the shops on the rue St.-Honoré put up their shutters.

After the terrible winter, spring was a blessing. It would have been a lovely spring if Paris had not been hungry. The months had lovely names, Germinal (month of seeding), Floréal (month of flowers), Prairial (month of meadows)—year II of the Republic, one nation, indivisible. Most people still said April, May, June.

To pay for the war the Convention went on putting out *assignats*. In theory they were still backed by the confiscated property of the *emigrés*. In practice they were only pieces of paper, worth less and less every day. Aside from those few articles controlled by the maximum, prices continued to rise. Everyone spent whatever he earned as fast as possible—why save? Whatever goods appeared in the shops were snapped up. Certain restaurants at the Palais-Egalité charged a month's salary of an ordinary worker for a dinner. But somehow they managed to offer delicacies that were available nowhere else; their menus were three pages long while Paris was starving. Their customers—merchants, speculators, and a new class known as "capitalists" who had made fortunes selling supplies to the army, all of them cheerfully getting rid of their money, which would be worth less the next day.

In three-score dance halls the *sans-culottes* jigged the carmagnole. On the *décadi* the boulevards were crowded. All of this gave the capital a false air of gaiety, like the flush of a fever that reddens the cheeks of a sick woman.

My section continued to meet twice a week at St.-Etienne-du-Mont. I went infrequently. Everyone went infrequently, aside from a small band of intriguers. Hué and Garnier were both arrested and rearrested on various accusations, one in April, one in June. It slowly became obvious that the Committee did not want anyone to protest the shortage of bread, the shortage of meat, the high price of everything else. Why not? We were at war.

The decree that ordered the property of all suspects distributed to the poor was never carried out. Delegations of workers went to the Hôtel de Ville and asked for higher wages. But Hébert was gone, Chaumette was gone; they were turned down. When they talked of striking they were threatened with the guillotine. The most ardent *sans-culottes* grew discouraged.

One bright day in May I met Daniol le Manceau, my former employee, on the Place Maubert. I had last seen him in July '92, the era of the *barrière de faveur*. I was sure then that he was trying to trap me, to prove that I was a royalist. To my surprise he greeted me with an affable smile:

"Hello boss, I'm glad to see you're still around. The Revolution is all fucked up, don't you think?"

"I wouldn't say that," I answered, on guard.

"We're back in '89 and I need some extra work. Do you have a place for an old friend?"

I told him I no longer had a shop. We talked. He had tried

to volunteer for the army but had been refused because he was too sick—a bad chest. He looked ten years older. He had married and had two children. They all lived in one room in an attic in the Faubourg St.-Antoine. He was sure his wife supplemented their income by walking the streets, but he didn't feel like asking her about it. Whatever money she earned was welcome.

"First that bitch stabbed Marat," he said. "Then they told us that *le Père Duchesne* was a traitor. Now I think they're all traitors since we don't have enough to eat."

"Even Robespierre?"

"A lawyer, a bourgeois, a speechmaker, a bastard like all the rest of them. His turn will come."

I reminded him of July '92, the terrace des Feuillants at the Tuileries. He grinned like the cocky redhead he has always been.

"I'm sorry about that, boss; some friends put me up to it. But you were too smart for us. I always thought you were a real *sans-culotte*. I've got a job setting type for a newspaper but I'd like some work for my spare time. Can you use me?"

As it happened I could. Poor Edmond was still sick and *Monsieur Nicolas* was going very slowly. But I could offer very little money. No matter; Daniol came to help me on the *décadi* and whenever else he was free.

I still went to the Café Manoury from time to time but there were fewer papers to read. Marat, Hébert, Desmoulins, all the great voices had been silençed. Those that remained all offered the same stuff—the minutes of the Convention, the speeches of Robespierre and Saint-Just, news from the front. No commentaries.

The Convention ordered that the remains of Rousseau were to be transported to the Panthéon. But it seemed a reflex action. Even Saint-Just admitted, "The Revolution has become a routine."

If Edmond was still sick, part of the trouble was the shortage of nourishing food. Meat was rationed in April but that only seemed to reduce the supply. Marion and I lived on vegetables and bread, giving Edmond our allotment of meat and poultry, sometimes that of the children also. But nothing seemed to help. He lay on his narrow camp bed, coughed, perspired and moaned. Poor Marion was haggard and drained, caring for him, caring for the children, nursing her baby, waiting in queues at the market, at the bakery, at the butcher's. Agnès came to help from time to time but not often enough. I understood her; so much of her youth had been wasted by her horrible marriage that she was in no mood for sacrifice now that she was free. I wrote to A. Lebègue, no longer my wife, thank god! asking her if she could do anything for the young couple. But the woman was as selfish as ever. She came by once with toys for the children, drank tea and left. Monster! Whatever was left of my savings from those days before the flood (before the Revolution) vanished rapidly. I had no regrets about the expense; each time the *assignat* fell what remained of my fortune was diminished.

I continued to work, to preserve my sanity and because work is the purpose of my life. When I was alone I set as many pages of *Monsieur Nicolas* as I have types for. When Daniol could help me the old press clanked away—we spun wheels, worked up a sweat, breathed the heady scent of printer's ink. For a few hours I was alive again. I felt that I had a clandestine shop; *Monsieur Nicolas* had become an underground work.

It is not counterrevolutionary, to be sure, but it is not in line with the Republic of Virtue as preached by those two Jesuits, Saint-Just and Robespierre. Its doctrine is a belief in the human heart and the human heart will always be the enemy of any despotism, the enemy of the Reason of State of the Old Regime that sent its enemies into exile or the Bastille, the enemy of the logic of the Terror, that sends the great chemist Lavoisier to the guillotine because he was once a tax collector. This Republic of Virtue chills my soul with its icy logic whose conclusion is the "national razor."

Why did Danton perish? Because he said, "I would rather be guillotined than a guillotiner." Why did Camille perish? Because he wept when Brissot and his associates were condemned to death, because he proposed a Committee of Clemency. Both of them had committed errors, even crimes, but it was neither their errors nor their crimes that led to their destruction, rather the goodness of their hearts. Readers of 1994, remember this! Judge any government by its humanity, not merely the humanity of its ideals but the humanity of its treatment of those who have erred, according to its lights.

True humanity has its source in love of the flesh; there is no other way to be a human being. The Puritans à la Robespierre will read *Monsieur Nicolas* and sneer, "Ah, what a terrible life!" Please don't pity me, automatons who have never felt anything! please don't pity me because in my sixtieth year I find myself almost penniless, alone, without hope, without consolation! because so many moments of happiness turned sour afterwards! Those moments were true when I felt them, even if my hopes were dashed. I prefer a thousand times to have felt, to have lost, than to have been a vegetable like you! I reject your pity because it is a blasphemy against joy!

There was only one area in which Robespierre proved more tolerant than his predecessors and that was a surprise. In an important speech on May 7th the Incorruptible reaffirmed his belief in freedom of religion, warning that persecution of priests and the pious would only turn many simple people against the Revolution. It seemed a bit late for that advice, but to tell the truth the lawyer from Arras had said the same thing many times before. Now that his power was almost absolute his advice became action. The Convention decreed that "France recognizes the existence of a Supreme Being."

The Commune eased its regulations on the *décadi,* permitting shops to stay open or closed whatever day they wished. Many chose days at random, a different day each *decade.* By chance these all happened to be Sundays, old style.

In May the sections ordered "Fraternal Suppers" all over Paris to cheer people up. We had one in the Place Maubert. Tables were constructed of planks, decorated with flowers. But the fraternal generosity of the great Fédération of 1790 had vanished. Everyone brought his own meal, the rich as little as possible to hide their affluence, the needy as much as possible to hide their poverty. Thus a sort of equality was achieved, but it was a stingy repast; fear had dried up charity. Only the children had a good time, crawling under the tables and playing tag in the long twilight.

Less fraternal were two attempted assassinations. Returning home at one in the morning, Collot d'Herbois was stopped by a Citizen Amiral, formerly a clerk for the lottery. Amiral pointed a pistol at Collot's face, pulled the trigger. The gun misfired. Word spread that the inept assassin, hauled off to jail, had declared that he meant to kill Robespierre but didn't know how to get to him.

The next day Cécile Renault, daughter of a stationer near Notre-Dame, tried to play Charlotte Corday. She muffed the part, specially the last scene. Knocking at the door of Robespierre's house, rue St.-Honoré, she asked to see the Incorruptible. Robespierre's hosts were more wary than Marat's housekeeper. The girl is seized, searched. There is nothing on her. Asked what she wanted with Robespierre she answers, "To see what a tyrant looks like." But it is found that she left a basket in a shop nearby. In it, two small knives and a change of clothing, the latter, she admits, the costume she had chosen to wear at the guillotine. She is carted off to jail.

The Jacobins, the sections, the Commune, the Convention—all send Robespierre messages of joy that he has escaped. But the fatal word has been spoken aloud—*tyrant.* In the report on this incredibly inept attempt—immediately attributed to Pitt—an English spy is quoted speaking of "Robespierre's troops . . . Robespierre's navy . . . Robespierre's government . . ." as if France were a dictatorship. The papers print the report, without comment.

A "Festival of the Supreme Being" had been ordered by the Convention in the same decree that renounced atheism. The day was set for June 8th (20 Prairial). We had seen so many fêtes in Paris in the last four years! The Fédération of 1790, the fête for the Constitution of 1791, the fête de la Liberté of 1792, the fête of August 10th the summer before, the absurd Fête de la Raison in the fall—not to mention all the grandiose funerals, Mirabeau, Lepelletier, etc.—yet another did not arouse much enthusiasm.

Nonetheless the preparations were immense. On every public building the inscription: "The people of France recognizes the existence of the Supreme Being and the Immortality of the Soul." Garlands everywhere, flowers, branches covered with the fresh leaves of spring. A plethora of flags and banners on the barges anchored in the Seine.

Anyone arriving in Paris that day would have thought the capital was celebrating the end of the war, the final triumph of the Revolution. Many people thought that that indeed was the case, that Robespierre would use this occasion to announce the end of the Terror. After all, our armies were successful and all factions annihilated, at least their leaders. Gone were the Royalists, the Girondins, the Enragés, the Hébertists, the Indulgents. The Revolutionary Tribunal took a holiday to attend the ceremonies and the guillotine on the Place de la Révolution was hidden by heavy draperies.

At eight in the morning cannon were fired to call everyone to the Tuileries, now the Jardin National. It was a serene June day, not a cloud in the sky. I set off in my old suit and to my surprise felt shabby. No red bonnets, instead everyone in the best clothes they had. I even saw women wearing jewelry, long avoided as a cause for *suspicion.* There were flowers at every window, flowers in every cap and coiffure, a sea of flowers at the Tuileries. A young girl offered me a rose. "Take this, Papa! you look sad!"

The crowd was so great that I couldn't get near the Jardin National. I went instead to the Ile St.-Louis, which I had neglected too long. A complete tour of the isle, all my *dates,* all my *inscriptions.* That was my own private fête.

I report what I learned the next day at the Café Manoury:

An amphitheater had been constructed before the palace. In the center, the seats reserved for the Convention. Four statues by David covered the basin of the great fountain in the center of the garden, four monsters constructed of flammable material: Atheism, Discord, Egotism, Ambition.

It was Robespierre's occasion, inspired by him, the consecration of his triumph, and every detail of his conduct was noticed. The Convention had elected him Presiding Officer for that week so that he should have the principal role in the ceremony.

He wore a new suit of sky-blue silk, his wig curled and powdered. In his hands a large bouquet of spring flowers and green wheat stalks. But he arrived a bit late, after everyone else had taken their places, and people murmured, "He thinks he is already king!"

The crowd greeted him with cheers. The Convention, already seated, was silent.

He made a long speech, printed in all the papers the next day. But only a few words floated across the vast space between the idol of the day and the crowd. "Today, transports of pure joy . . . Tomorrow we resume the struggle, etc. . . ."

It was enough. Everyone knew the Terror would continue.

That finished, the Incorruptible descended from the Tribune and walked alone across the open space to David's four monsters. There he lit a torch which he used to ignite the combustible allegories. The grotesque figures crinkled away and out of the flames there emerged yet another colossus, this time a statue of Wisdom. But as the four monsters had burned a bit too slowly, Wisdom appeared completely blackened by soot.

The next phase of the ceremony was to take place at the Champ-de-Mars. With Robespierre in the lead, the Convention set off on foot, the delegates encircled by a tricolor ribbon. Robespierre walked at his usual fast clip. The Convention followed with that slowness natural to a large body of men walking together. The distance between the leader and the led increased. When he had crossed the bridge Robespierre stopped, turned around, and found himself alone.

At the Champ-de-Mars, a new version of the now traditional "Mountain of the Fatherland," larger this year. Since he was the first to arrive Robespierre led the ascent and found himself at the summit of the peak. The Convention sat below him, then the Commune, etc. The people stood on the open space all about.

A *sans-culotte* in the crowd, looking up at this tableau, shouted, "The bastard! It isn't enough that he's in charge of everything—he wants to be God!"

Everyone sang a "Hymn to the Supreme Being" especially

composed for the occasion. There was an artillery salute. Then everyone went home.

The next morning the drapes were removed from the guillotine.

Instead of the end of the Terror we had the law of 22 Prairial.

This law was entirely the work of Robespierre, seconded by the rest of the Committee of Public Safety. When it was read to the Convention, a delegate shouted, "If this passes I'll blow my brains out!" It passed. He didn't.

When I read the text in the newspapers I could hardly believe my eyes. It was but one step short of being no law at all, a blank check to the Revolutionary Tribunal to execute anyone they wished.

"There are to be four Courts instead of one, each with three judges and nine jurors.

"The Revolutionary Tribunal is instituted to deal with the enemies of the people. Its sentence is either innocence or death.

"What is sufficient evidence in any case is to be determined by the good sense of the jurors, their conscience and patriotism.

"Every citizen has the duty to denounce all conspirators or counterrevolutionaries that he knows.

"Those accused will be interrogated in public. A preliminary investigation by the judges for purposes of investigation is not necessary.

"If there are written or moral proofs of guilt, no testimony need be heard.

"No lawyers for the defense. The innocent will be protected by the patriotism of the jurors. Conspirators do not deserve to have an attorney."

The term enemy of the people was defined as "anyone who corrupts public morals, spreads false rumors, spreads false opinions, spreads discouragement . . ."

With this law on the books, Robespierre seemed to have the perfect instrument in hand to do whatever he wanted. What was strange was that instead of acting he seemed to retire, avoiding the Convention, avoiding the meetings of the Committee, staying out of the public eye. But then he had done that before, saying he was sick.

As if to compensate for the terrible winter, summer came early. For weeks the inhabitants of the district near the Place de la Révolution and the citizens whose houses overlooked the cemeteries of the Madeleine and the Parc Monceau—in short, the neighbors of the guillotine and its debris—had been complaining of strange odors, miasmas, maladies. Imagination certainly played its role. The cemetery at the Parc Monceau had been open for more than a year and had received several thousand remains of natural deaths; the guillotine added less than two hundred. Moreover those districts contain mostly villas surrounded by gardens; they are open to the north wind, the west wind—almost the country. None the less people said the odor was intolerable and feared an epidemic.

And then the shopkeepers of the rue St.-Honoré, still the most frequented and elegant street of Paris, complained that they were losing business because of the daily passage of the fatal *charettes* on their way to the "little window." Rough crowds filled the street to cheer or jeer and the shops were forced to close their doors during the busiest hours of the day.

In response to this sentiment the Revolutionary Tribunal decided to move the guillotine to the ruins of the Bastille. Then it reconsidered. The neighborhood around the former fortress was heavily populated; the same complaints might be repeated. It was decided that the guillotine would be set up at the *barrière du Trône,* at the far edge of the Faubourg St.-Antoine, really an isolated spot with no houses close by aside from the deserted convent of Picpus. The courtyard of the convent could serve as a cemetery, protected as it was by high walls with open fields all about.

The guillotine was moved to this new location on June 12th, three days after the terrible law of 22 Prairial had begun to speed up the machinery of the Terror at an alarming rate. Previously there had been five, ten, fifteen victims a day. Now it shot up to thirty, forty, fifty, even sixty.

The site at the *barrière du Trône* was isolated, but to reach it the *charettes* had to pass through the whole length of the rue St.-Antoine and its extension, the rue du Faubourg St.-Antoine—one of the most crowded, agitated, bustling streets of Paris and one that went through the poorest and most violent neighborhoods. This meant that five or six times as many people were exposed to the sight of the victims on their way to the scaffold as when the route had been the rue St.-Honoré. And the new spectators were the same people who had created the Réveillon riots in April '89, stormed the Bastille, stormed the Tuileries August 10, 1792, and who now found themselves still as poor as ever.

St.-Antoine did not take the transfer as a compliment. When he came to help me with my press Daniol grumbled, "The Holy Guillotine stinks too much for the fine folk at the Madeleine with their fine noses, so now they've dumped it on us, the poor!"

Five days later (June 17–29 Prairial) the *faubourg* witnessed the longest procession of *charettes* yet seen in Paris, fifty-four men and women condemned for participation in what was called the Conspiracy of the Red Shirts—not because any red shirts were involved but because the Tribunal had them all dressed in red robes for their execution, men, women and two young girls. Sinister theatrics, inspired perhaps by the red robe worn by Charlotte Corday. (But for many people Charlotte Corday had become a sort of saint.)

The report on this conspiracy was strange, to say the least. It began with the girl who had fluffed the assassination of Robespierre (Cécile Renault), and the lottery clerk who had fired on Collot d'Herbois (Amiral). These two were linked together, along with their families and associates. It was then claimed that they were part of a grand plot involving, among others, a certain Mme. de Saint-Amaranthe, who ran one of the best-known gambling dens of the Palais-Royal. The whole tale was complicated and improbable. The family of Cécile Renault were implicated because portraits of Louis XVI and Marie-Antoinette were found in their house when it was searched. Imagine a plot, involving at least fifty-four persons, that ends with a gun that misfires and a girl who leaves her weapons in a shop on the rue St.-Honoré! In normal times such a trial would have taken months. Now they were all tried, sentenced and executed in one day. Included in the lot were several men who had been called to testify as witnesses and found themselves condemned to immediate death at the last minute.

It took the *charettes* three hours to go the whole length of the rue St.-Antoine. They were accompanied—and this was exceptional—by battalions of troops and fieldpieces. At the *barrière du Trône* it took the guillotine an hour of rising and falling to complete its grisly task. Which allowed only slightly more than a minute per victim.

Paris was impressed. But I heard people ask, "What more would be done to the *assassins of Robespierre* if Robespierre were the king?"

Everyone assumed that the Tribunal had acted under Robespierre's orders. But the whole affair was uncharacteristic. The Incorruptible had always remained a hidden and impersonal leader, rarely appearing in public, preferring the select audience of the Jacobins and the Convention to any more popular tribune, often working behind the scenes. People began to wonder if the Fête de l'Etre Suprême had gone to his head.

Street vendors suddenly appeared everywhere, hawking hastily written pamphlets: "The Holy Guillotine—the Fifty-Four Red Shirts—Robespierre's Assassins." In lurid terms these repeated the story of the conspiracy exposed by the vigilance of the Tribunal and its informers. All, of course, said the plot's success would have been a horrible disaster.

But Robespierre did not appear in a very good light. The more that was said about this affair, the less believable it became. And it was mentioned that Robespierre's brother had frequented Mme. de Saint-Amaranthe's gambling den. One pamphlet said that Robespierre himself had paid that establishment a visit in the company of a minor actor from the Comédie Française. More uncharacteristic behavior for the Incorruptible.

Even stranger was another exposé, *"Les Mystères de la Mère de Dieu*—The Mysteries of the Mother of God." Another plot, this one reported by Vadier of the Committee of Public Safety. A new kind of conspiracy—counterrevolutionary mysticism.

In an attic on the rue Contrescarpe behind the Panthéon

there lived an old woman, Catherine Theot or Theos, self-proclaimed prophetess and "Mother of God," head of an occult sect whose adepts were mostly young girls of the neighborhood. This ancient sorceress had first come to the attention of the police in 1779, ten years before the Revolution. She was sent to the Bastille, interrogated, then transferred to an insane asylum where she remained for three years. Once free she returned to her old practices, living in obscurity and poverty in her attic room. When the Revolution began she claimed it was the fulfillment of prophecies she had heard directly from the mouths of the Archangel Gabriel and the Virgin Mary. This convinced others of her special powers; her sect flourished in secret. One of her converts was an ex-monk and ex-deputy to the Constituent Assembly, Christopher Gerle.

The Committees were informed of the existence of this sect. Among a mass of other "evidence," their spies discovered that Gerle, an ardent Jacobin as well as devotee of la Mère de Dieu, had been given a certificate of patriotism signed by Robespierre himself.

There was a great deal more—the ceremonies in the attic, seven virgins each giving the eighty-four year old prophetess seven kisses as they washed her feet each morning, prophecies by Nostradamus, a book of black magic entitled, "The Clavicles of Rabbi Salomon," etc. Out of this information the police fashioned yet another "conspiracy."

Vadier made his report on June 15th, just a week after the Fête de l'Etre Suprême. From the sublime to the ridiculous. All of Catherine Theot's mumbo-jumbo was exposed to the Convention with the utmost gravity as a serious threat to the security of the Republic. Robespierre was presiding officer, but certain delegates could not help giggling. The titters spread from bench to bench.

When it was reported that the "Mother of God" had pronounced Robespierre the Messiah named in her revelations, the Redeemer who would appear after the death of Kings, the Prophet of the Supreme Being, the giggles became a great guffaw. Robespierre alone remained silent, twisting in his seat, his cheek twitching.

In the five long years of the Revolution, Robespierre had never made anyone laugh. Mirabeau could use the *esprit* of his caste when it suited him; Camille was quick with his wit; Danton always had some obscenity available to disarm the most hostile audience; even Marat had his moments of black humor.

Robespierre and Saint-Just were always serious. Words chiseled in marble—cold, abstract, imposing, uncompromising.

Now all of Paris was laughing. It was rumored that Robespierre had tried to quash the whole affair. In any event the "conspirators" were never brought to trial.

The Terror marched on at its accelerated rate. The "enemies of the people" were now brought before the court in batches, forty or fifty a day. Many of them had never seen one another before. They were accused *en masse* of some plot, judged, sentenced, carted off down the rue St.-Antoine to the guillotine.

Most of the suspects had been in prison a long while. The circumstances of their arrest were forgotten; they were accused of "conspiracy" while behind bars. First conspiracy, judged July 7th through 10th. First batch: 60 condemned. Second batch: 48 condemned. Third batch: 38 condemned. Second conspiracy, judged July 23rd through 26th. First batch: 46 condemned. Second batch: 25 condemned. Third batch: 25 condemned. Fourth batch: 25 condemned.

I scanned the lists every day, waiting for the name of Mercier or other friends. But the seventy-three delegates who had signed the petition were still protected by the clemency of Robespierre.

It was a torrid July. Paris became the Sahara. Day after day an implacable sun shone down out of a cloudless sky. The trees in the Tuileries and on the boulevards lost their leaves. Plants withered. Furniture cracked. We entered the month of Thermidor.

Will I be understood if I say that I was afraid? Too many people whom I had known at the salon of Mme. de Beauharnais were either dead or in prison. Mercier, Carra, Camille, Clootz, Fanny's daughter. There was still my old fool of a wife living in Paris and the *monster* Augé. I remembered my arrest of October 1789 when I was accused of writing three royalist tracts. In this era such an arrest would mean the guillotine the next afternoon.

But the people in the Place Maubert were not afraid; they were fed up. Our armies had won a great battle at Fleurus, but the shortages continued and prices remained high. People were tired of sacrifices, tired of the Terror, tired of appeals to their patriotism. The workers at the giant gunpowder factory in Grenelle demanded higher wages, unsuccessfully. On July 7th, incredibly enough, the printers employed by the Committee of Public Safety went on strike. Three of them were arrested.

Edmond was worse than ever, Marion exhausted. I did the marketing for our poor family. Everyone at the Place Maubert was bad-tempered, especially the market girls. Daniol reported that everyone in the Faubourg St.-Antoine felt the same way. The proximity of the guillotine was not amusing. The tiny cemetery at Picpus choked on the remains of the victims and the excessive heat did not help. When the wind blew from the east everyone in the neighborhood was sick.

The Commune at the Hôtel de Ville was now entirely staffed by men chosen by Robespierre. In the middle of July they decided to apply the *maximum* to wages. In some cases this meant a return to the salary level of a year before, taking no account of the rise in prices since then. Daniol was furious. "Robespierre not only wants to be pope," he said, "he wants the rest of us to fast every day!"

The heat wave broke suddenly on July 10th. After that the weather was stormy.

On the afternoon of the 27th (9 Thermidor) I set out to visit Agnès. It was a still, heavy afternoon, stifling, with high piled-up clouds that foretold a shower but as yet not a breath of air. I crossed to the Cité by the Petit-Pont, then to the right bank by the Pont-Notre-Dame, planning to take a route that would spare me the sight of the *charettes* departing for the guillotine. On the Grève, at the Hôtel de Ville, a sight that recalled the summer of '89—the square was covered by a milling throng, roughly dressed men, all *sans-culottes,* with others arriving from the direction of St.-Antoine. I got close enough to learn what was going on—a demonstration by wage earners against the new *maximum* on salaries.

With the menace of the crowd added to that of the thunder clouds overhead, I decided to return home, taking a short detour by the Ile St.-Louis.

I recrossed the Pont-Notre-Dame to the Cité, then took the narrow rue Marmousets to the Pont-Rouge. At the near end of the bridge I saw two men having an argument. They were Fouquier-Tinville, Chief Judge of the Revolutionary Tribunal, and Sanson, the executioner. Avoiding these two specters of death, I hurried on.

Months later I learned that Sanson, because of the disturbances in the Faubourg Saint-Antoine, had come into Paris to ask the judge for permission to postpone that day's execution. Fouquier refused. Neither of them knew then that those *charettes* would be the last to thread their way along the rue St.-Antoine.

I made a demi-promenade of the isle, then returned by the Pont-de-la-Tournelle.

When I reached the Place Maubert I heard a drum roll and saw a detachment of the Gardes riding down toward the river. Thinking the demonstration at the Hôtel de Ville must have gotten out of hand, I went directly to Marion's rooms and told her to lock herself in.

At six another drummer went by beating the *générale.* A short while later someone knocked on the door. It was Marion's neighbor, spreading the news that Robespierre had been arrested by the Convention along with his brother, Saint-Just, etc.

Were we pleased or alarmed? Chiefly astonished. Nothing so outlandish had occurred since the king's flight to Varennes. And even that had been foretold, warned against. This had never been suggested.

Besides, the news was premature. Robespierre had, in fact, been arrested and sent to the Luxembourg. But the officer in charge of that former palace refused to put him in a cell, told him instead that the Commune had asked him to come to the Hôtel de Ville to take command of an insurrection against the Convention. A group of his supporters filled the rue de Tournon at the entrance to the Luxembourg shouting, "To the Commune! to the Commune!"

I went out to see what was happening. At about eight a carriage clattered down the rue St.-Jacques at a terrific pace, several horsemen clearing the way. I learned later that it contained the Incorruptible, heading for the Hôtel de Ville, or rather the police headquarters on the quai des Orfèvres. Robespierre was apparently hesitant about taking charge of an insurrection. He was not Marat, the apostle of violence; he was not Danton, the great improviser; he was always the lawyer from Arras, respectful of authority. It was several hours before he went to the Hôtel de Ville, and that may have proved his undoing.

Paris was in a turmoil but it was a hesitant turmoil. I went no further than Mérigot's bookshop on the quai de la Vallée. Some people already spoke of the fall of the "tyrant"; others said it was the end of the Republic; most said only that it was an immense event.

The situation was dangerous, certainly for Paris. The Commune was behind Robespierre. The Commune officially controlled the Gardes. Their commander, Hanriot, was the man who had led the insurrection of May 31st–June 2nd a year before. Then as now it was the Commune versus the Convention and the Commune had triumphed. Why shouldn't the Commune triumph again?

There were rumors of a revolt in the prisons, fed by all the "conspiracies" uncovered by the Tribunal, fed by memories of '92. That afternoon the batch of condemned men, mostly aristocrats, had protested their execution, shouted to the people of the Faubourg St.-Antoine for help. Nothing like it had been seen since the start of the Terror, aside from Camille's vain cries. These too were unanswered; the guillotine did its work.

If the prisoners revolted, the massacres of September '92 might be resumed. The "Septembrists" were in hiding, condemned by all factions, but presumably they were still there.

The Gardes from the more fashionable neighborhoods would

probably support the Convention. Also the students of the Ecole Militaire.

As for our twelve victorious armies, who could predict their reaction if Paris went up in flames?

At ten o'clock the tocsin sounded. Drummers went through the streets, calling all patriots to meetings of their sections. The insurrection was official.

But the great *bourdon* of Notre-Dame was missing from the chorus of pealing bells in the sultry night. The section of the Cité had refused to let it ring. That was a portent of what followed.

I went home instead of to St.-Etienne-du-Mont. I was not the only one who preferred his own house. There was no great rush of patriots through the streets, no angry mob with pikes, few patrols.

Rollin told me later that the section disputed all night. For once the quarrel between Hué and Garnier (both of them now out of jail) was forgotten. At first the sentiment was in favor of Robespierre and the Commune. They sent a message to the Hôtel de Ville to that effect. But later word came that the Convention had declared that Robespierre, Saint-Just and the others arrested that afternoon were to be considered *outlaws*. Everyone became hesitant. Marat, after all, had been the first deputy arrested by the Convention. His trial had been his apotheosis. But if Robespierre was an *outlaw* he was already condemned.

The *sans-culottes* didn't feel like getting killed for a Commune that had just put a *maximum* on salaries. There were some who said, "Let's go home and let the bourgeois fight it out among themselves!"

At midnight the rain that had been threatening all day finally descended, a tropical torrent, hot heavy drops lashing down out of the July night. I sat in my room and watched the rain pour into the deserted street outside, making a running stream of the gutter. I thought, "Nothing will happen until tomorrow." The city was quiet.

It was hard to sleep. Too much hung in the balance. I woke up with the dawn at five. The sky had cleared, the street was dry. I went out. There were no queues at the bakeries—it was the *décadi,* the 10th of Thermidor. I decided to go to my isle, crossed the Pont-de-la-Tournelle. The Seine was iris and rose reflecting the dawn; the air felt newly washed.

At the guardhouse on the far side of the Pont-de-la-Tournelle, the same spot where I had been arrested the day the Bastille fell, two sentries with pikes were talking. I felt in my pocket to be sure I had my *carte civile,* then walked past them slowly. . . .

"He was shot in the jaw, a real mess," one said. "His brother jumped out the window but botched it."

"I'd bet they'll both be shortened by the national razor before this sun sets."

"*La sainte guillotine* is going to lose her patron."

"She'll work all the same. The basket has swallowed the king and the queen, *le Père Duchesne* and Danton—it's not going to spit up Robespierre."

"And afterwards?"

"*Eh bien,* when it's all over we'll dance!"

For all that I was curious I didn't dare ask any questions. I crossed my isle, took the quais. There were troops around the Hôtel de Ville. No lights inside.

The news vendors were already out on the rue St.-Honoré. A woman at the corner of the rue des Prouvaires was shouting, "Robespierre arrested! Saint-Just arrested! Hanriot arrested!"

The city was waking up; the stand was besieged with customers. Hastily printed sheets told the news of the previous day's events, but nothing about Robespierre's being shot.

(When the sentry said, "*He* was shot . . ." I knew it must be Robespierre. *He—he—he!* For the last two months whenever people said *"he"* it was always Robespierre.)

There was already a crowd at the Tuileries. I managed to enter the palace, shoved this way and that by the mob.

The palace had been completely transformed since the one other time I had seen it, on June 20th, 1792. Gone were the gilt furniture, the brocades, the paneling decorated with *fleurs-de-lis.* In their place plain wood and tricolor banners, the severe style of the Republic.

In an enormous room, antechamber to the meeting place of

the Committee of Public Safety, Robespierre lay stretched out on a plain table, already half a corpse.

Under his head, a small pine box. In his hand, a little purse of white leather that he touched to his bleeding jaw from time to time. He was breathing deeply and pale as death. His blood-stained silk suit was a sky-blue, no doubt the same one he had worn for the Fête de l'Etre Suprême, his day of ultimate triumph, just six weeks before. His eyes darted about, bright and piercing, but didn't deign to fix on anyone.

The crowd was cruel. A woman cried, "Your Majesty, are you in pain?" A man shoved his way through the press of bodies to get a good look, shouted hoarsely, "You seem to have lost your voice!" Perhaps they had relatives or friends who had perished on the scaffold, but in that room I felt the call of blood, the vicious instinct that adds cruelty to suffering, vultures descending on a cadaver.

I think I was the only man present who felt any pity.

It was already impossible to find out what had happened during the night. Most versions have it that a gendarme with the unfortunate name of Merda broke into the room in the Hôtel de Ville where the Commune was meeting and shot Robespierre, intending to kill him but only hitting his jaw. But later the Committee said that the wound resulted from an attempted suicide. Another enigma for the historians of 1994.

A surgeon arrived to dress the wound. Sure that the operation would be painful, I left.

The streets were already crowded. A holiday air. No one seemed surprised. So many other heroes of the Revolution had gone through the "little window," why not Robespierre?

It had already been announced that for this special occasion the guillotine would return to the Place de la Révolution. Porters along the rue St.-Honoré were renting space at windows to spectators who wanted to see the *charettes* go by. The prices were all exorbitant, but there was no shortage of subscribers.

During the morning, Robespierre, Saint-Just, etc., were all taken to the Conciergerie at the Palais de Justice. No need for a trial; the Convention had already declared them "outlaws."

It was a lovely July day.

The *charettes* set out at five. I had taken Agnès to dinner at the Mérigots. We all talked about Mercier's chances of being freed. It did not seem at all certain. Most of the men who had led the attack on Robespierre had called for the execution of the seventy-three. Robespierre had defended them.

Mérigot said he was sure the whole affair of the Red Shirts had been a trap set by Robespierre's enemies, designed to put him in a bad light. Also the story of *"la Mère de Dieu."* In retrospect that seemed reasonable.

After dinner we walked across the Pont-Neuf and tried to find a vantage point on the rue St.-Honoré. But every place was already taken. At all windows, up and down the street, as if they were at so many boxes at the Opéra, women wearing all their jewels, using the excuse of the fine weather to reveal almost all of their bosoms, radiant and smiling, drinking wine and sherbets offered by well-dressed men who stood at their backs. A whole layer of Parisian society that dared show itself once again.

Everyone knows the details of the execution. Twenty-two heads dropped into Sanson's basket that day. Robespierre was the last to go. With a barbarous cruelty, the executioner ripped off the bandage around his head, letting his shattered jaw dangle. Robespierre let out an inhuman cry of pain. When his suffering was cut short by the blade the executioner held up the bloody trophy. It was seven-thirty, the red sun was low in the west. The roar of the crowd was heard all over Paris.

The next day the entire Commune took the same route, seventy in all, a record. As they went by workers shouted, "There goes the fucking maximum!"

The guillotine swallowed one more batch, thirty associates of "the tyrant," the last day of July.

Then it stopped.

Only until the end of Thermidor, according to the men now in command, all of them Terrorists. The Tribunal had first to be purged of Robespierre's henchmen. But once stopped the machine refused to move again. When one of the victors of 10 Thermidor talked of resuming the Terror the Convention shouted, "Justice! Justice!" The infamous law of 22 Prairial was repealed on August 1st, just four days after Robespierre was killed.

In its last three days the guillotine had claimed one hundred heads. In its last six weeks, fifteen hundred. In all, since the start of the Terror in September '93, twenty-seven hundred victims in Paris alone.

Edmond died at the end of July. Marion was left alone with three small children to care for.

Agnès remarried. She is now Mme. Louis Vignon. Her husband works in a government bureau. They live modestly and happily.

Ten days after the fall of the Incorruptible the prostitutes reappeared at the Palais-Egalité. Humanity is always corruptible. The gambling dens sent out their barkers again. By the middle of August the public squares were filled with beggars, ballad singers, acrobats, musicians. Children stopped playing "the guillotine." The press revived, although none of it was notable. It ceased to be a crime to be on the right. The prisons emptied —too slowly for many, but then the laws had not changed, only the men in power. Fanny's daughter was released early in October, Mercier on October 23rd. He regained his seat at the Convention on December 8th.

Fall came, then winter, less harsh than the year before. But bread, meat, soap, wood, etc., were even more scarce. All uncontrolled prices continued to rise and the police tolerated an illegal market in controlled goods so that very little was ever available at the maximum. In short, the whole attempt to control wages and prices was abandoned. The poor no longer protested; instead they hid in corners, starved, shivered and died. It was again shameful to be *sans-culottes*.

Gone were the pikes and bonnets of '92. The Commune was abolished, the sections dissolved, the Gardes reorganized so that only solid bourgeois were found on patrol. Gone was the carmagnole vest, the well-tailored pants designed to prove the wearer a *sans-culotte* in his heart even if his wallet was bulging. "Monsieur" replaced "Citizen" as the term of address. Outside the theaters long lines of hacks waited for the show to empty. The coachman, hat in hand, bowed to the spectators—"May I help you, *sir?*"

Carriages remained scarce but the insolent cabriolets of '88 returned, driven by a new breed of dandy known as *muscadins* or *jeunesse dorée*. These callow gilded youths were the scions of obscure families that had grown rich on the war—speculators, profiteers, grafters. Waiting in the wings to ape the new bullies were impoverished nobles, the eternally pretentious clerks of the Place Dauphine, libertines of all ages. There is something slightly effeminate about the style affected by these new insolents, if only because it is so much a *style,* a flaunting of the latest quirk of fashion such as previously had been seen only in women's dress. These *incroyables* wear enormous mops of curly hair, parted in the middle and hanging down on either side of their faces like dogs' ears. Their jackets have enormous lapels and extra-long skirts; their vests of brushed chamois have eighteen buttons; their cravats are veritable tablecloths, billowing up to their perfumed chins, the preferred color green; bizarre spectacles perch on the bridge of their noses, whether necessary or not. Their breeches hang down to their ankles and their shoes would do better on a feminine foot, delicate, pointed and with paper-thin soles. In their hands they carry canes of knotty wood and not only for show—it was a brawl instigated by a band of this *jeunesse dorée* that provoked the closing of the Jacobin Club in November.

The girls who aspire to the favors of this bunch of prigs are now all *à la Grecque*. Whatever the weather, their feet are clad only in abominable flat sandals, a mere piece of leather held by ribbons tied around the leg. Their dresses are the filmiest of flowing gauze, artfully draped, almost transparent, worn with nothing at all underneath. No longer must Pyramus guess at the graces of his Thisbe; they are all there for a ready inventory, scarcely veiled.

The Palais-Egalité is once again as busy as in its palmiest days. Whores and pimps everywhere—girls, children, pederasts;

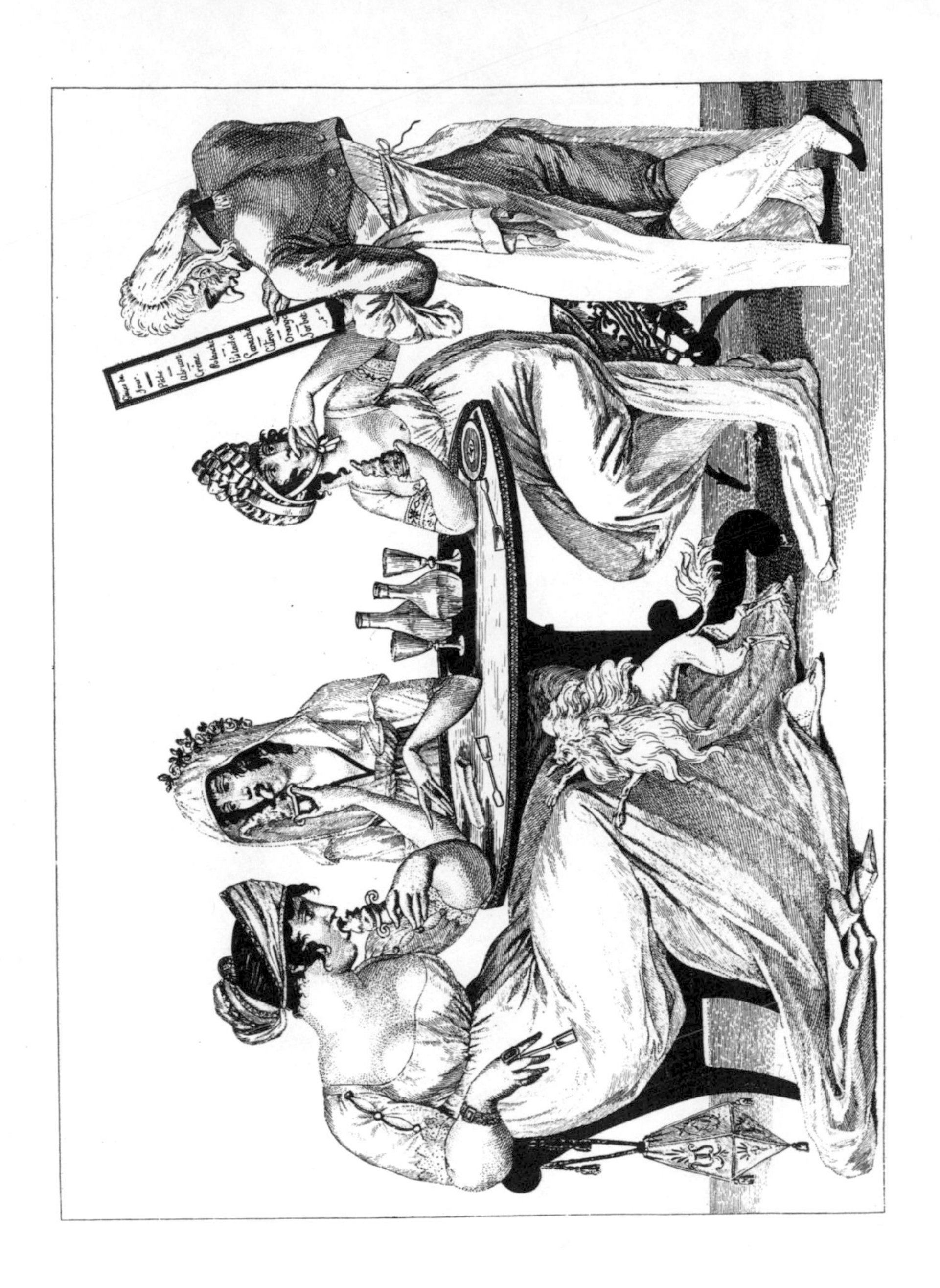
Jour.
Pêche
Abricot
Crème
Citron
Orange
Sorbet

PLATE 20: After the revolution. . . . From *Le Bon Genre,* Paris, 1827.

you take your pick so long as you have cash in your pocket. New restaurants have opened alongside the old; all of them have menus four pages long listing assorted delicacies at astronomical prices; all of them are crowded. A clever man has made a fortune by opening a well-appointed privy where, for a fee, the diners can relieve themselves of the ultimate products of all those Westphalia hams, Bologna sausages, wild boars' heads, liquors, sherbets and lemonades. The gambling dens are busy until dawn. But there is no Camille Desmoulins standing on the café tables.

We are still a Republic, One and Indivisible, in this year III of the new calendar. The remains of Marat have been deposited in the Panthéon with appropriate pomp. Also those of Jean-Jacques Rousseau. But busts of Marat have been cracked by the bully boys of the right and thrown into sewers, and the tricolor cockades in our ladies' coiffures, still prescribed by law, grow smaller and smaller.

Our armies remain victorious against all of Europe. How strange that the most durable legacy of the Revolution should be the most formidable army in the world.

It has been said many times since June '89, but now I believe it is really so: The Revolution is over.

Rich or poor, everyone danced. In the worker's cabarets where the carmagnole had been the rage during the Terror there was a new step, imported from Germany. How did it get to Paris? no one knew. Perhaps our soldiers brought it home. A light, new beat. What was scandalous, and a sign that the era was ready for anything at all, was that the dancing couples held on to each other, whirling around the dance floor in pairs. One can imagine the accidents that can occur in the heat of such an embrace, aided by the intoxication of the fiddles! This new aberration is called the *waltz*.

Meanwhile the aristocrats danced the carmagnole. All Paris talked of the *bals à la victime*. To be admitted you had to exhibit a document proving that you had lost a close relative to the guillotine. A mother, a father, a husband, a wife, a brother or sister—merely a cousin would not do. The men at these macabre festivities wore black armbands, the women red ribbons tied about their necks, to remind everyone of the blade they had escaped. Just as the prisoners had acted out the ceremony of the guillotine to pass the time of their detention, so these ex-suspects aped the manners and steps of the *sans-culottes* of the Terror.

Eighteen luxurious dance halls remained open all winter long. It was there that the new styles were seen to their best advantage. The women danced barefoot, their fingers festooned with diamonds, a tiny leather purse hanging between their breasts, their fans tied to their belts, their handkerchiefs in the pockets of their beaux. Among these bacchantes were some who carried their passion for the freedom of ancient Greece to the point that they left their breasts completely exposed, while their long hair swayed unfettered about their white shoulders.

Before the Revolution all fashion began at the Court and filtered down to the people. Now it moves both ways. By the beginning of 1795 some of our new aristocrats were taking up the waltz.

No one thought of reviving the minuet.

I attained the age of sixty on November 22, 1794 (old style), that is to say 2 Frimaire, year III of the Republic. The event was toasted at a dinner given by the generous Arthaud for Mercier, Louvet and other Girondin delegates who have finally been freed. We met in a restaurant at the Palais-Egalité and the meal must have cost a fortune in *assignats*.

What a joy to see Mercier again, but also what a disappointment. His year in prison has changed him greatly—or perhaps it is that the same year in Paris has changed me; we now disagree on almost everything. Mercier holds that nothing that was done by Robespierre or his followers had any value. He became furious when I suggested that there were other Terrorists, even more bloodthirsty, among the Thermidorians; that he and the rest of the "73" owed their lives to the grace of the Incorruptible. He claims that the "tyrant" held them as hostages to assure the submission of the right at the Convention, that their death was slated for the 10th of Thermidor, the same day when by

God's grace Robespierre mounted the scaffold himself. What astonished me most was the satisfaction Mercier expressed at Camille's death. For him nothing else could atone for *L'Histoire des Brissotins,* not even *Le Vieux Cordelier.*

So we talked instead of old friends, so many of them now gone. When we recalled Grimod's dinners it sounded like a fairy tale, and yet they were only eight years ago. The words "before the Revolution" now evoke a kind of nostalgia, like childhood memories. We were all children then, playing our philosophical games in a world that seemed destined to go on forever! Since then we have become wiser and sadder. I have not lost faith; I believe that the deeds and words of these six years will echo down through the centuries to come, overturning vast empires, changing the life of all the peoples of the earth. I believe that just as the revolution in America was but a dim foreshadowing of ours, so ours will prove the first glimmering of another, the Revolution predicted in the gospels, which will be greater and wiser and the last. But meanwhile we are left with war, famine and the reign of the hard men of money.

Afterwards we took a stroll in the arcades. Who would believe that whole sections of Paris are deserted, that the poor chew on crusts of bread in their cold garrets and make a feast of a plate of boiled turnips? Never have I seen so many nymphs, so many dandies, so many pickpockets. The cafés offer liquors from Martinique, wines stolen from the cellars of the *emigrés,* rum from Barbados, cargo of some captured English ship. Dozens of gambling dens. Cloth merchants who unroll their wares like Turks in the suks of Constantinople. Windows crammed with all sorts of jewelry, the heirlooms of all the old families of France, now so much merchandise. The bookstalls feature erotic engravings, pornographic novels—there is no appetite that cannot find its illustration, whether on paper or in the flesh.

The arcades offer a new sort of amusement—auction galleries where anything at all is sold to the highest bidder. A man with the voice of a Stentor proclaims that the object up for sale is going at a sacrifice. They bring out a woman's wig (and who cares about the fate of the head that wore it!), a clock, a shawl, a collection of shirts or handkerchiefs. Lackeys carry the stuff about but the buyers get no more than a glimpse. The bidding becomes ferocious and rivalry between the buyers makes the final bid an extravagance. If the audience is not attracted by some object, employees of the house make sure that it will be offered another time.

But then all of Paris has become a vast auction. Every house carries a sign, FOR SALE! Mansions are sold, churches are sold, convents are sold—all sold and then resold at ever higher prices. Those who know how to play the game dine at the Palais-Egalité; the dupes retreat to a corner and wait for better times. In front of houses on every street you see furniture, wardrobes, paintings, prints, jewelry—all exposed to the elements and marked FOR SALE! For thirty-five years I've walked the streets of Paris without knowing anything of the wealth hidden behind its gray façades. Now it is all out in the street.

An old wanderer, completely out-of-date, absorbed in memories of a vanished past, I still make occasional tours of my isle. My *inscriptions* are fading. One afternoon I encountered a living ghost, Sara, my last love. It was she who stopped me. I would not have recognized her otherwise; she looked so old I almost wept. She had married at last, a former abbé; somehow he had escaped arrest. The poor man has no trade; Sara works as a seamstress to support them both. She is now thirty-two and looks ten years older. We embraced, she called me her "dear papa." I did not feel like her "papa"; we both seemed too old for that.

Le Drame de la Vie is completed. Who will ever read it? Will it ever be performed? Not in my lifetime, of that I am sure.

Most of *Monsieur Nicolas* has been printed. I may add to it; I envision sections of "My Philosophy," "My Politics," "My Works." The pages containing the narration of my life are stacked up in my basement. Five hundred copies, no more. My legacy to posterity. Will posterity care? I doubt it. The days when I believed in my grand scheme for selling the work by subscription are gone. A glance at the list shows its absurdity; it begins, "The King, the Queen. . . ."

I continue to work, as much out of habit as anything else. There is a new project that I scribble at from time to time. It is called *The Anti-Justine.* I began my career with the reputation of a pornographer, and I might as well end it the same way. The times are ripe. I have already expressed my opinion of the *Justine* of de Sade, that cloaca of horrors. I should like to write something that will distract our soldiers but at the same time teach them to be tender instead of cruel. But to compete with de Sade, the work will have to be as obscene as possible; the antidote must be as strong as the poison, if not stronger. . . .

As always, it is based on the story of my life. What else have I ever written?

We begin with a hearty peasant lad in Sacy. He loses his virginity at the age of ten one night when he climbs into bed with his mother. Adventures with the girls of the village. Each time he ejaculates he faints. Skip ahead twenty years. He has a lovely daughter, Coquette-Ingénue. At the age of eleven she is wildly attractive—to her father. At the age of fifteen she falls in love with a MONSTER, Vitnègre. She persuades her father to sign the marriage contract by letting him lick . . . but let it pass. Description of the monstrous deeds of Vitnègre which I am afraid do recall de Sade, because Augé was *a creature of de Sade's imagination in real life.* Vitnègre sells his wife to a horrible monk called Foutamort. Some more scenes à la Sade, the only such aberrations in the book and put there to disgust the reader with such practices. Coquette-Ingénue is rescued from the clutches of the wicked monk Foutamort; another girl put in her place whom Foutamort kills in a most revolting way, eating her heart for dinner when he has gratified himself on her body. Various episodes, all things that I've actually seen. A cheap old whore on her knees for carters behind the market wagons on the quai du Louvre.

The Puritans à la Robespierre will be shocked by this work, but they are all gone. I have not yet decided whether it should be distributed, but I have begun printing it and I must arrange for some illustrations. In the end there is a fornication club including the hero, his daughters Ingénue and Victoire, and a whole company of gallant young men and women who demonstrate that the normal pleasures of love (albeit incestuous and orgiastic) are more satisfying than the perverted *sadism* of Vitnègre and Foutamort.

One of this jolly company cries, "Hurray for down-to-earth love-making, the best position of the famous forty-four!"

Vive l'amour! Vive la tendresse! Vive la Révolution!

RESTIF DE LA BRETONNE IN ENGLISH

The corrupted ones; le Paysan et la paysanne pervertis; translation and introduction by Alan Hull Walton; London, Spearman, 1967

Les Nuits de Paris, or the nocturnal spectator; translation by Linda Asher and Ellen Fertig, introduction by Jacques Barzun; New York, Random House, 1964

Monsieur Nicolas; translation by R. Crowdy Mathers, introduction by Havelock Ellis, 6 volumes; London, J. Rodker, 1930–31

Monsieur Nicolas, or the human heart laid bare; translated and edited by Robert Baldrick; London, Barrie & Rockliff, 1966; New York, C. N. Potter, 1967

Pleasures and follies of a good-natured libertine (l'Anti-Justine); translation by Pierallessandro Casavini; Paris, Olympia Press, 1955

Sara; translation by R. C. Mathers; London, J. Rodker, 1927

ABOUT THE AUTHOR

Alex Karmel grew up in New York and began to write while attending Columbia. After taking his M.A. in cultural history, he went to Paris on a Fulbright Scholarship to do research on the Resistance. His years in Paris were the beginning of an intimate acquaintance with the city that is very much in evidence in *My Revolution.* They were also occupied by his marriage and the birth of his son, which in turn led eventually to Marjorie Karmel's book, *Thank You, Dr. Lamaze.* His first novel, *Mary Ann* was made into the film "Something Wild." His second novel, *Last Words,* was published by McGraw-Hill in 1968. Mr. Karmel lives in New York and is presently at work on a study of the relevance of the French revolution to present-day events.

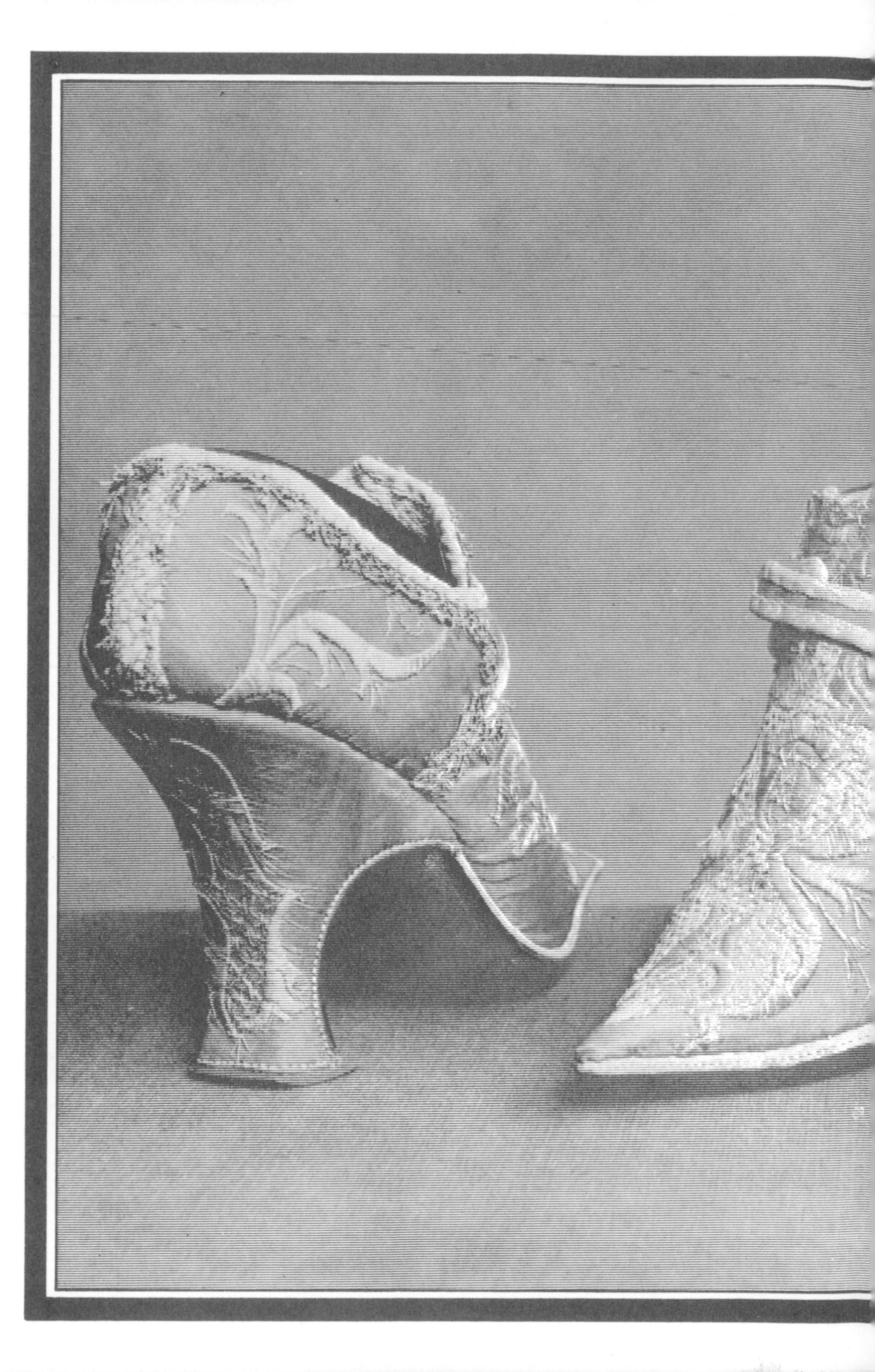